Name_____

Address_____

City_____

State_____ _____Zip_____

Phone (___)_____

Email_____

The New National Baptist Hymnal

21st Century Edition

Praise ye the Lord. Praise God in his sanctuary: praise him in the firmament of his power. Praise him for his mighty acts; praise him according to his excellent greatness. Praise him with the sound of the trumpet: praise him with the psaltery and harp. Praise him with the timbrel and dance: praise him with stringed instruments and organs. Praise him upon the loud cymbals: praise him upon the high sounding cymbals. Let every thing that hath breath praise the Lord. Praise ye the Lord. (Psalm 150 KJV)

First Printing - October 2001

ISBN 0-9675029-0-X (Red)
ISBN 0-9675029-1-8 (Blue)
ISBN 0-9675029-2-6 (Loose Leaf)
ISBN 0-9675029-3-4 (Special Presentation-Leather)

A Word from the Publisher

The centrality of music in the Christian experience always has been recognized and affirmed by church leaders. In fact, music is called the universal language because it not only transcends cultural and linguistic barriers; it also rises above denominational barriers and serves to unite people of different faiths.

When God is recognized as the motivation and inspiration for the music we sing, and Jesus Christ is exalted through its melody, people are brought to joyous recognition of God's faithfulness and greatness. In fact, for hymns and songs to be meaningful they should have their foundation in the Word of God. It is God's Word that provides the context and foundation for this 21st Century Edition.

The conception and publication was for a two-fold purpose: first, to enhance all aspects of our worship; second, to preserve our great religious heritage and music for generations to come. With this in mind, this hymnal has been published using a standard that all other hymnals will follow. This hymnal encompasses hymns that have added so much richness and diversity in our worship services. This new hymnal is inclusive of many features that will add both enjoyment and proficiency in the utilization of this comprehensive collection of Christian songs by both church congregations and individually. This 21st century hymnal includes such features as a glossary of musical terms, scriptural based meditations, benedictions, offertory appeals, anthems, praise songs, children's songs, contemporary gospel songs, scriptural references for each hymn title, and many other features.

As the publisher, it is our prayer that God will continue to be glorified through the hymns and songs contained in these pages. We also pray that souls will be moved to praise God, from whom all blessings flow. As God is glorified in praise, may your spirit soar to higher heights and may your faith evolve to experience deeper depths.

It is with immense gratitude that we thank those of the household of faith who have given their time and talent to bring this project to fruition. This hymnal publication was undertaken with a sincere prayer that it finds a meaningful place of inspiration and edification in every church and every heart.

It is my pleasure to present this 21st Century Edition, an outstanding collection of both old and new offerings and is truly one of the great music resources of our time.

Dr. T. B. Boyd, III
Publisher

Speaking to yourselves in psalms and hymns and spiritual songs, singing and making melody in your heart to the Lord. (Ephesians 5:19 KJV)

Purpose

The writing of music is a gift from the Italian culture. Its language tells us how music is to be sung and played. If each country used its own language, it would be difficult for us to understand this art form that is so dear to all cultures. Consequently, all countries have adopted Italian terms for their music. If we know these terms, we will understand how to sing and play music of any country.

Creating a new hymnal brings many challenges and rewards. As we reflect upon the first two thousand years of the Christian faith, the family of faith throughout the world has made great contributions by telling the gospel message of Christ through its experience, music, and theology.

Christians have always been noted as a singing people. The early chants, psalms, hymns, spirituals, and early and modern gospel songs, all reflect the Christian experience. We are grateful to great composers and lyricists like Thomas A. Dorsey, John Wesley, Luci Campbell, Martin Luther, Charlotte Elliott, Isaac Watts, John Newton, Fanny J. Crosby, Dottie Rambo, and others for their musical genius and contributions to the community of faith.

This 21st Century Edition brings together the European chants and hymns, the African-American spirituals and contemporary gospel music telling in narrative form the experiences of a Christian nation. This great music gives meaning and purpose to our worship as we proclaim the beliefs and tenets of the Christian faith.

Music is the language and hope of the soul, when lifted up in the presence of the Divine, by those who have been set sin free for the glory of God and service to all people. As did the psalmist of old, let us call the people of God to worship.

O sing unto the Lord a new song: sing unto the Lord, all the earth. Sing unto the Lord, bless his name; show forth his salvation from day to day.
(Psalm 96:1-2 KJV)

Dedication

Special thanks to the men and women who have worked tirelessly over the years.

Mrs. Ruth Lomax Davis
Mr. W. Elmo Mercer
Mrs. Juanita Griffey Hines
Mrs. Virgie C. DeWitty
Dr. A. Charles Bowie
Mrs. Marena Belle Williams
Mr. Anderson T. Dailey
Mrs. Margaret Pleasant Douroux
Mrs. Mamie E. Taylor
Mrs. Odessa Jackson
Mr. John T. Benson, III
Mr. E. D. Thompson
Mr. Robert B. McConnell, III
Mr. Glenn Smotherman
Mr. Grant Browning
Mr. Don Sheffield
Dr. J. P. Nightingale
Dr. N. Samuel Jones
Dr. N. E. Douglas
Rev. Henry Smith
Mrs. Julia C. Jones
Ms. Karen F. Brown
Triad Publications
Rev. Jesse P. Nightingale, Sr.
Dr. T. B. Boyd, III

Dr. A Charles Bowie
Mrs. Edith McKinney
Mrs. Ruth Sauls
Ms. Norma Noble
Mrs. Lovie G. Kellar
Mr. John T. Benson
Mr. Allen Tuten
Rev. Willie Paul
Rev. Walter Grant
Mrs. Julia Hoover
Mrs. Brenda Boyd-Walker
Ms. Beulah Vaughn
Ms. Sheila P. Kellar
Dr. F. Benjamin Davis
Dr. B. W. Noble
Dr. W. N. Daniel
Dr. Nehemiah Davis
Dr. H. L. Hudson
Mrs. Mabel Boyd
Rev. Pamela Kellar
Rev. Olivia Cloud
Mr. Brian Goodwin
Ms. Barbara Perkins
Mrs. Ida Black
Mr. Paul Kwame
Mr. Derrick Lee

Make a joyful noise unto the Lord, all ye lands. Serve the Lord with gladness: come before his presence with singing. Know ye that the Lord he is God: it is he that hath made us, and not we ourselves; we are his people, and the sheep of his pasture. Enter into his gates with thanksgiving, and into his courts with praise: be thankful unto him, and bless his name. For the Lord is good; his mercy is everlasting; and his truth endureth to all generations. (Psalm 100)

How to Care for Your New Hymnal

•*Never* lay open hymnal face down
•*Never* fold hymnal page corners
•*Never* use pen, pencil, or any other object to mark in or on hymnal
•*Always* use a bookmark
•*Never* fold the spine of hymnal
•Keep away from excessive heat
•Keep in a dry area

Make a joyful noise to the Lord, all the earth; break forth and sing for joy, yes, sing praises! Sing praises to the Lord with the lyre; and the voice of melody. With trumpets and sound of the horn make a joyful noise before the King, the Lord! (Psalm 98:4-6 The Amplified Bible)

Let the word of Christ dwell in you richly in all wisdom; teaching and admonishing one another in psalms and hymns and spiritual songs, singing with grace in your hearts to the Lord. (Colossians 3:16 KJV)

Table of Contents

Holy, Holy, Holy

Holy, holy, holy is the Lord — Isaiah 6:3 KJV

1

1. Ho-ly, Ho-ly, Ho - ly,   Lord   God   Al - might - y!
2. Ho-ly, Ho-ly, Ho - ly!   All   the saints a - dore   Thee,
3. Ho-ly, Ho-ly, Ho - ly!   Tho' the dark-ness hide   Thee,
4. Ho-ly, Ho-ly, Ho - ly,   Lord   God   Al - might - y!

Ear - ly   in   the   morn - ing our song shall rise   to Thee;
Cast - ing down their gold - en crowns a - round the glass - y   sea;
Tho'   the   eye   of   sin - ful man Thy glo - ry may not see;
All   Thy works shall praise Thy name in   earth and sky   and sea;

Ho - ly, Ho - ly, Ho - ly!   Mer - ci - ful and might - y!
Cher-u - bim and ser - a-phim   fall - ing down be - fore   Thee,
On - ly Thou art ho - ly –   there is none be - side   Thee,
Ho - ly, Ho - ly, Ho - ly!   Mer - ci - ful and might - y!

God   in Three Per - sons,   bless - ed Trin - i - ty!
Which   wert and   art,   and   ev - er - more shalt be.
Per - fect   in   pow'r,   in   love and pur - i - ty.
God   in Three Per - sons,   bless - ed Trin - i - ty!

WORDS: Reginald Heber
MUSIC: John B. Dykes

NICAEA

2 Praise to the Lord, the Almighty

Praise and extol and honor the King of heaven — Daniel 4:37 KJV

1. Praise to the Lord, the Al-might-y, the King of cre-a-
2. Praise to the Lord, who o'er all things so won-drous-ly reign-
3. Praise to the Lord, who doth pros-per thy work and de-fend
4. Praise to the Lord, O let all that is in me a-dore

tion! O my soul, praise Him, for He is thy health and sal-
eth, Shel-ters thee un-der His wings, yea, so gent-ly sus-
thee; Sure-ly His good-ness and mer-cy here dai-ly at-
Him! All that hath life and breath, come now with prais-es be-

va-tion! All ye who hear, Now to His tem-ple draw
tain-eth! Hast thou not seen How thy de-sires e'er have
tend thee. Pon-der a-new What the Al-might-y can
fore Him. Let the A-men Sound from His peo-ple a-

near; Praise Him in glad ad-o-ra-tion.
been Grant-ed in what He or-dain-eth?
do, If with His love He be-friend thee.
gain, Glad-ly for aye we a-dore Him. A-men.

WORDS: Joachim Neander; trans. by Catherine Winkworth (Psalm 103:1-6; Psalm 150)   LOBE DEN HERREN
MUSIC: From *Stralsund Gesangbuch; harm. by W. Sterndale Bennett*

All Hail the Power

For the same Lord over all is rich unto all that call upon Him — Romans 10:12 KJV

1. All hail the pow'r of Je - sus' name! Let an - gels pros-trate
2. Ye cho - sen seed of Is - rael's race, Ye ran-somed from the
3. Let ev - 'ry kin - dred, ev - 'ry tribe, On this ter - res - trial
4. O that with yon - der sa - cred throng We at His feet may

fall; Bring forth the roy - al di - a - dem, And
fall, Hail Him who saves you by His grace, And
ball, To Him all maj - es - ty as - cribe, And
fall! We'll join the ev - er - last - ing song, And

crown Him Lord of all; Bring forth the roy - al
crown Him Lord of all; Hail Him who saves you
crown Him Lord of all; To Him all maj - es -
crown Him Lord of all; We'll join the ev - er -

di - a - dem, And crown Him Lord of all!
by His grace, And crown Him Lord of all!
ty as - cribe, And crown Him Lord of all!
last - ing song, And crown Him Lord of all!

WORDS: Edward Perronet; alt. by John Rippon
MUSIC: Oliver Holden

CORONATION

4 Bless His Holy Name

Bless the Lord, O my soul and all that is within me, bless His holy name — Psalm 103:1 KJV

Bless the Lord, O my soul, and all that is with-in me, Bless His

Fine

ho - ly name. He has done great things, He has done great

D.C. al Fine

things, He. has done great things, Bless His ho - ly name.

WORDS: Psalm 103
MUSIC: Andraé Crouch
© Copyright 1973 Bud John Songs, Inc. (ASCAP)

5 All Hail the Power

And a crown was given unto Him — Revelation 6:2 KJV

1. All hail the pow'r of Je - sus' name! Let
2. Ye cho - sen seed of Is - rael's race, Ye
3. Let ev - 'ry kin - dred, ev - 'ry tribe, On
4. Oh, that with yon - der sa - cred throng We

WORDS: Edward Perronet; alt. by John Rippon   DIADEM
MUSIC: James Ellor

All Hail the Power

6   O Worship the King

Thus saith the Lord, thy redeeemer — Isaiah 44:24 KJV

1. O wor - ship the King, all - glo - rious a - bove,
2. O tell of His might, O sing of His grace,
3. Thy boun - ti - ful care what tongue can re - cite?
4. Frail chil - dren of dust, and fee - ble as frail,

And grate - ful - ly sing His pow'r and His love;
Whose robe is the light, whose can - o - py space;
It breathes in the air, it shines in the light;
In Thee do we trust, nor find Thee to fail;

Our Shield and De - fend - er, the An - cient of Days,
His char - iots of wrath the deep thun - der-clouds form,
It streams from the hills it de - scends to the plain,
Thy mer - cies how ten - der! how firm to the end!

Pa - vil - ioned in splen-dor and gird - ed with praise.
And dark is His path on the wings of the storm.
And sweet - ly dis - tills in the dew and the rain.
Our Mak - er, De - fend - er, Re - deem - er and Friend.

WORDS: Robert Grant
MUSIC: Attr. to Johann Michael Haydn

LYONS

Rejoice, Ye Pure in Heart

7

Blessed are the pure in heart: for they shall see God — Matthew 5:8 KJV

1. Re - joice, ye pure in heart, Re - joice, give thanks and
2. Bright youth and snow-crowned age, Strong men and maid - ens
3. With all the an - gel choirs, With all the saints on
4. Yes, on thru life's long path, Still chant - ing as ye
5. Then on, ye pure in heart, Re - joice, give thanks and

sing; Your fes - tal ban - ner wave on high, The
meek Raise high your free, ex - ult - ing song, God's
earth, Pour out the strains of joy and bliss, True
go; From youth to age, by night and day, In
sing; Your glo - rious ban - ner wave on high, The

Refrain

cross of Christ your King.
won - drous prais - es speak. Re - joice, re -
rap - ture, no - blest mirth.
glad - ness and in woe.
cross of Christ your King. Re - joice,

joice, Re - joice, give thanks and sing.
re - joice,

WORDS: Edward H. Plumptre
MUSIC: Arthur H. Messiter

MARION

8   For the Beauty of the Earth

And God saw everything that He had made, and, behold, it was very good — Genesis 1:31 KJV

1. For the beau-ty of the earth, For the glo-ry of the skies,
2. For the won-der of each hour Of the day and of the night,
3. For the joy of hu-man love, Broth-er, sis-ter, par-ent, child,
4. For Thy Church that ev-er-more Lift-eth ho-ly hands a-bove,

For the love which from our birth O-ver and a-round us lies:
Hill and vale, and tree and flow'r, Sun and moon and stars of light:
Friends on earth and friends a-bove, For all gen-tle thoughts and mild:
Of-f'ring up on ev-'ry shore Her pure sac-ri-fice of love:

Refrain

Christ our God, to Thee we raise This our hymn of grate-ful praise.

WORDS: Folliott S. Pierpoint
MUSIC: Conrad Kocher

DIX

9   Alleluia

Let everything that hath breath praise the Lord — Psalm 150:6 KJV

1. Al-le-lu-ia, Al-le-lu-ia, Al-le-lu-ia, Al-le-lu-ia,
2. Lord, I love You, Al-le-lu-ia, Lord, I love You, Al-le-lu-ia,

3. I will serve Him, 4. I will praise Him, 5. He is coming, 6. Thank You, Jesus;

WORDS: Jerry Sinclair
MUSIC: Jerry Sinclair

ALLELUIA

Alleluia

Al - le - lu - ia, Al - le - lu - ia, Al - le - lu - ia, Al - le - lu - ia.
Lord, I love You, Al - le - lu - ia, Lord, I love You, Al - le - lu - ia.

Jesus Shall Reign   10

Of the increase of His government and peace there shall be no end — Isaiah 9:7 KJV

1. Je - sus shall reign wher - e'er the sun Does his suc -
2. From north to south the princ - es meet To pay their
3. To Him shall end - less pray'r be made And end - less
4. Peo - ple and realms of ev - 'ry tongue Dwell on His

ces - sive jour - neys run, His king-dom spread from
hom - age at His feet, While west - ern em - pires
prais - es crown His head; His name like sweet per -
love with sweet - est song, And in - fant voic - es

shore to shore Till moons shall wax and wane no more.
own their Lord And sav - age tribes at - tend His word.
fume shall rise With ev - 'ry morn - ing sac - ri - fice.
shall pro - claim Their ear - ly bless - ings on His name.

WORDS: Isaac Watts
MUSIC: John Hatton

DUKE STREET

11   Let All the People Praise Thee

O magnify the Lord with me, and let us exalt His name together Psalm 34:3 KJV

1. O mag-ni-fy the Lord with me, Ye peo-ple of His choice,
2. O praise Him for His ho-li-ness, His wis-dom and His grace;
3. Had I a thou-sand tongues to sing, The half could ne'er be told

Let all to whom He lend-eth breath Now in His name re-joice;
Sing prais-es for the pre-cious blood Which ran-somed all our race;
Of love so rich, so full and free, Of bless-ings man-i-fold;

For love's blest rev-e-la-tion, For rest from con-dem-na-tion,
In ten-der-ness He sought us, From depths of sin He brought us,
Of grace that fail-eth nev-er, Peace flow-ing like a riv-er,

For ut-ter-most sal-va-tion To Him give thanks.
The way of life then taught us, To Him give thanks.
From God the glo-rious Giv-er, To Him give thanks.
To Him give thanks.

Refrain

Let all (let all) the peo-ple praise Thee, Let all (let all) the peo-ple

WORDS: Mrs. C. H. Morris
MUSIC: Mrs. C. H. Morris

Let All the People Praise Thee

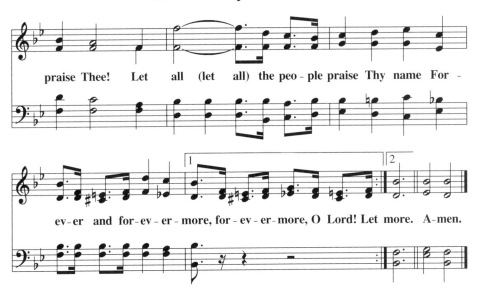

praise Thee! Let all (let all) the peo - ple praise Thy name For -

ev- er and for-ev - er - more, for - ev - er- more, O Lord! Let more. A- men.

Glory Be to the Father   12

All men glorified God for that which was done — Acts 4:21 KJV

Glo - ry be to the Fa-ther, and to the Son, and to the

Ho - ly Ghost; As it was in the be - gin-ning, is now, and ev-er

shall be, world with-out end. A - men, A - men.

WORDS: Lesser Doxology, 3rd-4th century
MUSIC: Henry W. Greatorex

GREATOREX

13   Holy God, We Praise Thy Name

I will be glad and rejoice in Thee, I will sing praises to Thy name,
O Thou most High — Psalm 9:2 KJV

1. Ho - ly God, we praise Thy name – Lord of all, we
2. Hark! the loud ce - les - tial hymn An - gel choirs a -
3. Lo, the ap - os - tol - ic train Joins Thy sa - cred
4. Ho - ly Fa - ther, Ho - ly Son, Ho - ly Spir - it,

bow be - fore Thee! All on earth Thy scep - ter claim,
bove are rais - ing; Cher - u - bim and Ser - a - phim,
name to hal - low; Proph - ets swell the glad re - frain,
Three we name Thee; While in es - sence on - ly One,

All in heav'n a - bove a - dore Thee; In - fi - nite Thy
In un - ceas - ing cho - rus prais - ing, Fill the heav'ns with
And the white-robed mar - tyrs fol - low; And, from morn to
Un - di - vid - ed God we claim Thee, And a - dor - ing

vast do - main, Ev - er - last - ing is Thy reign.
sweet ac - cord – Ho - ly, ho - ly, ho - ly Lord!
set of sun, Thru the Church the song goes on.
bend the knee, While we sing our praise to Thee.

WORDS: From the *Te Deum*, c. 4th century; attr. to Ignace Franz; trans. by Clarence Walworth   GROSSER GOTT
MUSIC: From *Katholisches Gesangbuch*, Vienna, c. 1774

His Name Is Wonderful

His name shall be called Wonderful, Counselor, The mighty God — Isaiah 9:6 KJV

His name is Won-der-ful,
He is the might-y King,
His name is Won-der-ful,
Mas - ter of ev - 'ry-thing,

His name is Won-der-ful, Je-sus, my Lord.
Je-sus, my Lord.

He's the great Shep-herd, the Rock of all a - ges, Al-might-y

God is He; _____ Bow down be-fore Him, Love and a-

dore Him, His name is Won-der-ful, Je - sus, my Lord.

WORDS: Audrey Mieir
MUSIC: Audrey Mieir

HIS NAME IS WONDERFUL

15 Glorious Is Thy Name

*Now therefore, our God, we thank Thee,
and praise Thy glorious name* — 1 Chronicles 29:13 KJV

1. Bless-ed Sav-ior, we a - dore Thee, We Thy love and
2. Great Re-deem-er, Lord and Mas-ter, Light of all e -
3. From the throne of heav-en's glo - ry To the cross of
4. Come, O come, im-mor - tal Sav-ior, Come and take Thy

grace pro-claim; Thou art might - y, Thou are ho - ly,
ter - nal days; Let the saints of ev - ery na - tion
sin and shame, Thou didst come to die a ran - som,
roy - al throne; Come, and reign, and reign for - ev - er,

Refrain

Glo - rious is Thy match-less name!
Sing Thy just and end - less praise!
Guilt - y sin - ners to re - claim!
Be the king - dom all Thine own!

Glo - rious

Glo - rious is Thy

ri-ous, Glo - ri-ous, Glo-rious is Thy

name, O Lord! Glo-rious is Thy name, O Lord!

WORDS: B. B. McKinney
MUSIC: B. B. McKinney
GLORIOUS NAME

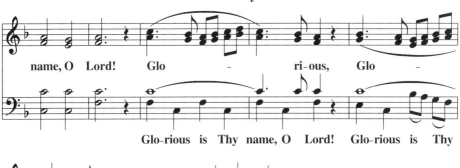

name, O Lord! Glo - ri-ous, Glo -

Glo-rious is Thy name, O Lord! Glo-rious is Thy

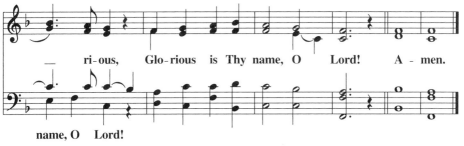

_ ri-ous, Glo-rious is Thy name, O Lord! A - men.

name, O Lord!

Praise the Name of Jesus 16

The Lord is my Rock, my Fortress, and my Deliverer — 2 Samuel 22:2 KJV

Praise the name of Je - sus, Praise the name of Je - sus.

He's my Rock, He's my For - tress, He's my De - liv - er - er, In

Him will I trust. Praise the name of Je - sus.

WORDS: Roy Hicks, Jr.
MUSIC: Roy Hicks, Jr.
© 1976 Latter Rain Music (ASCAP)

HICKS

17   To God Be the Glory

The Lord hath done great things for us; whereof we are glad — Psalm 126:3 KJV

1. To God be the glo - ry – great things He hath
2. O per - fect re - demp - tion, the pur - chase of
3. Great things He hath taught us, great things He hath

done! So loved He the world that He gave us His Son, Who
blood! To ev - 'ry be - liev - er the prom-ise of God; The
done, And great our re - joic - ing thru Je - sus the Son; But

yield - ed His life an a - tone-ment for sin And o - pened the
vil - est of - fen - der who tru - ly be - lieves, That mo-ment from
pur - er and high-er and great - er will be Our won-der, our

Refrain

Life - gate that all may go in.
Je - sus a par - don re - ceives.
trans-port, when Je - sus we see.

Praise the Lord, Praise the
Lord, Let the earth hear his voice! Praise the Lord, Praise the

WORDS: Fanny J. Crosby
MUSIC: William H. Doane

TO GOD BE THE GLORY

To God Be the Glory

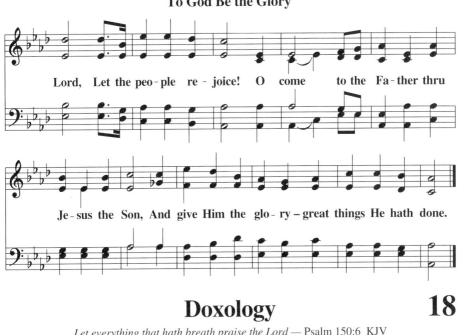

Lord, Let the peo-ple re-joice! O come to the Fa-ther thru

Je-sus the Son, And give Him the glo-ry – great things He hath done.

Doxology 18

Let everything that hath breath praise the Lord — Psalm 150:6 KJV

Praise God, from whom all bless-ings flow; Praise Him, all crea-tures

here be-low: Praise Him, a-bove ye heav'n-ly host;

Praise Fa-ther, Son, and Ho-ly Ghost. A-men.

WORDS: Thomas Ken
MUSIC: Attr. to Louis Bourgeois in the *Genevan Psalter*, 1551

OLD 100th

19 Praise Him! Praise Him!

And did all drink the same spiritual drink:
for they drank of that spiritual Rock — 1 Corinthians 10:4 KJV

1. Praise Him! Praise Him! Je-sus, our bless-ed Re-deem - er!
2. Praise Him! Praise Him! Je-sus, our bless-ed Re-deem - er!
3. Praise Him! Praise Him! Je-sus, our bless-ed Re-deem - er!

Sing, O earth – His won-der-ful love pro-claim! Hail Him!
For our sins He suf-fered and bled and died; He our
Heav'n - ly por - tals loud with ho-san-nas ring! Je - sus,

hail Him! high-est arch-an-gels in glo - ry, Strength and
Rock, our hope of e - ter-nal sal - va - tion, Hail Him!
Sav - ior, reign-eth for - ev - er and ev - er, Crown Him!

hon - or give to His ho - ly name! Like a shep - herd
hail Him! Je - sus the Cru - ci - fied. Sound His prais - es –
crown Him! Proph-et and Priest and King! Christ is com - ing,

WORDS: Fanny J. Crosby
MUSIC: Chester G. Allen

JOYFUL SONG

Praise Him! Praise Him!

Je - sus will guard His chil - dren – In His arms He
Je - sus who bore our sor - rows – Love un - bound - ed,
o - ver the world vic - to - rious – Pow'r and glo - ry

Refrain

car - ries them all day long:
won - der - ful, deep and strong: Praise Him! Praise Him! tell of His ex-cel-lent
un - to the Lord be - long:

great - ness! Praise Him! Praise Him! ev - er in joy - ful song!

Bless the Lord, O My Soul   20

And forget not all His benefits — Psalm 103:2 KJV

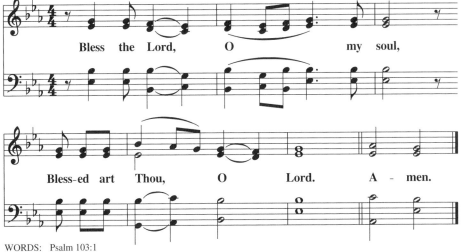

Bless the Lord, O my soul,

Bless-ed art Thou, O Lord. A - men.

WORDS: Psalm 103:1
MUSIC: Milkail Ippolitof-Ivanoff

21 Let's Just Praise the Lord

Let them praise the name of the Lord: for His name alone is excellent — Psalm 148:13 KJV

1. We thank You for Your kind-ness, we thank You for Your love, We've been in heav'n-ly plac-es, felt bless-ings from a-bove; We've been shar-ing all the good things the fam-'ly can af-ford, Let's just

2. Just the pre-cious name of Je-sus is wor-thy of our praise, Let us bow our knee be-fore Him, our hands to heav-en raise; When He comes in clouds of Glo-ry, with Him to ev-er reign, Let's

WORDS: William J. and Gloria Gaither
MUSIC: William J. and Gloria Gaither

LET'S JUST PRAISE THE LORD

Let's Just Praise the Lord

22 There's Something About That Name

*Salvation is found in no one else, for there is no other name under heaven
given to men by which we must be saved — Acts 4:12 NIV*

Je - sus, Je - sus, Je - sus! There's just some-thing a -
bout that name! ___ Mas-ter, Sav-ior, Je - sus! Like the
fra-grance af - ter the rain; _____ Je - sus,
Je - sus, Je - sus! Let all heav-en and earth pro -
claim: ___ Kings and king-doms will all pass a -

WORDS: Gloria Gaither and William J. Gaither
MUSIC: William J. Gaither

There's Something About That Name

way, But there's some-thing a - bout that name! _____

O For a Thousand Tongues to Sing   23

For the Lord knoweth the way of the righteous:
but the way of the ungodly shall perish — Psalm 1:6 KJV

1. O for a thou - sand tongues to sing My
2. My gra - cious Mas - ter and my God, As -
3. Je - sus! the name that charms our fears, That
4. He breaks the pow'r of can - celed sin, He
5. Hear Him, ye deaf; His praise, ye dumb, Your
6. Glo - ry to God and praise and love Be

great Re - deem - er's praise, The glo - ries of my
sist me to pro - claim, To spread thru all the
bids our sor - rows cease, 'Tis mu - sic in the
sets the pris - 'ner free, His blood can make the
loos-ened tongues em - ploy; Ye blind, be - hold your
ev - er, ev - er giv'n By saints be - low and

God and King, The tri - umphs of His grace.
earth a - broad The hon - ors of Thy name.
sin - ner's ears, 'Tis life and health and peace.
foul - est clean – His blood a - vailed for me.
Sav - ior come; And leap, ye lame, for joy.
saints a - bove – The Church in earth and heav'n.

WORDS: Charles Wesley
MUSIC: Carl G. Gläser; arr. by Lowell Mason

AZMON

24 Praise Him

For from the rising of the sun, even to its going down, My name shall be great — Malachi 1:11 KJV

1., 3. Praise Him! Praise Him! _ Praise Him! _____
2. Glo - ry! Glo - ry! In all things give Him

Praise Him! Je - sus, bless-ed Sav - ior, He's
glo - ry. Je - sus, bless-ed Sav - ior, He's

Fine

wor - thy to be praised. From the ris - ing of the
wor - thy to be praised. For God is our

sun un - til the go - ing down of the same; He's
Rock, hope of sal - va - tion; A

D.C.

wor - thy, Je-sus is wor - thy, He's wor-thy to be praised.
strong de-liv-er - er, in Him I will al-ways trust.

WORDS: Donnie Harper
MUSIC: Donnie Harper

High Praise

25

*Worthy is the Lamb, who was slain, to receive power and wealth
and wisdom and strength and honor and glory and praise* — Revelation 5:12 KJV

Unison

Pre-cious, ho-ly, bless-ed Sav-ior, You are wor-thy to be praised.

Heav-en and earth bow be-fore You. You are wor-thy to be praised.

Parts

Pre-cious ho-ly bless-ed Sav-ior, You are wor-thy to be prais-ed.

Hal - le - lu - jah, Hal - le - lu - jah,
Hal - le - lu - jah, Hal - le - lu - jah,

Hal - le - lu - jah,

Heav-en and earth bow be-fore You, You're wor-thy to be praised.

Hal - le - lu - jah, You're wor-thy to be praised.

WORDS: Margaret Pleasant Douroux
MUSIC: Margaret Pleasant Douroux

26 We Give You Praise

I will declare your name to my brothers;
in the presence of the congregation I will sing your praises — Hebrew 2:12 NIV

We give You praise, we give You praise;

Lord, now and al-ways, we give You praise. we give You praise.

we give You praise. We give You praise, praise,

praise, we give You praise: With our hands lift-ed high and our

voic-es to the sky, we give You praise.

WORDS: Morris Chapman
MUSIC: Morris Chapman

© Copyright 1982 Word Music, Inc. (ASCAP), 65 Music Square West, Nashville, TN 37203 /
M.U.D.A.S.A International admin. by Word Music, Inc.) (ASCAP), 65 Music Square West, Nashville, TN 37203.
All rights reserved. Made in the USA. International copyright secured. Used by permission.

How Majestic Is Your Name

27

O Lord, our Lord, how majestic is your name in all the earth — Psalm 8:1 NIV

O Lord, our Lord, how ma - jes - tic is Your name in all the earth. O earth. O Lord, _____ we praise Your name. O Lord, _____ we mag - ni - fy Your name: Prince of Peace, might - y God; O Lord God Al - might - y, O y. _____

WORDS: Michael W. Smith
MUSIC: Michael W. Smith
© 1981 Meadowgreen Music Company (ASCAP)

HOW MAJESTIC

28 Praise the Lord! Ye Heavens Adore Him

Praise ye the Lord. Praise ye the Lord from the heavens;
praise Him in the heights — Psalm 148:1 KJV

1. Praise the Lord! ye heav'ns a - dore Him; Praise Him, an - gels, in the height; Sun and moon re - joice be - fore Him; Praise Him, all ye stars of light. Praise the Lord, for He hath spo - ken; Worlds His might - y

2. Praise the Lord! for He is glo - rious; Nev - er shall His prom - ise fail; God hath made His saints vic - to - rious; Sin and death shall not pre - vail. Praise the God of our sal - va - tion! Hosts on high His

3. Wor - ship, hon - or, glo - ry, bless - ing, Lord, we of - fer un - to Thee; Young and old, Thy praise ex - press - ing, In glad hom - age bend the knee. All the saints in heav'n a - dore Thee. We would bow be -

WORDS: Stanzas 1-2: anonymous; Stanza 3: Edward Osler (Psalm 148)
MUSIC: Rowland H. Prichard

HYFRYDOL

Praise the Lord, Ye Heavens Adore Him

voice o - beyed; Law which nev - er shall be
pow'r pro - claim; Heav'n and earth and all cre -
fore Thy throne. As thine an - gels serve be -

bro - ken For their guid - ance hath He made.
a - tion Laud and mag - ni - fy His name.
fore Thee, So on earth Thy will be done.

He Is Lord   29

As I live, saith the Lord, every knee shall bow to me,
and every tongue shall confess to God — Romans 14:11 KJV

He is Lord, He is Lord, He is ris-en from the dead and He is

Lord; Ev-'ry knee shall bow, ev-'ry tongue con-fess that Je-sus Christ is Lord.

WORDS: Philippians 2:9-11
MUSIC: Source unknown

30   We Have Come into This House

Come, let us bow down in worship; let us kneel before the Lord our Maker; for He is our
God and we are the people of His pasture, the flock under His care — Psalm 95:6,7 NIV

1. We have come in-to His house and gath-ered in His name to
2. So for - get a-bout your-self and con - cen-trate on Him and
3. Let us lift up ho - ly hands and mag - ni - fy His name and

wor - ship Him. _____ We have come in - to His house and
wor - ship Him. _____ So for - get a - bout your-self and
wor - ship Him. _____ Let us lift up ho - ly hands and

gath-ered in His name to wor - ship Him. _____ We have
con - cen-trate on Him and wor - ship Him. _____ So for -
mag - ni - fy His name and wor - ship Him. _____ Let us

come in - to His house and gath-ered in His name to
get a - bout your - self and con - cen-trate on Him and
lift up ho - ly hands and mag - ni - fy His name and

WORDS: Bruce Ballinger
MUSIC: Bruce Ballinger

We Have Come into This House

wor-ship Christ the Lord. Wor-ship Him, Christ, the Lord. _
wor-ship Christ the Lord. Wor-ship Him, Christ, the Lord. _
wor-ship Christ the Lord. Wor-ship Him, Christ, the Lord. _

Glory, Glory, Hallelujah 31

Come unto me, all you who are weary and burdened,
and I will give you rest — Matthew 11:28 NIV

1. Glo - ry, glo - ry, ____ hal - le - lu - jah! ____ Since I laid my __
2. I feel bet - ter, ____ so much bet - ter, ____ Since I laid my __
3. Feel like shout - ing, ____ "Hal - le - lu - jah!" __ Since I laid my __

__ bur - den down, _____ Glo - ry, glo - ry, ____ hal - le -
__ bur - den down, _____ I feel bet - er, ____ so much
__ bur - den down, _____ Feel like shout - ing, ____ "Hal - le -

lu - jah! ____ Since I laid my ____ bur - den down. ____
bet - ter, ____ Since I laid my ____ bur - den down. ____
lu - jah!" ___ Since I laid my ____ bur-den down. ____

4. I am climbing Jacob's ladder...   5. Ev'ry round goes higher, higher...

WORDS: Traditional
MUSIC: Traditional

32 We've Come to Praise Your Name

*Sing praises to the Lord, which dwelleth in Zion:
declare among the people His doings* — Psalm 9:11 KJV

Thou art ho - ly, Thou art might-y, Praise Your name!

Praise Your name! Lord and Sav - ior, Mine for-ev - er,

Praise Your name! Praise Your name! Won - der-ful! Coun - sel-or!

King of kings and Lord of lords! Thou art ho - ly,

Thou art might - y, We've come to praise Your name! _

WORDS: Deborah Rae Thomson
MUSIC: Deborah Rae Thomson

We've Come to Praise Your Name

33 All Creatures of Our God and King

Let the heaven and earth praise Him, the seas,
and every thing that moveth therein — Psalm 69:34 KJV

1. All crea-tures of our God and King, Lift
2. Thou rush-ing wind that art so strong, Ye
3. Dear moth-er earth, who day by day Un -
4. And all ye men of ten-der heart, For -
5. Let all things their Cre - a - tor bless, And
6. *Praise God, from whom all bless-ings flow;* *Praise*

up your voice and with us sing Al - le - lu - ia,
clouds that sail in heav'n a - long, O praise Him!
fold - est bless-ings on our way, O praise Him!
giv - ing oth - ers, take your part, O sing ye!
wor - ship Him in hum - ble - ness – O praise Him!
Him, all crea-tures here be - low; *Al - le - lu - ia,*

Al - le - lu - ia! Thou burn - ing sun with gold - en
Al - le - lu - ia! Thou ris - ing morn, in praise re -
Al - le - lu - ia! The flow'rs and fruits that in thee
Al - le - lu - ia! Ye who long pain and sor - row
Al - le - lu - ia! Praise, praise the Fa - ther, praise the
Al - le - lu - ia! *Praise Him a - bove, ye heav'n - ly*

WORDS: St. 1-5, Francis of Assisi; trans. by William H. Draper;
st. 6, Thomas Ken
MUSIC: From *Geistliche Kirchengesäng;* arr. by Norman Johnson

LASST UNS ERFREUEN

All Creatures of Our God and King

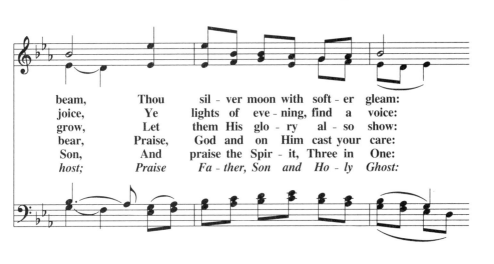

beam,   Thou sil - ver moon with soft - er gleam:
joice,   Ye   lights of eve - ning, find a voice:
grow,   Let   them His glo - ry al - so show:
bear,   Praise, God and on Him cast your care:
Son,   And   praise the Spir - it, Three in One:
host;   *Praise* *Fa - ther, Son and Ho - ly Ghost:*

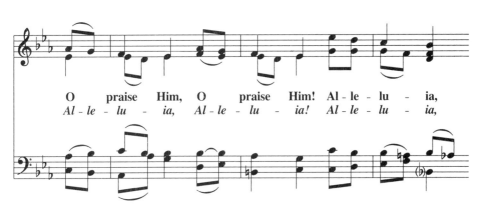

O praise Him, O praise Him! Al - le - lu - ia,
Al - le - lu - ia, Al - le - lu - ia! Al - le - lu - ia,

Al - le - lu - ia! Al - le - lu ia!
Al - le - lu - ia! Al - le - lu ia!

34 Majesty

To the only wise God our Savior, be glory and majesty, dominion and power —Jude 25 KJV

Maj - es - ty, _____ wor-ship His maj - es - ty. _____ Un - to

Je - sus be all glo - ry, hon - or, and praise. _____

Maj - es - ty, _____ king-dom au - thor - i - ty _____ flow from His

throne un - to His own; His an-them raise. _____ So ex -

WORDS: Jack Hayford
MUSIC: Jack Hayford

MAJESTY

Majesty

alt, lift up on high the name of Je - sus._____ Mag - ni -

fy, come glo - ri - fy Christ Je - sus, the King.

Maj - es - ty, _____ wor-ship His maj - es - ty; _____ Je - sus who

died, now glo - ri - fied, King of all kings. _____

35 Blessed Be the Name

Blessed be the name of the Lord from this time forth and for evermore — Psalm 113:2 KJV

1. O for a thou - sand tongues to sing,
2. Je - sus, the name that charms our fears,
3. He breaks the pow'r of can - celed sin,

Bless-ed be the name of the Lord! The glo - ries of my God and King,
Bless-ed be the name of the Lord! 'Tis mu - sic in the sin - ner's ears,
Bless-ed be the name of the Lord! His blood can make the foul-est clean,

Refrain

Bless-ed be the name of the Lord!
Bless-ed be the name of the Lord!   Bless-ed be the name,
Bless-ed be the name of the Lord!

Bless-ed be the name,   Bless-ed be the name of the Lord!

WORDS: Charles Wesley and Ralph E. Hudson
MUSIC: Ralph E. Hudson

BLESSED NAME

Blessed Be the Name

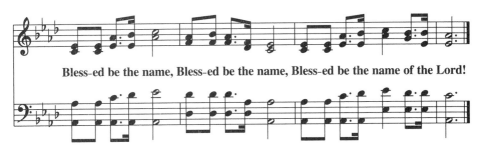

Bless-ed be the name, Bless-ed be the name, Bless-ed be the name of the Lord!

All People That on Earth Do Dwell   36

Make a joyful noise unto the Lord ... to all generations — Psalm 100:1, 5 KJV

1. All peo-ple that on earth do dwell, Sing to the Lord with cheer-ful voice; Him serve with fear, His praise forth-tell, Come ye be-fore Him and re-joice.

2. Know that the Lord is God in-deed: With-out our aid He did us make; We are His folk, He doth us feed, and for His sheep He doth us take.

3. O en-ter then His gates with praise, Ap-proach with joy His courts un-to; Praise, laud and bless His name al-ways, For it is seem-ly so to do.

4. For why? the Lord our God is good, His mer-cy is for-ev-er sure; His truth at all times firm-ly stood, And shall from age to age en-dure.

WORDS: From Psalm 100, attr. to William Kethe
MUSIC: Louis Bourgeois in the *Genevan Psalter*

OLD HUNDREDTH

37　A Mighty Fortress Is Our God

The Lord is my Rock, and my Fortress, and my Deliverer — Psalm 18:2　KJV

1. A might - y for - tress is our God, A
2. Did we in our own strength con - fide Our
3. And tho this world, with dev - ils filled, Should
4. That word a - bove all earth - ly pow'rs – No

bul - wark nev - er fail - ing; Our help - er He a - mid the flood
striv - ing would be los - ing, Were not the right Man on our side,
threat - en to un - do us, We will not fear, for God hath willed
thanks to them – a - bid - eth; The Spir - it and the gifts are ours

Of mor - tal ills pre - vail - ing. For still our an - cient foe
The Man of God's own choos - ing. Dost ask who that may be?
His truth to tri - umph thru us. The prince of dark - ness grim –
Thru Him who with us sid - eth. Let goods and kin - dred go,

Doth seek to work us woe – His craft and pow'r are great,
Christ Je - sus, it is He – Lord Sab - a - oth His name,
We trem - ble not for him; His rage we can en - dure,
This mor - tal life al - so; The bod - y they may kill:

WORDS:　Martin Luther; trans. Frederick H. Hedge
MUSIC:　Martin Luther

EIN' FESTE BURG

A Mighty Fortress Is Our God

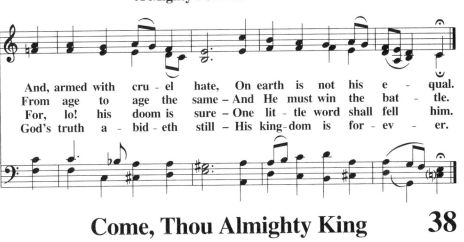

And, armed with cru - el hate, On earth is not his e - qual.
From age to age the same – And He must win the bat - tle.
For, lo! his doom is sure – One lit - tle word shall fell him.
God's truth a - bid - eth still – His king-dom is for - ev - er.

Come, Thou Almighty King 38

Lord, which is, and which was, and which is to come, the Almighty — Revelation 1:8 KJV

1. Come, Thou Al - might - y King, Help us Thy name to sing,
2. Come, Thou In - car - nate Word, Gird on Thy might - y sword,
3. Come, Ho - ly Com - fort - er, Thy sa-cred wit - ness bear
4. To the great One in Three E - ter-nal prais - es be,

Help us to praise: Fa - ther, all glo - ri - ous, O'er all vic -
Our prayer at - tend: Come, and Thy peo - ple bless, And give Thy
In this glad hour: Thou who al - might - y art, Now rule in
Hence ev - er - more: His sov-'reign maj - es - ty May we in

to - ri - ous, Come and reign o - ver us, An - cient of Days.
word suc-cess – Spir - it of ho - li - ness, On us de - scend.
ev - 'ry heart, And ne'er from us de-part, Spir - it of pow'r.
glo - ry see, And to e - ter - ni - ty Love and a - dore.

WORDS: Source unknown
MUSIC: Felice de Giardini

ITALIAN HYMN

39 My Jesus, I Love Thee

Thou knowest that I love Thee — John 21:15 KJV

1. My Je - sus, I love thee, I know Thou art mine For
2. I love Thee be - cause Thou hast first lov - ed me – And
3. I'll love Thee in life, I will love Thee in death, And
4. In man - sions of glo - ry and end - less de - light, I'll

Thee all the fol - lies of sin I re - sign; My
pur - chased my par - don on Cal - va - ry's tree; I
praise Thee as long as Thou lend - est me breath; And
ev - er a - dore Thee in heav - en so bright; I'll

gra - cious Re - deem - er, my Sav - ior art Thou: If
love Thee for wear - ing the thorns on Thy brow: If
say when the death - dew lies cold on my brow, "If
sing with the glit - ter - ing crown on my brow, "If

ev - er I loved Thee, my Je - sus, 'tis now.
ev - er I loved Thee, my Je - sus, 'tis now.
ev - er I loved Thee, my Je - sus, 'tis now."
ev - er I loved Thee, my Je - sus, 'tis now."

WORDS: William R. Featherston
MUSIC: Adoniram J. Gordon

GORDON

Joyful, Joyful, We Adore Thee 40

Mine head be lifted up above mine enemies ... I will sing praises unto the Lord — Psalm 27:6 KJV

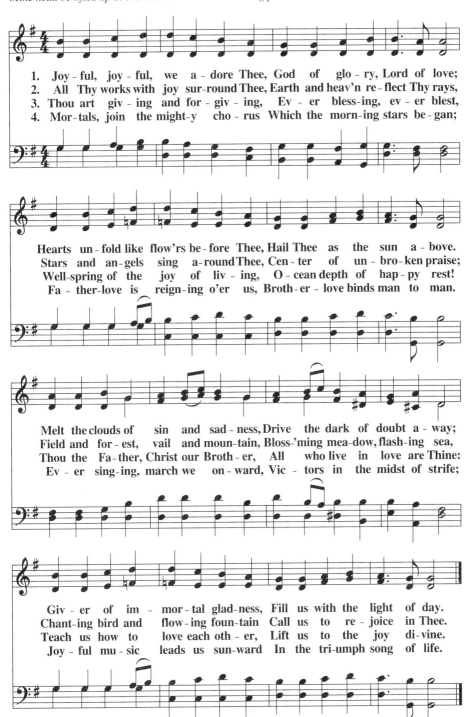

1. Joy-ful, joy-ful, we a-dore Thee, God of glo-ry, Lord of love;
2. All Thy works with joy sur-round Thee, Earth and heav'n re-flect Thy rays,
3. Thou art giv-ing and for-giv-ing, Ev-er bless-ing, ev-er blest,
4. Mor-tals, join the might-y cho-rus Which the morn-ing stars be-gan;

Hearts un-fold like flow'rs be-fore Thee, Hail Thee as the sun a-bove.
Stars and an-gels sing a-round Thee, Cen-ter of un-bro-ken praise;
Well-spring of the joy of liv-ing, O-cean depth of hap-py rest!
Fa-ther-love is reign-ing o'er us, Broth-er-love binds man to man.

Melt the clouds of sin and sad-ness, Drive the dark of doubt a-way;
Field and for-est, vail and moun-tain, Bloss-'ming mea-dow, flash-ing sea,
Thou the Fa-ther, Christ our Broth-er, All who live in love are Thine:
Ev-er sing-ing, march we on-ward, Vic-tors in the midst of strife;

Giv-er of im-mor-tal glad-ness, Fill us with the light of day.
Chant-ing bird and flow-ing foun-tain Call us to re-joice in Thee.
Teach us how to love each oth-er, Lift us to the joy di-vine.
Joy-ful mu-sic leads us sun-ward In the tri-umph song of life.

WORDS: Henry van Dyke
MUSIC: Melody from *Ninth Symphony*, Ludwig van Beethoven

HYMN TO JOY

41 This Is My Father's World

The earth is the Lord's, and the fulness thereof;
the world, and they that dwell therein — Psalm 24:1 KJV

1. This is my Fa-ther's world, And to my list-'ning ears All
2. This is my Fa-ther's world – The birds their car - ols raise; The
3. This is my Fa-ther's world – O let me ne'er for - get That

na - ture sings, and round me rings The mu - sic of the spheres.
morn-ing light, the li - ly white, De - clare their Ma - ker's praise.
tho' the wrong seems oft so strong God is the Rul - er yet.

This is my Fa-ther's world! I rest me in the thought Of
This is my Fa-ther's world! He shines in all that's fair; In the
This is my Fa-ther's world! The bat - tle is not done; Je -

rocks and trees, of skies and seas – His hand the won - ders wrought.
rus-tling grass I hear Him pass – He speaks to me ev-'ry-where.
sus who died shall be sat - is - fied, And earth and heav'n be one.

WORDS: Maltbie D. Babcock
MUSIC: Franklin L. Sheppard

TERRA BEATA

Father, I Stretch My Hands to Thee 42

For whosoever calls upon the name of the Lord shall be saved — Romans 10:13 KJV

1. Fa - ther, I stretch my hands to Thee, No oth - er
2. What did Thine on - ly Son en - dure, Be - fore I
3. O Je - sus, could I this be - lieve, I now should
4. Au - thor of Faith, to Thee I lift My wea - ry
5. Sure - ly Thou canst not let me die; O speak and
6. The worst of sin - ners would re - joice, Could they but

help I know; If Thou with - draw Thy
drew my breath! What pain, what la - bor,
feel Thy power! Now my poor soul Thou
long - ing eyes: O let me now re -
I should live; And here I will un -
see Thy face; O let me hear Thy

self from me, Ah! with - er shall I go?
to se - cure My soul from end - less death!
wouldst re - trieve, Nor let me wait one hour.
ceive that gift, My soul with - out it dies!
wea - ried lie, Till Thou Thy Spir - it give.
quick - 'ning voice And taste Thy par - d'ning grace.

WORDS: Charles Wesley
MUSIC: Hugh Wilson

MARTYRDOM

43 How Great Thou Art

Bless the Lord, O my soul; O Lord, my God, Thou art very great – Psalm 104:1 KJV

1. O Lord my God, when I in awe-some won - der
2. When thru the woods and for - est glades I wan - der
3. And when I think that God, His Son not spar - ing,
4. When Christ shall come with shout of ac - cla - ma - tion

Con - sid - er all the *worlds Thy hands have made,
And hear the birds sing sweet - ly in the trees,
Sent Him to die, I scarce can take it in —
And take me home, what joy shall fill my heart!

I see the stars, I hear the *roll - ing thun - der,
When I look down from loft - y moun-tain gran - deur
That on the cross, my bur - den glad - ly bear - ing,
Then I shall bow in hum - ble ad - o - ra - tion

Thy pow'r thru - out the un - i - verse dis - played!
And hear the brook and feel the gen - tle breeze,
He bled and died to take a - way my sin!
And there pro - claim, my God, how great Thou art!

Author's original words are "works" and "mighty."

WORDS: Stuart K. Hine
MUSIC: Stuart K. Hine

HOW GREAT THOU ART

How Great Thou Art

Refrain

Then sings my soul, my Sav-ior God, to thee; How great Thou art, how great Thou art, Then sings my soul, my Sav-ior God, to Thee, How great Thou art, how great Thou art!

Awesome God 44

For the Lord your God is God of gods, and Lord of lords, the great God, mighty and awesome, who shows no partiality — Deuteronomy 10:17 NIV

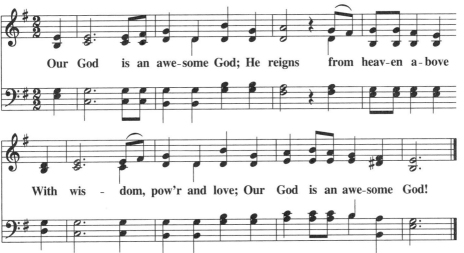

Our God is an awe-some God; He reigns from heav-en a-bove With wis - dom, pow'r and love; Our God is an awe-some God!

WORDS: Rich Mullins
MUSIC: Rich Mullins
© Copyright 1988 BMG Songs, Inc. (ASCAP)

AWESOME GOD

45   Great Is Thy Faithfulness

It is of the Lord's mercies that we are not consumed, because His compassions fail not.
They are new every morning: great is Thy faithfulness — Lamentations 3:22-23 KJV

1. "Great is Thy faith-ful-ness," O God, my Fa-ther, There is no
2. Sum-mer and win-ter, and spring-time and har-vest, Sun, moon and
3. Par-don for sin and a peace that en-dur-eth, Thine own dear

shad-ow of turn-ing with Thee; Thou chang-est not, Thy com -
stars in their cours-es a-bove Join with all na-ture in
pres-ence to cheer and to guide; Strength for to-day and bright

pas-sions, they fail not; As Thou hast been, Thou for-ev-er wilt be.
man-i-fold wit-ness To Thy great faith-ful-ness, mer-cy and love.
hope for to-mor-row; Bless-ings all mine, with ten thou-sand be-side!

Refrain

"Great is Thy faith-ful-ness! Great is Thy faith-ful-ness!" Morn-ing by

WORDS: Thomas O. Chisholm
MUSIC: William M. Runyan

FAITHFULNESS

Great is Thy Faithfulness

morn-ing new mer - cies I see; All I have need - ed, Thy

hand hath pro - vid-ed; "Great is Thy faith-ful-ness," Lord, un - to me!

O God, Our Help in Ages Past   46

Lord, Thou hast been our dwelling place in all generations — Psalm 90:1 KJV

1. O   God, our help in   a - ges past, Our hope for years to   come,
2. Un - der the shad-ow   of Thy throne Still may we dwell se - cure;
3. Be - fore the hills in   or - der stood   Or earth re-ceived her frame,
4. Time, like an ev - er   roll-ing stream, Bears all   its sons a - way;
5. O   God, our help in   a - ges past, Our hope for years to   come,

Our shel - ter from the storm - y blast, And   our e - ter - nal home!
Suf - fi - cient is Thine arm   a - lone, And   our de - fense is   sure.
From ev - er - last - ing, Thou art God, To   end - less years the same.
They fly for - got - ten, as   a dream Dies at the ope-ning day.
Be Thou our guide while life shall last, And   our e - ter - nal home.

WORDS: Isaac Watts
MUSIC: William Croft

ST. ANNE

47 He Will Hold Me Fast

Now unto Him that is able to keep you from falling — Jude 24 KJV

1. When I fear my faith will fail, Christ will hold me fast;
2. I could nev-er keep my hold, He must hold me fast;
3. I am pre-cious in His sight, He will hold me fast;
4. He'll not let my soul be lost, Christ will hold me fast;

When the tempt-er would pre-vail, He can hold me fast.
For my love is oft-en cold, He must hold me fast.
Those He saves are His de-light, He will hold me fast.
Bought by Him at such a cost, He will hold me fast.

Refrain, in harmony

He will hold me fast, He will hold me fast;
hold me fast, hold me fast;

For my Sav-ior loves me so, He will hold me fast. A-men.

WORDS: Ada R. Habershon
MUSIC: Robert Harkness

How Firm a Foundation

48

Who laid the foundations of the earth, that it should not be removed for ever — Psalm 104:5 KJV

1. How firm a foun - da - tion, ye saints of the Lord,
2. "Fear not, I am with thee, O be not dis - mayed,
3. "When thru the deep wa - ters I call thee to go,
4. "When thru fi - ery tri - als thy path - way shall lie,
5. "The soul that on Je - sus hath leaned for re - pose

Is laid for your faith in His ex - cel - lent Word!
For I am thy God, I will still give thee aid;
The riv - ers of woe shall not thee o - ver - flow;
My grace, all - suf - fi - cient, shall be thy sup - ply;
I will not, I will not de - sert to his foes;

What more can He say than to you He hath said
I'll strength - en thee, help thee, and cause thee to stand,
For I will be with thee, thy trou - bles to bless,
The flame shall not hurt thee – I on - ly de - sign
That soul, tho all hell should en - deav - or to shake,

To you, who for ref - uge to Je - sus hath fled?
Up - held by my gra - cious, om - ni - po - tent hand."
And sanc - ti - fy to thee thy deep - est dis - tress."
Thy dross to con - sume, and thy gold to re - fine."
I'll nev - er – no, nev - er – no, nev - er for - sake!"

WORDS: "K" — in Rippon's *Selection of Hymns*, 1787
MUSIC: American melody, from Caldwell's *Union Harmony*, 1837

FOUNDATION

49 He Brought Me Out

Restore unto me the joy of Thy salvation, and uphold me with Thy free spirit — Psalm 51:12 KJV

1. My heart was dis-tressed 'neath Je - ho - vah's dread frown, And
2. He placed me up - on the strong Rock by His side, My
3. He gave me a song, 'twas a new song of praise; By
4. I'll sing of His won - der - ful mer - cy to me, I'll

low in the pit where my sins dragged me down; I
steps were es - tab - lished and here I'll a - bide; No
day and by night its sweet notes I will raise; My
praise Him till all men His good - ness shall see; I'll

cried to the Lord from the deep mir - y clay, Who
dan - ger of fall - ing while here I re - main, But
heart's o - ver - flow - ing, I'm hap - py and free, I'll
sing of sal - va - tion at home and a - broad, Till

ten - der - ly brought me out to gold - en day.
stand by His grace un - til the crown I gain.
praise my Re - deem - er, who has res - cued me.
man - y shall hear the truth and trust in God.

WORDS: Henry J. Zelley; refrain by Henry L. Gilmour
MUSIC: Henry L. Gilmour

He Brought Me Out

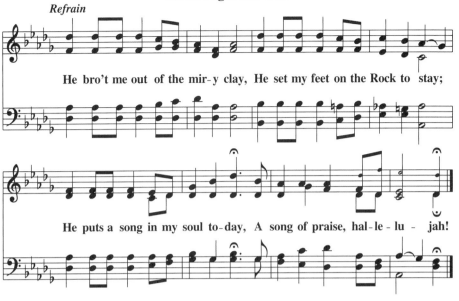

He bro't me out of the mir-y clay, He set my feet on the Rock to stay;

He puts a song in my soul to-day, A song of praise, hal-le-lu-jah!

Be Still and Know   50

Be still, and know that I am God — Psalm 46:10 KJV

1. Be still and know that I am God. Be still and know that
2. I am the Lord that heal-eth thee. I am the Lord that
3. My bound-less mer-cy shall en-dure. My bound-less mer-cy
4. I love you with a stead-fast love. I love you with a
5. In Thee, O Lord, I put my trust. In Thee, O Lord, I

I am God. Be still and know that I am God.
heal-eth thee. I am the Lord that heal-eth thee.
shall en-dure. My bound-less mer-cy shall en-dure.
stead-fast love. I love you with a stead-fast love.
put my trust. In Thee, O Lord, I put my trust.

WORDS: Stanzas 1, 2, and 5 Anonymous; stanzas 3 and 4 Tom Fettke   BE STILL AND KNOW
MUSIC: Anonymous, arranged by Lee Herrington

51 Hold to God's Unchanging Hand

Let Thine hand help me — Psalm 119:173 KJV

1. Time is filled with swift tran - si - tion,
2. Trust in Him who will not leave you,
3. Cov - et not this world's vain rich - es,
4. When your jour - ney is com - plet - ed,

Naught of earth un-moved can stand, Build your hopes on things e -
What - so - ev - er years may bring, If by earth - ly friends for -
That so rap - id - ly de - cay; Seek to gain the heav'n - ly
If to God you have been true, Fair and bright the home in

ter - nal, Hold to God's un-chang-ing hand!
sak - en, Still more close - ly to Him cling!
treas - ures, They will nev - er pass a - way!
glo - ry, Your en - rap-tured soul will view!

Refrain

Hold to God's un-chang-ing hand! Hold to
Hold to His hand, Hold to His hand,

God's un-chang-ing hand! Build your hopes on things e -

WORDS: Jennie Wilson
MUSIC: F. L. Eiland

Hold to God's Unchanging Hand

(repeat Refrain softly)

ter - nal,   Hold   to God's un-chang-ing hand!   A - men.

God Will Take Care of You   52

Casting all you care upon Him; for He careth for you — 1 Peter 5:7 KJV

1. Be not dis-mayed what-e'er be-tide, God will take care of you;
2. Thru days of toil when heart doth fail, God will take care of you;
3. All you may need He will pro-vide, God will take care of you;
4. No mat-ter what may be the test, God will take care of you;

Be-neath His wings of love a-bide, God will take care of you.
When dan-gers fierce your path as-sail, God will take care of you.
Noth-ing you ask will be de-nied, God will take care of you.
Lean, wea-ry one, up-on His breast, God will take care of you.

Refrain

God will take care of you, Thru ev-'ry day, O'er all the way;

He will take care of you, God will take care of you.
              take care of you.

WORDS: Civilla D. Martin
MUSIC: W. Stillman Martin

GOD CARES

53   My Father Watches Over Me

Your Father knoweth what things ye have need of, before ye ask Him — Matthew 6:8 KJV

Solo or Unison

1. I trust in God, wher - ev - er I may be, Up - on the land, or on the roll - ing sea, For, come what may, From day to day, My heav'n-ly Fa - ther watch-es o - ver day,

2. He makes the rose an ob - ject of His care, He guides the ea - gle thru the path-less air, And sure - ly He Re - mem-bers me, My heav'n-ly Fa - ther watch-es o - ver me,

3. I trust in God, for, in the li - on's den, On bat - tle field, or in the pris - on pen, Thru praise or blame, Thru flood or flame, My heav'n-ly Fa - ther watch-es o - ver flame,

4. The val - ley may be dark, the shad - ows deep, But, O, the Shep - herd guards His lone - ly sheep; And thru the gloom He'll lead me home, My heav'n-ly Fa - ther watch-es o - ver home,

WORDS: Rev. W. C. Martin
MUSIC: Charles H. Gabriel

My Father Watches Over Me

Refrain (parts)

me.
me.
me.
me.

I trust in God, I know He cares for

me, On moun-tain bleak or on the storm-y

He cares for me, On moun-tain bleak or on the

sea; Tho' bil-lows roll, He keeps my

sea, the storm-y sea; Tho' bil-lows roll, tho' bil-lows roll, He

soul, My heav'n-ly Fa-ther watch-es o - ver me.

keeps my soul,

54 Savior, Like a Shepherd Lead Us

Lead me in the way everlasting — Psalm 139:24 KJV

1. Sav - ior, like a shep-herd lead us, Much we need Thy ten-der care;
2. We are Thine, do Thou be - friend us, Be the Guard-ian of our way;
3. Thou hast prom-ised to re - ceive us, Poor and sin - ful tho' we be;
4. Ear - ly let us seek Thy fa - vor, Ear - ly let us do Thy will;

In Thy pleas - ant pas-tures feed us, For our use Thy folds pre-pare.
Keep Thy flock, from sin de - fend us, Seek us when we go a - stray.
Thou hast mer - cy to re - lieve us, Grace to cleanse and pow'r to free.
Bless - ed Lord and on - ly Sav - ior, With Thy love our bos-oms fill.

Bless-ed Je - sus, Bless-ed Je - sus, Thou hast bought us, Thine we are;
Bless-ed Je - sus, Bless-ed Je - sus, Hear, O hear us when we pray;
Bless-ed Je - sus, Bless-ed Je - sus, Ear - ly let us turn to Thee;
Bless-ed Je - sus, Bless-ed Je - sus, Thou hast loved us, love us still;

Bless-ed Je - sus, Bless-ed Je - sus, Thou hast bought us, Thine we are.
Bless-ed Je - sus, Bless-ed Je - sus, Hear, O hear us when we pray.
Bless-ed Je - sus, Bless-ed Je - sus, Ear - ly let us turn to Thee.
Bless-ed Je - sus, Bless-ed Je - sus, Thou hast loved us, love us still.

WORDS: From *Hymns for the Young,* 1836; attr. to Dorothy A. Thrupp
MUSIC: William B. Bradbury

BRADBURY

Like a River Glorious 55

I will extend peace to her like a river — Isaiah 66:12 KJV

1. Like a riv - er glo - rious Is God's per - fect peace,
2. Hid - den in the hol - low Of His bless - ed hand,
3. Ev - 'ry joy or tri - al Fall - eth from a - bove,

O - ver all vic - to - rious In its bright in - crease; Per - fect, yet it
Nev - er foe can fol - low, Nev - er trai - tor stand; Not a surge of
Traced up - on our di - al By the Sun of Love; We may trust Him

flow - eth Full - er ev - 'ry day, Per - fect, yet it grow - eth
wor - ry, Not a shade of care, Not a blast of hur - ry
ful - ly All for us to do — They who trust Him whol - ly

Refrain

Deep - er all the way.
Touch the spir - it there. Stayed up - on Je - ho - vah, Hearts are ful - ly
Find Him whol - ly true.

blest — Find-ing, as He prom - ised, Per - fect peace and rest.

WORDS: Frances R. Havergal
MUSIC: James Mountain

WYE VALLEY

56 Peace! Be Still!

And the wind ceased, and there was a great calm — Mark 4:39 KJV

1. Mas-ter, the tem-pest is rag - ing! The bil-lows are toss-ing high! The
2. Mas-ter, with an-guish of spir - it I bow in my grief to - day; The
3. Mas-ter, the ter - ror is o - ver, The el - e-ments sweet-ly rest; Earth's

sky is o'er-shad-owed with black - ness, No shel - ter or help is nigh:
depths of my sad heart are trou - bled; O wak - en and save, I pray!
sun in the calm lake is mir - rored, And heav-en's with - in my breast.

"Car - est Thou not that we per - ish?" How canst Thou lie a - sleep, When each
Tor-rents of sin and of an-guish Sweep o'er my sink-ing soul! And I
Lin - ger, O bless-ed Re-deem-er, Leave me a - lone no more; And with

mo-ment so mad - ly is threat-'ning A grave in the an - gry deep?
per - ish! I per - ish, dear Mas - ter; O has-ten, and take con - trol!
joy I shall make the blest har - bor, And rest on the bliss - ful shore.

WORDS: Mary A. Baker
MUSIC: H. R. Palmer

Peace! Be Still!

57 Think of His Goodness to You

For the Lord is good; His mercy is everlasting — Psalm 100:5 KJV

1. When waves of af - flic - tion sweep o - ver the soul,
2. The world may for - sake you, and those whom you trust
3. Mis - for - tune's dark cloud may hang o - ver the way,
4. When dear ones are tak - en a - way from you here,

And sun - light is hid - den from view,
May prove to be false and un - true;
De - spite your best ef - forts to do;
You loved with af - fec - tion so true;

If ev - er you're tempt - ed to fret or com - plain,
There's One you can trust, e - ven un - to the end;
The Sav - ior is guard - ing your treas - ures up there;
Look un - to the Sav - ior for strength to en - dure,

Just think of His good - ness to you.
Just think of His good - ness to you.
Just think of His good - ness to you.
And think of His good - ness to you.

WORDS: R. C. Ward
MUSIC: R. C. Ward

Think of His Goodness to You

Just think of His good - ness to you;

good - ness, His good - ness to you;

Yes, think of His good - ness to you;

good - ness, His good - ness to you;

Tho' storms o'er thee sweep, He is a - ble to keep;

O think of His good - ness to you.

58 Without God I Could Do Nothing

God is our refuge and strength — Psalm 46:1 KJV

With-out God I could do noth-ing, _____ With-out Him I would fail; _____ With-out Him my life would be rug-ged, Like a ship with-out a sail. _____

1. With-out a doubt He is my Sav-ior, ____ My strength a-long life's way; _____ In deep wa-ter He is my
2. I'm lean-ing and de-pend-ing on Je-sus, ____ I'm trust-ing and I know He cares; _____ I'm wait-ing, just wait-ing for my
3. My soul is an-chored in Je-sus, ____ Tho' storms and bil-lows may roll; _____ Sa-tan has so man-y temp-

WORDS: Beatrice Brown
MUSIC: Beatrice Brown; arr. by Kenneth Morris

Without God I Could Do Nothing

D.C.

an - chor; _____	Thru	faith	He'll be	my	stay. _____
Sav-ior; _____	I	know He'll	dry all	my	tears. _____
ta - tions; _____	God's the cap - tain	of		my	soul. _____

Great God, We Sing That Mighty Hand 59

For the Lord upholdeth him with His hand — Psalm 37:24 KJV

1. Great God, we sing that might - y hand By which sup -
2. By day, by night, at home, a - broad, Still are we
3. With grate-ful hearts the past we own; The fu - ture,
4. In scenes ex - alt - ed or de-pressed Thou art our

port - ed still we stand; The ope - ning year Thy
guard - ed by our God; By His in - ces - sant
all to us un - known, We to Thy guard - ian
joy, and Thou our rest; Thy good-ness all our

mer - cy shows, That mer - cy crowns it till it close.
boun - ty fed, By His un - err - ing coun - sel led.
care com - mit, And, peace - ful, leave be - fore Thy feet.
hopes shall raise, A - dored thru all our chang - ing days.

WORDS: Philip Doddridge
MUSIC: George J. Elvey

ST. CRISPIN

60 His Eye Is On the Sparrow

The eyes of the Lord are upon the righteous — Psalm 34:15 KJV

Unison

1. Why should I feel dis-cour-aged, Why should the shad-ows come, Why should my heart be lone-ly And long for heav'n and home, When Je-sus is my por-tion? My con-stant Friend is He:

2. "Let not your heart be trou-bled," His ten-der word I hear, And rest-ing on His good-ness, I lose my doubts and fears; Tho' by the path He lead-eth But one step I may see: But

3. When-ev-er I am tempt-ed, When-ev-er clouds a-rise, When song gives place to sigh-ing, When hope with-in me dies, I draw the clos-er to Him, From care He sets me free: His

WORDS: Mrs. C. D. Martin
MUSIC: Charles H. Gabriel

His Eye Is On the Sparrow

61 What a Friend We Have in Jesus

A friend loveth at all times — Proverbs 17:17 KJV

1. What a friend we have in Je - sus, All our sins and griefs to bear!
2. Have we tri - als and temp-ta - tions? Is there trou-ble an - y-where?
3. Are we weak and heav - y la - den, Cum-bered with a load of care?

What a priv - i - lege to car - ry Ev - 'ry-thing to God in prayer!
We should nev - er be dis-cour-aged – Take it to the Lord in prayer.
Pre - cious Sav-ior, still our ref - uge – Take it to the Lord in prayer.

O what peace we oft - en for - feit, O what need-less pain we bear,
Can we find a friend so faith - ful Who will all our sor-rows share?
Do thy friends de-spise, for-sake thee? Take it to the Lord in prayer;

All be - cause we do not car - ry Ev - 'ry-thing to God in prayer!
Je - sus knows our ev - 'ry weak-ness – Take it to the Lord in prayer.
In His arms He'll take and shield thee – Thou wilt find a sol-ace there.

WORDS: Joseph Scriven
MUSIC: Charles C. Converse

CONVERS

No, Not One!

62

Greater love hath no man than this,
that a man lay down his life for his friends — John 15:13 KJV

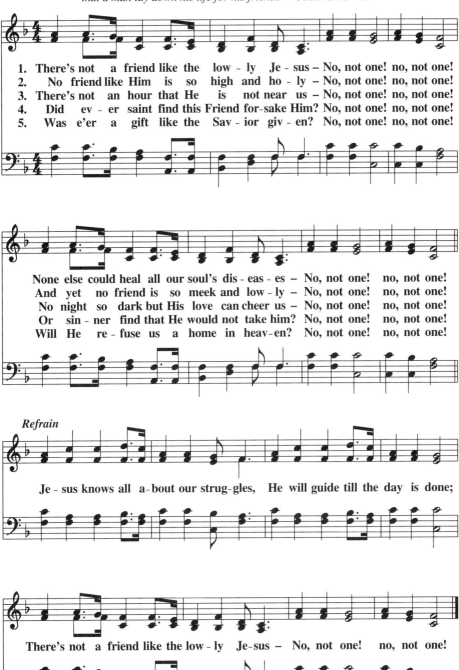

1. There's not a friend like the low - ly Je - sus – No, not one! no, not one!
2. No friend like Him is so high and ho - ly – No, not one! no, not one!
3. There's not an hour that He is not near us – No, not one! no, not one!
4. Did ev - er saint find this Friend for-sake Him? No, not one! no, not one!
5. Was e'er a gift like the Sav - ior giv - en? No, not one! no, not one!

None else could heal all our soul's dis - eas - es – No, not one! no, not one!
And yet no friend is so meek and low - ly – No, not one! no, not one!
No night so dark but His love can cheer us – No, not one! no, not one!
Or sin - ner find that He would not take him? No, not one! no, not one!
Will He re - fuse us a home in heav - en? No, not one! no, not one!

Refrain

Je - sus knows all a-bout our strug-gles, He will guide till the day is done;

There's not a friend like the low - ly Je-sus – No, not one! no, not one!

WORDS: Johnson Oatman, Jr.
MUSIC: George C. Hugg

HARPER MEMORIAL

63 The Name of Jesus

At the name of Jesus every knee should bow — Philippians 2:10 KJV

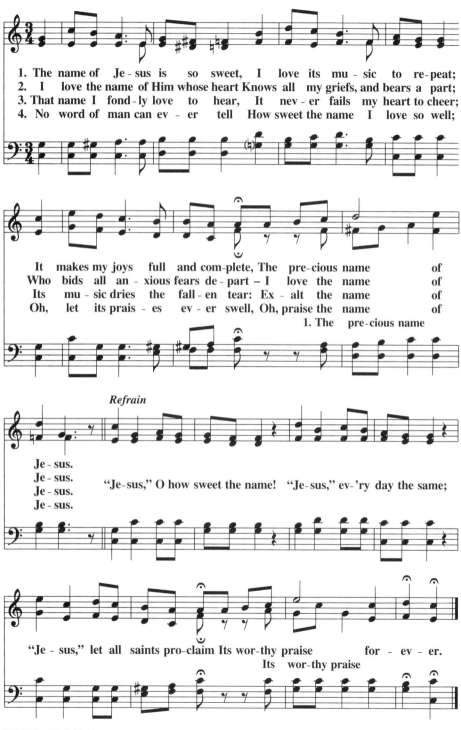

1. The name of Je-sus is so sweet, I love its mu-sic to re-peat;
2. I love the name of Him whose heart Knows all my griefs, and bears a part;
3. That name I fond-ly love to hear, It nev-er fails my heart to cheer;
4. No word of man can ev-er tell How sweet the name I love so well;

It makes my joys full and com-plete, The pre-cious name of
Who bids all an-xious fears de-part – I love the name of
Its mu-sic dries the fall-en tear: Ex-alt the name of
Oh, let its prais-es ev-er swell, Oh, praise the name of

1. The pre-cious name

Refrain

Je-sus.
Je-sus.
Je-sus.
Je-sus.

"Je-sus," O how sweet the name! "Je-sus," ev-'ry day the same;

"Je-sus," let all saints pro-claim Its wor-thy praise for-ev-er.

Its wor-thy praise

WORDS: W. C. Martin
MUSIC: Edmund S. Lorenz

Jesus, Lover of My Soul 64

For in the time of trouble He shall hide me in His pavillion — Psalm 27:5 KJV

1. Je - sus, lov - er of my soul, Let me to Thy bos - om fly,
2. Oth - er ref - uge have I none – Hangs my help-less soul on Thee;
3. Thou, O Christ, are all I want, More than all in Thee I find;
4. Plen-teous grace with Thee is found, Grace to cov - er all my sin;

While the near - er wa - ters roll, While the tem-pest still is high!
Leave, ah, leave me not a - lone, Still sup-port and com - fort me!
Raise the fall - en, cheer the faint, Heal the sick and lead the blind.
Let the heal-ing streams a-bound, Make and keep me pure with - in.

Hide me, O my Sav - ior, hide – Till the storm of life is past;
All my trust on Thee is stayed – All my help from Thee I bring;
Just and ho - ly is Thy name – I am all un - right-eous - ness;
Thou of life the foun-tain art – Free-ly let me take of Thee;

Safe in - to the ha - ven guide, O re - ceive my soul at last!
Cov - er my de-fense-less head With the shad-ow of Thy wing.
False and full of sin I am, Thou art full of truth and grace.
Spring Thou up with-in my heart, Rise to all e - ter - ni - ty.

WORDS: Charles Wesley
MUSIC: Simeon B. Marsh

MARTYN

65 Love Divine

1. Love di-vine, all love ex-cel-ling, Joy of heav'n, to earth come down!
2. Breathe, O breathe Thy lov-ing Spir-it In-to ev-'ry trou-bled breast!
3. Come, Al-might-y to de-liv-er, Let us all Thy life re-ceive;
4. Fin-ish then Thy new cre-a-tion; Pure and spot-less let us be;

Fix in us Thy hum-ble dwell-ing; All Thy faith-ful mer-cies crown.
Let us all in Thee in-her-it, Let us find that se-cond rest.
Sud-den-ly re-turn and nev-er, Nev-er-more Thy tem-ples leave:
Let us see Thy great sal-va-tion, Per-fect-ly re-stored in Thee:

Je-sus, Thou are all com-pas-sion, Pure, un-bound-ed love Thou art;
Take a-way our bent to sin-ning; Al-pha and O-me-ga be;
Thee we would be al-ways bless-ing, Serve Thee as Thy hosts a-bove,
Changed from glo-ry in-to glo-ry, Till in heav'n we take our place,

Vis-it us with Thy sal-va-tion; En-ter ev-'ry trem-bling heart.
End of faith as its be-gin-ning, Set our hearts at lib-er-ty.
Pray and praise Thee with-out ceas-ing, Glo-ry in Thy per-fect love.
Till we cast our crowns be-fore Thee, lost in won-der, love, and praise.

WORDS: Charles Wesley
MUSIC: John Zundel

BEECHER

Jesus Loves Even Me

66

For God is love — 1 John 4:8 KJV

1. I am so glad that our Fa-ther in heav'n Tells of His love in the
2. Tho I for-get Him and wan-der a - way, Still He doth love me wher-
3. O if there's on - ly one song I can sing When in His beau-ty I

Book He has giv'n; Won-der-ful things in the Bi - ble I see —
ev - er I stray; Back to His dear lov-ing arms would I flee
see the great King, This shall my song in e - ter - ni-ty be:

Refrain

This is the dear-est, that Je - sus loves me. I am so glad that
When I re-mem-ber that Je - sus loves me.
"O what a won-der that Je - sus loves me!"

Je - sus loves me, Je - sus loves me, Je - sus loves me;

I am so glad that Je-sus loves me, Je-sus loves e - ven me.

WORDS: Philip P. Bliss
MUSIC: Philip P. Bliss

GLADNESS

67 Tell Me the Stories of Jesus

Hosanna in the highest — Mark 11:10 KJV

Unison or two-part

1. Tell me the sto - ries of Je - sus I love to hear;
2. First let me hear how the chil - dren Stood 'round His knee,
3. In - to the cit - y I'd fol - low The chil - dren's band,

Things I would ask Him to tell me If He were here:
And I shall fan - cy His bless - ing Rest - ing on me;
Wav-ing a branch of the palm tree High in my hand;

Scenes by the way - side, Tales of the sea,
Words full of kind - ness, Deeds full of grace,
One of His her - alds, Yes, I would sing

Sto - ries of Je - sus, Tell them to me.
All in the love - light Of Je - sus' face.
Loud - est ho - san - nas, "Je - sus is King!" A - men.

WORDS: William H. Parker
MUSIC: Frederic A. Challinor

STORIES OF JESUS

Only One

68

The Lord our God is one Lord — Mark 12:29 KJV

1. There is but One with change-less love, On - ly One, on - ly One;
2. There is but One who leads us right, On - ly One, on - ly One;
3. There is but One who saves by grace, On - ly One, on - ly One;
4. There is but One who died to save, On - ly One, on - ly One;

Close to our souls He bends a - bove, And this One is Je - sus.
One who is near by day and night; And this One is Je - sus.
Free - ly He bless - es all the race, And this One is Je - sus.
Free - ly His life for us He gave, And this One is Je - sus.

Refrain

On - ly One who can save the soul, Wash it, cleanse it and make it whole,

On - ly One who can sin con - trol, And this One is Je - sus.

WORDS: Clarence A. Truli
MUSIC: Clarence A. Truli

69 Put Your Hand in the Hand

He arose and rebuked the wind and said to the sea, "Peace, be still!"
And the wind ceased, and there was a great calm — Mark 4:39 KJV

Put your hand in the hand of the man who stilled the wa - ter.

Put your hand in the hand of the man who calmed the

sea. Take a look at your-self and - a

you can look at oth - ers dif - f'rent - ly. By put-tin' your

Fine

hand in the hand of the man from-a Gal - i - lee.

WORDS: Gene MacLellan
MUSIC: Gene MacLellan

Put Your Hand in the Hand

Ev - 'ry time I look in - to the Ho - ly Book I wan-na trem - ble. _____

When I read a - bout the part where a car-pen-ter cleared the

tem - ple, _____ For the buy-ers and the sell-ers were

no dif-f'rent fel - las than what I pro - fess to be, And it

D.C. al Fine

caus-es me pain to know I'm not the per-son I should be; _____

70 Jesus Is the Answer

Whosoever drinketh of the water that I shall give Him shall never thirst — John 4:14 KJV

Je - sus is the an - swer for the world to - day; A -
bove Him there's no oth - er, Je - sus is the Way.
Je - sus is the an - swer for the world to - day; A -
bove Him there's no oth - er, Je - sus is the Way.

WORDS: Andraé Crouch and Sandra Crouch
MUSIC: Andraé Crouch and Sandra Crouch; arranged by Dennis Allen

Bless That Wonderful Name

71

Rejoice in the Lord always. I will say it again: rejoice! — Philippians 4:4 NIV

1. Bless that won-der-ful name _ of Je - sus,

Bless that won-der-ful name _ of Je - sus,

Bless that won-der-ful name _ of Je - sus,

No oth-er name _ I know.

2. Sing... 3. Preach... 4. Praise... 5. Share...

WORDS: Traditional African American
MUSIC: Traditional African American

WONDERFUL NAME

72 Jesu, Joy of Man's Desiring

I am the way, the truth, and the life — John 14:6 KJV

1. Je - su, joy of man's de - sir - ing, Ho - ly
2. Through the way where hope is guid-ing, Hark what

wis - dom love most bright, Drawn by Thee our souls as -
peace - ful mu - sic rings Where the flock in Thee con -

pir - ing Soar to un - cre - at - ed light. Word of
fid - ing Drink of joy from death - less springs. Theirs is

God, our flesh that fash-ioned with the fire of
beau - ty's fair - est plea-sure, theirs is wis - dom's

WORDS: Martin Janus
MUSIC: Johann Schop; arranged and harmonized by J.S. Bach

Jesu, Joy of Man's Desiring

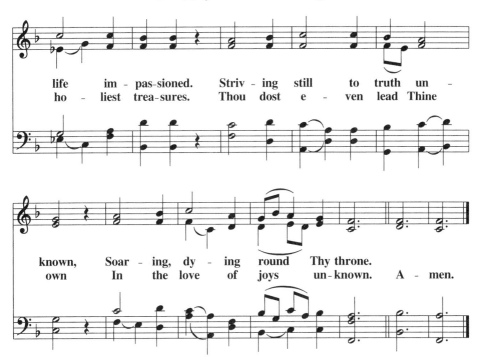

life | im - pas-sioned. | Striv - ing | still | | to | truth | un -
ho - liest | trea-sures. | Thou | dost | e - | ven | lead | Thine

known, | Soar - ing, | dy - ing | round | Thy throne.
own | In | the love | of | joys | un- known. | A - men.

Jesus in the Morning   73

My tongue will speak of Your righteousness
and of Your praises all the day long — Psalm 35:28 NIV

Je - sus, Je - sus, Je-sus in the morn-ing, Je-sus in the noon-time.

Je - sus, Je - sus, Je-sus when the sun goes down.

2. Praise Him… 3. Love Him… 4. Serve Him… 5. Jesus…

WORDS: Traditional
MUSIC: Traditional

74   Jesus, Priceless Treasure

Christ, in whom are hidden all the treasures of wisdom and knowledge — Colossians 2:2-3 KJV

1. Je - sus, price - less trea - sure, Source of pur - est plea - sure,
2. In Thy strength I rest me; Foes who would mo - lest me
3. Ban - ished is our sad - ness! For the Lord of glad - ness,

Tru - est Friend to me. Long my heart hath pant - ed,
Can - not reach me here. Tho' the earth be shak - ing,
Je - sus en - ters in. Those who love the Fa - ther,

'Til it well - nigh faint - ed, Thirst-ing af - ter Thee.
Ev - 'ry heart be quak - ing, God dis - pels our fear.
Tho' the storms may gath - er, Still have peace with - in.

Thine I am, O spot - less Lamb, I will suf - fer naught to
Sin and hell in con - flict fell With their heav-iest storms as -
Yea, what-e'er we here must bear, Still in Thee lies pur - est

WORDS: Johann Franck; translated by Catherine Winkworth
MUSIC: Traditional German melody; adapted by Johann Crüger

JESU, MEINE FREUDE

Jesus, Priceless Treasure

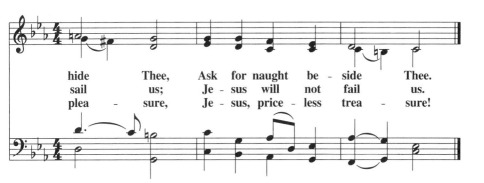

hide Thee, Ask for naught be - side Thee.
sail us; Je - sus will not fail us.
plea - sure, Je - sus, price - less trea - sure!

Fairest Lord Jesus   75

Thou art of purer eyes than to behold evil — Habakkuk 1:13 KJV

1. Fair - est Lord Je - sus! Rul - er of all na - ture!
2. Fair are the mead - ows, Fair - er still the wood - lands,
3. Fair is the sun - shine, Fair - er still the moon - light,

O Thou of God and man the Son! Thee will I cher - ish,
Robed in the bloom - ing garb of spring; Je - sus is fair - er,
And all the twin - kling star - ry host; Je - sus shines bright-er,

Thee will I hon - or, Thou my soul's glo-ry, joy, and crown!
Je - sus is pur - er, Who makes the woe-ful heart to sing!
Je - sus shines pur - er, Than all the an-gels heav'n can boast!

WORDS: Anonymous, from *Münster Gesangbuch*; st. 4. trans. by Joseph A. Seiss   CRUSADERS' HYMN
MUSIC: From *Schlesische Volkslieder*, 1842; arr. by Richard S. Willis

76   Wonderful, Wonderful Jesus

But we see Jesus ... crowned with glory and honor — Hebrews 2:9 KJV

1. There is nev - er a day so drear - y,
2. There is nev - er a cross so heav - y,
3. There is nev - er a care or bur - den,
4. There is nev - er a guilt - y sin - ner,

There is nev - er a night so long, (so long,)
There is nev - er a weight of woe, (of woe,)
There is nev - er a grief or loss, (or loss,)
There is nev - er a wan - d'ring one, (not one,)

But the soul that is trust - ing Je - sus
But that Je - sus will help to car - ry
But that Je - sus in love will light - en
But that God can in mer - cy par - don

Will some - where find a song. (a song.)
Be - cause He lov - eth so. (loves so.)
When car - ried to the cross. (the cross.)
Thru Je - sus Christ, His Son. (His Son.)

WORDS: Anna B. Russell

MUSIC: Ernest O. Sellers

NEW ORLEANS

Wonderful, Wonderful Jesus

77 Jesus Is Coming Again

I will come again and receive you unto myself — John 14:3 KJV

1. Mar - vel - ous mes-sage we bring, Glo - ri - ous car - ol we
2. For - est and flow - er ex - claim, Moun-tain and mead-ow the
3. Stand-ing be - fore Him at last, Tri - al and trou - ble all

sing, Won - der - ful word of the King:
same, All earth and heav - en pro - claim:
past, Crowns at His feet we will cast:

Refrain, in Unison

Je - sus is com-ing a - gain! (a - gain!)
Je - sus is com-ing a - gain! (a - gain!) Com - ing a -
Je - sus is com-ing a - gain! (a - gain!)

gain, Com - ing a - gain;

WORDS: John W. Peterson COMING AGAI
MUSIC: John W. Peterson

Jesus Is Coming Again

78 He's the One

Christ is all, and is in all — Colossians 3:11 NIV

1. Is there an-y-one can help us – one who un-der-stands our hearts,
2. Is there an-y-one can help us when the load is hard to bear.
3. Is there an-y-one can help us who can give the sin-ner peace,
4. Is there an-y-one can help us when the end is draw-ing near,

When the thorns of life have pierced them till they bleed;
And we faint and fall be-neath it in a-larm;
When his heart is bur-dened down with pain and woe;
Who will go thru death's dark wa-ters by our side;

One who sym-pa-thiz-es with us, who in won-drous love im-parts
Who in ten-der-ness will lift us, and the heav-y bur-den share,
Who can speak the word of par-don, that af-fords a sweet re-lease,
Who will light the way be-fore us, and dis-pel all doubt and fear,

Just the ver-y, ver-y bless-ing that we need?
And sup-port us with an ev-er-last-ing arm?
And whose blood can wash and make us white as snow?
And will bear our spir-its safe-ly o'er the tide?

WORDS: J. B. Mackay
WORDS: J. B. Mackay

He's the One

Refrain

Yes, there's One, Yes, there's one, on - ly One! on - ly one! The bless-ed, bless-ed Je-sus, He's the One! When af-flic-tions press the soul, When waves of trou-ble roll, And you need a Friend to help you, He's the One!

He Keeps Me Singing 79

A name which is above every name — Phillipians 2:9 KJV

Je - sus, Je - sus, Je - sus — Sweet-est name I know, Fills my ev - 'ry long - ing, Keeps me sing-ing as I go.

WORDS: Luther B. Bridgers
MUSIC: Luther B. Bridgers

SWEETEST NAME

80 The Lily of the Valley

I am the rose of Sharon, and the lily of the valleys — Song of Solomon 2:1 KJV

1. I have found a friend in Je-sus – He's ev-'ry-thing to me,
2. He all my griefs has tak-en and all my sor-rows borne,
3. He will nev-er, nev-er leave me nor yet for-sake me here,

He's the fair-est of ten thou-sand to my soul;
In temp-ta-tion He's my strong and might-y tow'r;
While I live by faith and do His bless-ed will;

The Lil-y of the Val-ley – in Him a-lone I see
I have all for Him for-sak-en and all my i-dols torn
A wall of fire a-bout me, I've noth-ing now to fear –

All I need to cleanse and make me ful-ly whole.
From my heart, and now He keeps me by His pow'r.
With His man-na He my hun-gry soul shall fill.

WORDS: Charles W. Fry
MUSIC: William S. Hays

SALVATIONIST

The Lily of the Valley

81   Jesus, the Light of the World

I am the Light of the World — John 8:12 KJV

1. Hark! the her - ald an - gels sing, Je-sus, the light of the
2. Joy - ful, all ye na - tions, rise, Je-sus, the light of the
3. Christ, by high - est heav'n a - dored, Je-sus, the light of the
4. Hail the heav'n-born Prince of Peace! Je-sus, the light of the

world; Glo - ry to the new - born King, Je-sus, the light of the
world; Join the tri - umph of the skies, Je-sus, the light of the
world; Christ, the ev - er - last - ing Lord, Je-sus, the light of the
world; Hail the Sun of right-eous - ness! Je-sus, the light of the

Refrain

world. We'll walk in the light, beau - ti - ful light,

Come where the dew-drops of mer-cy are bright, Shine all a-round us by

day and by night. Je-sus, the light of the world. A - men.

WORDS: Charles Wesley and George D. Elderkin
MUSIC: George D. Elderkin

O Come, O Come, Emmanuel 82

Behold...Emmanuel, which being interpreted is, God with us — Matthew 1:23 KJV

1. O come, O come, Em - man - u - el, And ran - som cap - tive
2. O come, O come, Thou Lord of might, Who to Thy tribes on
3. O come, Thou Rod of Jes - se, free Thine own from Sa - tan's
4. O come, Thou Day - spring, come and cheer Our spir - its by Thine
5. O come, Thou Key of Da - vid, come And o - pen wide our

Is - ra - el, That mourns in lone - ly ex - ile here Un -
Si - nai's height, In an - cient times didst give the law In
tyr - an - ny; From depths of hell Thy peo - ple save And
ad - vent here; O drive a - way the shades of night And
heav'n - ly home Where all Thy saints with Thee shall dwell – O

Refrain

til the Son of God ap - pear.
cloud and maj - es - ty and awe.
give them vic - t'ry o'er the grave.   Re - joice! re - joice!
pierce the clouds and bring us light.
come, O come, Em - man - u - el!

Em - man - u - el shall come to thee, O Is - ra - el.

WORDS: 9th century Latin hymn; trans. by John M. Neale   VENI EMMANUEL
MUSIC: 15th century French plainsong; adapt. Thomas Helmore

83 While Shepherds Watched Their Flocks

For unto you is born this day ... a Savior, which is Christ the Lord — Luke 2:11 KJV

1. While shep-herds watched their flocks by night, All seat - ed
2. "Fear not!" said he, for might - y dread Had seized their
3. "To you in Da - vid's town this day Is born of
4. "The heav'n - ly Babe you there shall find To hu - man
5. "All glo - ry be to God on high, And to the

on the ground, The an - gel of the Lord came down,
trou - bled mind; "Glad ti - dings of great joy I bring
Da - vid's line, The Sav - ior who is Christ the Lord,
view dis - played, All mean - ly wrapt in swath - ing bands
earth be peace: Good will hence - forth from heav'n to men

And glo - ry shone a - round, And glo - ry shone a - round.
To you and all man - kind, To you and all man - kind."
And this shall be the sign — And this shall be the sign:
And in a man - ger laid, And in a man - ger laid."
Be - gin and nev - er cease! Be - gin and nev - er cease!"

WORDS: Nahum Tate
MUSIC: Arr. from George F. Handel in Weyman's *Melodia sacra*, 1815

CHRISTMAS

It Came upon the Midnight Clear 84

The angel of the Lord came upon them,
and the glory of the Lord shone round about them — Luke 2:9 KJV

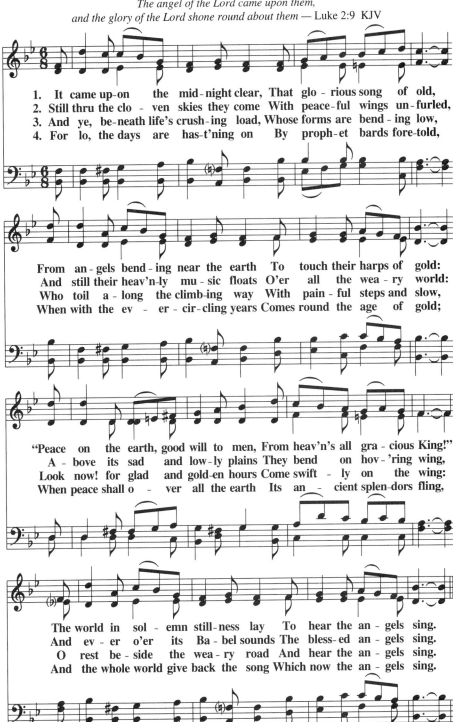

1. It came up-on the mid-night clear, That glo-rious song of old,
2. Still thru the clo-ven skies they come With peace-ful wings un-furled,
3. And ye, be-neath life's crush-ing load, Whose forms are bend-ing low,
4. For lo, the days are has-t'ning on By proph-et bards fore-told,

From an-gels bend-ing near the earth To touch their harps of gold:
And still their heav'n-ly mu-sic floats O'er all the wea-ry world:
Who toil a-long the climb-ing way With pain-ful steps and slow,
When with the ev-er-cir-cling years Comes round the age of gold;

"Peace on the earth, good will to men, From heav'n's all gra-cious King!"
A-bove its sad and low-ly plains They bend on hov-'ring wing,
Look now! for glad and gold-en hours Come swift-ly on the wing:
When peace shall o-ver all the earth Its an-cient splen-dors fling,

The world in sol-emn still-ness lay To hear the an-gels sing.
And ev-er o'er its Ba-bel sounds The bless-ed an-gels sing.
O rest be-side the wea-ry road And hear the an-gels sing.
And the whole world give back the song Which now the an-gels sing.

WORDS: Edmund H. Sears
MUSIC: Richard S. Willis

CAROL

85 Angels, from the Realms of Glory

There was with the angel a multitude of the heavenly host praising God — Luke 2:13 KJV

1. An - gels, from the realms of glo - ry, Wing your flight o'er
2. Shep-herds in the fields a - bid - ing, Watch-ing o'er your
3. Sag - es, leave your con - tem-pla - tions, Bright - er vi - sions
4. Saints be - fore the al - tar bend - ing, Watch-ing long in

all the earth; Ye who sang cre - a - tion's sto - ry,
flocks by night, God with man is now re - sid - ing,
beam a - far; Seek the great De - sire of na - tions,
hope and fear, Sud - den - ly the Lord, de-scend - ing,

Now pro - claim Mes - si - ah's birth: Come and wor - ship,
Yon - der shines the in - fant Light: Come and wor - ship,
Ye have seen His na - tal star: Come and wor - ship,
In His tem - ple shall ap - pear: Come and wor - ship,

come and wor - ship, Wor - ship Christ the new - born King.
come and wor - ship, Wor - ship Christ the new - born King.
come and wor - ship, Wor - ship Christ the new - born King.
come and wor - ship, Wor - ship Christ the new - born King.

WORDS: James Montgomery
MUSIC: Henry Smart

REGENT SQUARE

What Child Is This? 86

They that heard it wondered at those things which were told them — Luke 2:18 KJV

1. What Child is this, Who, laid to rest On Ma-ry's lap, is
2. Why lies He in such mean e - state, Where ox and ass are
3. So bring Him in - cense, gold, and myrrh, Come peas - ant, king to

sleep-ing? Whom an - gels greet with an-thems sweet, While shep-herds watch are
feed-ing? Good Chris-tian fear: for sin - ners here The si - lent Word is
own Him, The King of kings, sal-va - tion brings, Let lov - ing hearts en-

keep - ing? This, this is Christ the King; Whom shep-herds guard and
plead - ing: Nails, spear, shall pierce Him through, The Cross be borne, for
throne Him. Raise, raise the song on high, The Vir - gin sings her

an-gels sing: Haste, haste to bring Him laud, The Babe, the Son of Ma-ry!
me for you: Hail, hail, the Word made flesh, The Babe, the Son of Ma-ry!
lul - la - by: Joy, joy, for Christ is born, The Babe, the Son of Ma-ry!

WORDS: William C. Dix
MUSIC: Old English Air; arr. by John Stainer

GREENSLEEVES

87   The First Noel

There were … shepherds …in the field, keeping watch over their flock — Luke 2:8 KJV

1. The first no - el the an - gel did say Was to
2. They look - ed up and saw a star Shin-ing
3. And by the light of that same star, Three
4. This star drew nigh to the north - west, O'er
5. Then en - tered in those wise men three, Full
6. Then let us all with one ac - cord Sing

cer - tain poor shep-herds in fields as they lay – In
in the east be - yond them far; And
wise men came from coun - try far; To
Beth - le - hem it took its rest; And
rev - 'rent - ly up - on their knee, And
prais - es to our heav'n - ly Lord, That

fields where they lay keep - ing their sheep, On a
to the earth it gave great light, And
seek for a king was their in - tent, And to
there it did both stop and stay, Right
of - fered there, in His pres - ence, Their
hath made heav'n and earth of naught, And

WORDS: English carol, before 1823
MUSIC: English melody from Sandy's *Christmas Carols*, 1833

THE FIRST NOEL

The First Noel

Refrain

cold win-ter's night that was so deep.
so it con - tin-ued both day and night.
fol-low the star wher - ev - er it went.
o - ver the place where Je - sus lay.
gold and myrrh and frank - in - cense.
with His blood man - kind hath bought.

No - el, no -

el! No - el, no - el! Born is the King of Is - ra - el!

Glory Be to God on High   88

Glory to God in the highest, and on earth peace, good will toward men — Luke 2:14 KJV

Unison

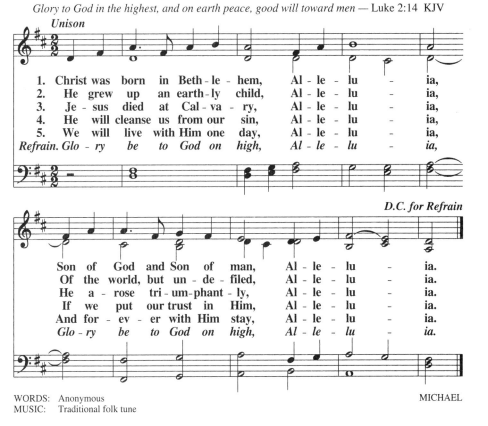

1. Christ was born in Beth - le - hem,   Al - le - lu - ia,
2. He grew up an earth - ly child,   Al - le - lu - ia,
3. Je - sus died at Cal - va - ry,   Al - le - lu - ia,
4. He will cleanse us from our sin,   Al - le - lu - ia,
5. We will live with Him one day,   Al - le - lu - ia,
Refrain. Glo - ry be to God on high,   Al - le - lu - ia,

D.C. for Refrain

Son of God and Son of man,   Al - le - lu - ia.
Of the world, but un - de - filed,   Al - le - lu - ia.
He a - rose tri - um - phant - ly,   Al - le - lu - ia.
If we put our trust in Him,   Al - le - lu - ia.
And for - ev - er with Him stay,   Al - le - lu - ia.
Glo - ry be to God on high,   Al - le - lu - ia.

WORDS: Anonymous
MUSIC: Traditional folk tune

MICHAEL

89   Angels We Have Heard on High

The angel said ... "I bring you good tidings of great joy" — Luke 2:10 KJV

1. An - gels we have heard on high, Sing - ing sweet-ly through the night.
2. Shep-herds, why this ju - bi - lee? Why these songs of hap - py cheer?
3. Come to Beth-le - hem and see Him whose birth the an - gels sing;

And the moun-tains in re - ply Ech - o - ing their brave de - light.
What great bright-ness did you see? What glad tid - ings did you hear?
Come, a - dore on bend - ed knee Christ, the Lord, the new - born King.

Refrain

Glo - ri - a in ex - cel - sis De - o, Glo - ri - a in ex-cel-sis De - o.

WORDS: French carol
MUSIC: French carol melody; arr. by Edward Shippen Barnes

GLORIA

O Little Town of Bethlehem 90

Jesus was born in Bethlehem of Judaea — Matthew 2:1 KJV

1. O lit - tle town of Beth - le - hem, How still we see thee lie!
2. For Christ is born of Ma - ry — And gath - ered all a - bove,
3. How si - lent - ly, how si - lent - ly The won - drous gift is giv'n!
4. O ho - ly Child of Beth - le - hem, De - scend to us, we pray;

A - bove thy deep and dream-less sleep The si - lent stars go by;
While mor - tals sleep, the an - gels keep Their watch of won-d'ring love.
So God im - parts to hu - man hearts The bless - ings of His heav'n.
Cast out our sin and en - ter in — Be born in us to - day.

Yet in thy dark streets shin - eth The ev - er - last - ing Light —
O morn-ing stars, to - geth - er Pro - claim the ho - ly birth,
No ear may hear His com - ing, But, in this world of sin,
We hear the Christ-mas an - gels The great glad ti - dings tell;

The hopes and fears of all the years Are met in thee to-night.
And prais - es sing to God the King, And peace to men on earth.
Where meek souls will re - ceive Him, still The dear Christ en - ters in.
O come to us, a - bide with us, Our Lord Em - man - u - el!

WORDS: Phillips Brooks
MUSIC: Lewis H. Redner

ST. LOUIS

91   Rise Up, Shepherd

Let us go now even unto Bethlehem, and see this thing which is come to pass — Luke 2:15 KJV

1. Dere's a Star in de East on Christ-mas morn; Rise up,
2. Leave yo' sheep, leave yo' sheep, and leave yo' lambs; Rise up,
3. If you take good heed to de an - gel's words; Rise up,

shep-herd, and fol - ler; It will lead to de place where de
shep-herd, and fol - ler; Leave yo' sheep, leave yo' sheep, leave yo'
shep-herd, and fol - ler; You'll for - get all yo' flocks, you'll for -

Sav - ior's born; Rise up, shep-herd, and fol - ler.
ewes and lambs; Rise up, shep-herd, and fol - ler.
get yo' herds; Rise up, shep-herd, and fol - ler.

Refrain

Rise up, shep - herd, Rise up shep-herd and fol- ler; O

p

fol- ler the Star of Beth-le - hem, Rise up, shep-herd, and fol - ler.

WORDS: Anonymous
MUSIC: Anonymous; arr. by J. B. Herbert

Go, Tell It On the Mountain 92

They made known abroad the saying which was told them
concerning this child — Luke 2:17 KJV

Refrain, in Unison

Go, tell it on the moun - tain, O - ver the hills and ev - 'ry-where,

Fine

Go, tell it on the moun - tain That Je - sus Christ is born.

Parts

1. While shep-herds kept their watch-ing O'er si - lent flocks by night,
2. The shep-herds feared and trem-bled When lo! a - bove the earth
3. Down in a lone - ly man - ger The hum-ble Christ was born,

D.C.

Be - hold through-out the heav-ens There shone a ho - ly light.
Rang out the an - gel cho - rus That hailed our Sav - ior's birth.
And God sent us sal - va - tion That bless - ed Christ-mas morn.

WORDS: Spiritual; adapt. by John W. Work III
MUSIC: American Negro melody; arr. by John W. Work, III

GO TELL IT

93   O Come, All Ye Faithful

We ... have come to worship Him — Matthew 2:2 NIV

WORDS: 18th century Latin hymn; attr. to John F. Wade; trans. by Frederick Oakeley and others   ADESTE FIDELES
MUSIC: John F. Wade

Joy to the World

94

Of the increase of His government and peace there shall be no end — Isaiah 9:7 KJV

1. Joy to the world! the Lord is come! Let earth receive her King; Let ev - 'ry heart pre - pare Him room, And heav'n and na - ture sing, And heav'n and na - ture sing, And heav'n, and heav'n and na - ture sing.

2. Joy to the earth! the Sav - ior reigns! Let men their songs em - ploy; While fields and floods, rocks, hills and plains Re - peat the sound - ing joy, Re - peat the sound - ing joy, Re - peat, re - peat the sound - ing joy.

3. No more let sins and sor - rows grow, Nor thorns in - fest the ground; He comes to make His bless - ings flow Far as the curse is found, Far as the curse is found, Far as, far as the curse is found.

4. He rules the world with truth and grace, And makes the na - tions prove The glo - ries of His right - eous - ness, And won - ders of His love, And won - ders of His love, And won - ders, won - ders of His love.

WORDS: Isaac Watts (Psalm 98)
MUSIC: Arr. from G. F. Handel by Lowell Mason

ANTIOCH

95 Hark! the Herald Angels Sing

Glory to God in the highest, and on earth peace, good will toward men — Luke 2:14 KJV

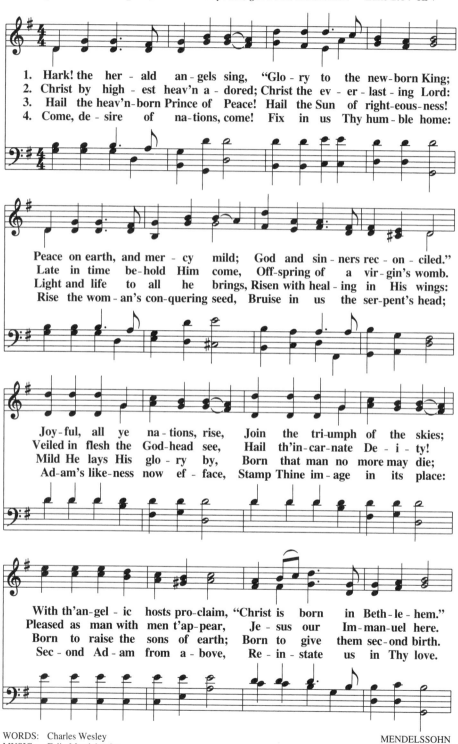

1. Hark! the her - ald an - gels sing, "Glo - ry to the new-born King;
2. Christ by high - est heav'n a - dored; Christ the ev - er - last - ing Lord:
3. Hail the heav'n-born Prince of Peace! Hail the Sun of right-eous-ness!
4. Come, de - sire of na - tions, come! Fix in us Thy hum - ble home:

Peace on earth, and mer - cy mild; God and sin - ners rec - on - ciled."
Late in time be - hold Him come, Off-spring of a vir - gin's womb.
Light and life to all he brings, Risen with heal - ing in His wings:
Rise the wom - an's con-quering seed, Bruise in us the ser-pent's head;

Joy - ful, all ye na - tions, rise, Join the tri-umph of the skies;
Veiled in flesh the God-head see, Hail th'in-car-nate De - i - ty!
Mild He lays His glo - ry by, Born that man no more may die;
Ad-am's like-ness now ef - face, Stamp Thine im-age in its place:

With th'an-gel - ic hosts pro-claim, "Christ is born in Beth-le - hem."
Pleased as man with men t'ap-pear, Je - sus our Im-man-uel here.
Born to raise the sons of earth; Born to give them sec-ond birth.
Sec - ond Ad - am from a - bove, Re - in - state us in Thy love.

WORDS: Charles Wesley
MUSIC: Felix Mendelssohn

MENDELSSOHN

Hark! the Herald Angels Sing

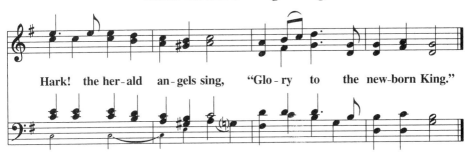

Hark! the her-ald an-gels sing, "Glo-ry to the new-born King."

Away in a Manger   96

And'she laid Him in a manger; because there was no room for them in the inn — Luke 2:7 KJV

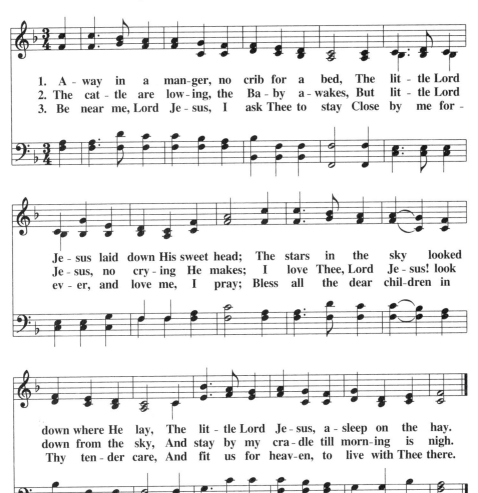

1. A - way in a man-ger, no crib for a bed, The lit - tle Lord
2. The cat - tle are low-ing, the Ba - by a - wakes, But lit - tle Lord
3. Be near me, Lord Je - sus, I ask Thee to stay Close by me for -

Je - sus laid down His sweet head; The stars in the sky looked
Je - sus, no cry - ing He makes; I love Thee, Lord Je - sus! look
ev - er, and love me, I pray; Bless all the dear chil-dren in

down where He lay, The lit - tle Lord Je - sus, a - sleep on the hay.
down from the sky, And stay by my cra - dle till morn-ing is nigh.
Thy ten - der care, And fit us for heav-en, to live with Thee there.

WORDS: Stanzas 1-2: anonymous; stanza 3: John Thomas McFarland   AWAY IN A MANGER
MUSIC: James R. Murray

97 We Three Kings of Orient Are

They presented unto Him gifts;
gold, frankincense, and myrrh — Matthew 2:11 KJV

1. We three kings of O - ri - ent are, Bear - ing
2. Born a King on Beth - le - hem's plain, Gold I
3. Frank - in - cense to of - fer have I, In - cense
4. Myrrh is mine; its bit - ter per - fume Breathes a
5. Glo - rious now be - hold Him a - rise, King and

gifts we trav - erse a - far, Field and foun - tain,
bring to crown Him a - gain, King for - ev - er,
owns a De - i - ty nigh; Prayer and prais - ing,
life of gath - er - ing gloom; Sorrow - ing, sigh - ing,
God and Sac - ri - fice; A - le - lu - ia,

moor and moun - tain, Fol - low - ing yon - der star.
ceas - ing nev - er O - ver us all to reign.
all men rais - ing, Wor-ship Him, God on high. O
bleed - ing, dy - ing, Sealed in the stone cold tomb.
Al - le - lu - ia! Peals thru the earth and skies.

star of won - der, star of light, Star with roy - al beau - ty bright,

WORDS: John H. Hopkins
MUSIC: John H. Hopkins

KINGS OF ORIENT

We Three Kings of Orient Are

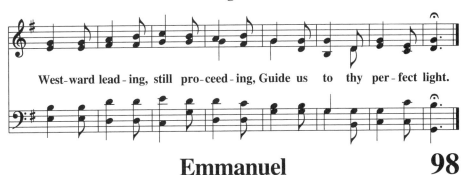

West-ward lead - ing, still pro-ceed - ing, Guide us to thy per - fect light.

Emmanuel 98

The virgin will be with child ... and they will call Him Immanuel — Matthew 1:23 NIV

Unison

Em-man - u - el, Em-man - u - el,

His name is called Em-man - u - el;

God with us, re-vealed in us;

His name is called Em-man-u - el.

McGEE

WORDS: Bob McGee
MUSIC: Bob McGee

99 The Angels Sang

Behold a virgin shall conceive and bear a son,
and shall call His name Immanuel — Isaiah 7:14 KJV

1. How pre-cious is the gift God gave to all man-kind.
2. God, let this Child be born in a man-ger filled with hay.
3. When that great Child was born, His par-ents loved Him so.
4. God let this Child be born to save this world from sin.

1. There is no great-er gift I know you'll ev-er find.
2. A bright and shin-ing star showed Wise men where He lay.
3. But when the time had come, they knew that He would go.
4. It was the great-est gift that God could give to men.

Refrain

The an-gels sang, "Hal - le - lu - jah, Glo - ry, hal - le - lu - jah!

WORDS: Margaret Pleasant Douroux
MUSIC: Margaret Pleasant Douroux

The Angels Sang

Peace on Earth, good-will to men. Je-sus Christ is born."

I Heard the Bells on Christmas Day 100

Peace I leave with you, My peace I give you — John 14:27 KJV

1. I heard the bells on Christ-mas day, Their
2. I thought how, as the day had come, The
3. And in de-spair I bowed my head: "There
4. Then pealed the bells more loud and deep: "God
5. Till ring-ing, sing-ing on its way. The

old fa-mil-iar car-ols play, And wild and sweet the
bel-fries of all Chris-ten-dom Had rolled a-long th'un-
is no peace on earth," I said, "For hate is strong, and
is not dead, nor doth He sleep; The wrong shall fail the
world re-volved from night to day, A voice, a chime, a

words re-peat Of peace on earth, good will to men.
bro-ken song Of peace on earth, good will to men.
mocks the song Of peace on earth, good will to men."
right pre-vail, With peace on earth, good will to men."
chant sub-lime, Of peace on earth, good will to men!

WORDS: Henry W. Longfellow
MUSIC: J. Baptiste Calkin
WALTHAM

101 Silent Night! Holy Night!

They saw the young Child with Mary His mother — Matthew 2:11 KJV

1. Si - lent night! ho - ly night! All is calm,
2. Si - lent night! ho - ly night! Shep - herds quake
3. Si - lent night! ho - ly night! Son of God,

all is bright Round yon vir - gin moth - er and Child,
at the sight; Glo - ries stream from heav - en a - far,
love's pure light Ra - diant beams from Thy ho - ly face

Ho - ly In - fant, so ten - der and mild – Sleep in heav - en - ly
Heav'n - ly hosts sing al - le - lu - ia – Christ the Sav - ior is
With the dawn of re - deem - ing grace – Je - sus, Lord at Thy

peace, Sleep in heav - en - ly peace.
born! Christ the Sav - ior is born!
birth, Je - sus, Lord at Thy birth.

WORDS: Joseph Mohr; trans. by John F. Young
MUSIC: Franz Grüber

STILLE NACHT

All Glory, Laud, and Honor 102

*Who is the blessed and only Potentate, the King of kings,
and Lord of lords — 1 Timothy 6:15 KJV*

Refrain

All glo - ry, laud, and hon - or To Thee, Re-deem-er King, To

whom the lips of chil - dren Make sweet ho-san-nas ring. ring. A-men.

to stanza *to end*

1. Thou art the King of Is - rael, Thou Da - vid's roy - al Son,
2. The com - pa - ny of an - gels Are prais-ing Thee on high,
3. The peo - ple of the He - brews With palms be - fore Thee went;
4. To Thee, be - fore Thy pas - sion, They sang their hymns of praise;
5. Thou didst ac - cept their prais - es; Ac - cept the prayers we bring,

Who in the Lord's name com - est, The King and Bless-ed One.
And mor - tal men, and all things Cre - at - ed, make re - ply.
Our praise and prayer and an - thems Be - fore Thee we pre - sent.
To Thee, now high ex - alt - ed, Our mel - o - dy we raise.
Who in all good de - light - est Thou good and gra-cious King.

D.C.

WORDS: Theodulph of Orleans; trans. by John Mason Neale
MUSIC: Melchior Teschner

ST. THEODULPH

103 Near the Cross

But one of the soldiers with a spear pierced His side, and
forthwith came there out blood and water — John 19:34 KJV

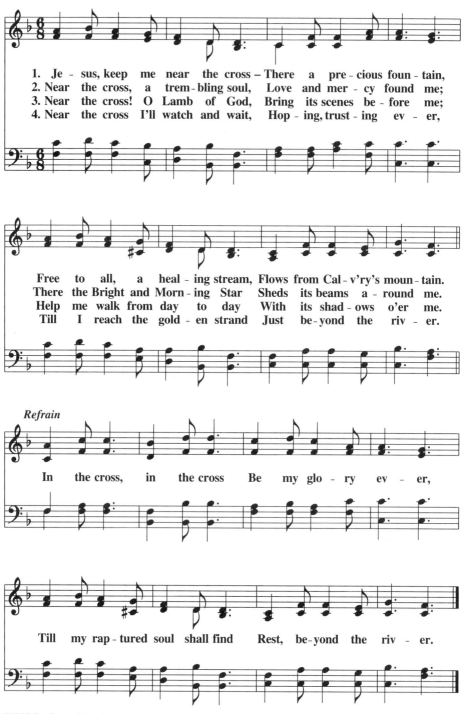

1. Je - sus, keep me near the cross – There a pre - cious foun - tain,
2. Near the cross, a trem - bling soul, Love and mer - cy found me;
3. Near the cross! O Lamb of God, Bring its scenes be - fore me;
4. Near the cross I'll watch and wait, Hop - ing, trust - ing ev - er,

Free to all, a heal - ing stream, Flows from Cal - v'ry's moun - tain.
There the Bright and Morn - ing Star Sheds its beams a - round me.
Help me walk from day to day With its shad - ows o'er me.
Till I reach the gold - en strand Just be - yond the riv - er.

Refrain

In the cross, in the cross Be my glo - ry ev - er,

Till my rap - tured soul shall find Rest, be - yond the riv - er.

WORDS: Fanny J. Crosby
MUSIC: William H. Doane

NEAR THE CROSS

In the Cross of Christ I Glory 104

We also joy in God through our Lord Jesus Christ, by whom we
have now received the atonement — Romans 5:11 KJV

1. In the cross of Christ I glo - ry,
2. When the woes of life o'er - take me,
3. When the sun of bliss is beam - ing
4. Bane and bless - ing, pain and pleas - ure,

Tow - 'ring o'er the wrecks of time;
Hopes de - ceive and fears an - noy,
Light and love up - on my way,
By the cross are sanc - ti - fied;

All the light of sa - cred sto - ry
Nev - er shall the cross for - sake me:
From the cross the ra - diance stream - ing
Peace is there that knows no meas - ure,

Gath - ers 'round its head sub - lime.
Lo! it glows with peace and joy.
Adds more lus - ter to the day.
Joys that thru all time a - bide.

WORDS: John Bowring
MUSIC: Ithamar Conkey

RATHBUN

105   The Old Rugged Cross

*And when the chief Shepherd shall appear, ye shall receive a
crown of glory that fadeth not away — 1 Peter 5:4 KJV*

1. On a hill far a - way stood an old rug-ged cross,
2. O that old rug-ged cross, so de - spised by the world,
3. In the old rug-ged cross, stained with blood so di - vine,
4. To the old rug-ged cross I will ev - er be true,

The em - blem of suf - f'ring and shame;
Has a won - drous at - trac - tion for me;
A won - drous beau - ty I see;
Its shame and re - proach glad - ly bear;

And I love that old cross where the dear - est and best
For the dear Lamb of God left His glo - ry a - bove
For 'twas on that old cross Je - sus suf - fered and died
Then He'll call me some - day to my home far a - way,

For a world of lost sin - ners was slain.
To bear it to dark Cal - va - ry.
To par - don and sanc - ti - fy me.
Where His glo - ry for - ev - er I'll share.

WORDS: George Bennard
MUSIC: George Bennard

OLD RUGGED CROSS

The Old Rugged Cross

Refrain

So I'll cher - ish the old rug - ged cross,
cross, the old rug - ged cross,

Till my tro - phies at last I lay down;

I will cling to the old rug - ged cross,
cross, the old rug - ged cross,

And ex - change it some day for a crown.

106   Beneath the Cross of Jesus

They shall look on Him whom they pierced — John 19:37 KJV

1. Be-neath the cross of Je-sus I fain would take my stand,
2. Up-on that cross of Je-sus Mine eye at times can see
3. I take, O cross, thy shad-ow For my a-bid-ing place –

The shad-ow of a might-y Rock With-in a wea-ry land;
The ver-y dy-ing form of One Who suf-fered there for me;
I ask no oth-er sun-shine than The sun-shine of His face;

A home with-in the wil-der-ness, A rest up-on the way
And from my smit-ten heart with tears Two won-ders I con-fess –
Con-tent to let the world go by, To know no gain nor loss,

From the burn-ing of the noon-day heat And the bur-den of the day.
The won-ders of His glo-rious love And my own worth-less-ness.
My sin-ful self my on-ly shame, My glo-ry all the cross.

WORDS: Elizabeth C. Clephane
MUSIC: Frederick C. Maker

ST. CHRISTOPHER

Bearing His Cross for Me 107

He humbled Himself and became obedient unto … the death of the cross — Philippians 2:8 KJV

1. I see my Sav-ior with thorn-crowned head, Bear-ing His cross for
2. I see Him pass thru the cit-y gate, Bear-ing His cross for
3. I see Him bur-dened with this world's sin, Bear-ing His cross for

me; Thorn-pierced His brow, as by sol-diers led,
me; On midst the taunts and the peo-ple's hate,
me; Will-ing to suf-fer, all hearts to win,

Refrain (parts)

Bear-ing His cross for me. Bear-ing His cross for me, (for me,)

Bear-ing His cross for me, (for me,) Won-der-ful Sav-ior, what

an-guish He bore, Bear-ing His cross for me. (for me.)

WORDS: Robert Harkness
MUSIC: Robert Harkness

108 O Sacred Head, Now Wounded

Then came Jesus forth, wearing the crown of thorns, and the purple robe — John 19:5 KJV

1. O sa - cred Head, now wound - ed, With grief and shame weighed
2. What lan-guage shall I bor - row To thank Thee, dear - est
3. Be near me when I'm dy - ing, Oh! show Thy cross to

down, Now scorn-ful - ly sur-round - ed With thorns, Thine on - ly
Friend, For this, Thy dy - ing sor - row, Thy pit - y with - out
me; And for my suc-cor fly - ing, Come, Lord, and set me

crown; O sa - cred Head, what glo - ry, What bliss, till now was
end? Oh! make me Thine for - ev - er; And should I faint-ing
free; These eyes, new faith re - ceiv - ing, From Je - sus shall not

Thine! Yet, tho' de-spised and gor - y, I joy to call Thee mine.
be, Lord, let me nev - er, nev - er, Out-live my love to Thee.
move; For he who dies be - liev - ing, Dies safe-ly, thru Thy love.

WORDS: Paul Gerhardt; trans. by James W. Alexander
MUSIC: From *Meiningen Gesangbuch*, 1693; harm. by Felix Mendelssohn

MUNICH

Were You There?

109

They all said unto Him, "Let Him be crucified!" — Matthew 27:22 KJV

1. Were you there when they cru - ci - fied my Lord? (were you there?)
2. Were you there when they nailed Him to the tree? (to the tree?)
3. Were you there when they pierced Him in the side? (in the side?)
4. Were you there when the sun re - fused to shine? (were you there?)
5. Were you there when they laid Him in the tomb? (in the tomb?)

Were you there when they cru - ci - fied my Lord? Oh!
Were you there when they nailed Him to the tree? Oh!
Were you there when they pierced Him in the side? Oh!
Were you there when the sun re - fused to shine? Oh!
Were you there when they laid Him in the tomb? Oh!

Some - times it caus - es me to trem - ble, trem - ble,

Were you there when they cru - ci - fied my Lord?
Were you there when they nailed Him to the tree?
trem - ble, Were you there when they pierced Him in the side?
Were you there when the sun re - fused to shine?
Were you there when they laid Him in the tomb?

WORDS: African-American spiritual
MUSIC: African-American spiritual; adapt. John W. Work, Jr. and Frederick J. Work

WERE YOU THERE?

110 Surely He Died on Calvary

And when they were come to the place, which is called Calvary,
there they crucified Him — Luke 23:33 KJV

Cal - va - ry, _____ Cal - va - ry, Cal - va -

ry, _____ Cal - va - ry, Cal - va - ry, ___

__ Cal - va - ry, _____ Sure - ly He died on Cal - va -

ry. 1. Ev - 'ry time I ___ think a - bout Je - sus, Ev - 'ry

time I ___ think a - bout Je - sus, ___ Ev - 'ry time I ___

WORDS: African-American spiritual
MUSIC: African-American spiritual; arr. by J. D. Bushell

CALVARY

Surely He Died on Calvary

think a-bout Je - sus, __ Sure - ly He died on __ Cal - va - ry.

2. Don't you hear the hammer ringing?
3. Don't you hear Him calling His Father?
4. Don't you hear Him say, "It is finished?"
5. Jesus furnished my salvation.
6. Sinner, do you love my Jesus?

Wounded for Me 111

But He was wounded for our transgressions ...
and with His stripes we are healed — Isaiah 53:5 KJV

1. Wound-ed for me, wound-ed for me, Wound-ed for me, He was wound-ed for me. Gone my trans-gres-sions and now I am free, All be-cause Je - sus was wound-ed for me.
2. Dy - ing for me, dy - ing for me, Dy - ing for me, He was dy - ing for me. Gone my trans-gres-sions and now I am free, All be-cause Je - sus was dy - ing for me.
3. Ris - en for me, ris - en for me, Ris - en for me, He is ris - en for me. Gone my trans-gres-sions and now I am free, All be-cause Je - sus is ris - en for me.
4. Com - ing for me, com - ing for me, Com - ing for me, He is com - ing for me. Then with what joy His dear face I shall see, Oh, how I praise Him, He's com - ing for me.

WORDS: St. 1: W. G. Ovens; st. 2-4: Gladys Westcott Roberts
MUSIC: W. G. Ovens

112 Blessed Redeemer

Then said Jesus, "Father, forgive them; for they know not what they do" — Luke 23:34 KJV

1. Up Cal-v'ry's moun - tain, one dread-ful morn, Walked Christ my
2. "Fa - ther, for - give them!" thus did He pray, E'en while His
3. O how I love Him, Sav - ior and Friend! How can my

Sav - ior, wea - ry and worn; Fac - ing for sin - ners
life - blood flowed fast a - way; Pray - ing for sin - ners
prais - es ev - er find end! Thru years un - num - bered

death on the cross, That He might save them from end-less loss.
while in such woe – No one but Je - sus ev - er loved so.
on heav-en's shore, My tongue shall praise Him for - ev - er - more.

Refrain

Bless-ed Re - deem - er, pre-cious Re - deem - er! Seems now I

see Him on Cal-va-ry's tree, Wound-ed and bleed - ing,

WORDS: Avis B. Christiansen
MUSIC: Harry Dixon Loes

REDEEMER

Blessed Redeemer

for sin-ners plead - ing – Blind and un - heed - ing – dy-ing for me!

When I Survey the Wondrous Cross 113

Jesus … who for the joy that was set before Him endured the cross — Hebrews 12:2 KJV

1. When I sur - vey the won - drous cross On which the
2. For - bid it, Lord, that I should boast, Save in the
3. See, from His head, His hands, His feet, Sor - row and
4. Were the whole realm of na - ture mine, That were a

Prince of glo - ry died, My rich - est gain I
death of Christ, my God; All the vain things that
love flow min - gled down; Did e'er such love and
pres - ent far too small: Love so a - maz - ing,

count but loss, And pour con-tempt on all my pride.
charm me most – I sac - ri - fice them to His blood.
sor - row meet, Or thorns com - pose so rich a crown?
so di - vine, De-mands my soul, my life, my all.

WORDS: Isaac Watts
MUSIC: Lowell Mason

HAMBURG

114　He Wore a Crown of Thorns

And they clothed Him with purple, and platted a crown of thorns,
and put it about His head — Mark 15:17

1. 'Twas God's own Son who came to earth, Who chose to know a
2. Won - der - ful Coun - sel - lor was He, Match-less His grace; how
3. Kind were the deeds that crowned each day, Gra-cious the words His
4. Nev - er a - gain His brow shall know Pierc-ings of ag - o -

low - ly birth; But, tho' a King of match - less worth,
could it be That at the last, He wore for me
lips would say, While He pur-sued the fate - ful way
ny and woe But 'twas for us that, here be - low,

Refrain

He wore a crown of thorns.
That bit - ter crown of thorns?
To wear that crown of thorns.
He wore the crown of thorns.

He wore a crown of

thorns that I might wear a crown of glo - ry!

WORDS: William M. Runyan
MUSIC: George S. Schuler

He Wore a Crown of Thorns

He laid His heav'n-ly splen-dors by to bring me love's sweet sto - ry. In pov-er-ty He walked life's way, In Ol-ive's gar-den bowed to pray; He wore a crown of thorns that I might wear a crown of glo - ry!

115 Alone

And they came to a place which was named Gethsemane: and He saith
"Sit ye here, while I shall pray" — Mark 14:32 KJV

Duet

1. It was a - lone   the Sav - ior prayed   In
2. It was a - lone   the Sav - ior stood   In
3. A - lone up - on   the cross He hung   That
4. Can you re - ject   such match-less love?   Can

dark   Geth-sem - a - ne;   A - lone He
Pi - late's judg-ment hall;   A - lone the
oth - ers He might save;   For - sak - en
you   His claim dis - own?   Come, give your

drained   the bit - ter cup   And suf-fered there for me.
crown   of thorns He wore,   For - sak - en thus by all.
then   by God and man,   A - lone, His life He gave.
all   in grat - i - tude,   Nor leave Him thus a - lone.

Refrain (Quartet or Parts)

A - lone,   a - lone,   He
A - lone, it was a - lone,

a - lone, yes, all a - lone,

WORDS: Ben H. Price
MUSIC: Ben H. Price

Alone

bore it all a - lone;
bore it all a - lone, yes, all a-lone; He gave Him-self to save His

own, He suf-fered, bled and died a - lone, a - lone.

They went to a place called Gethsemane, and Jesus said to his disciples, "Sit here while I pray." He took Peter, James and John along with him, and he began to be deeply distressed and troubled. "My soul is overwhelmed with sorrow to the point of death," he said to them. "Stay here and keep watch." Going a little farther, he fell to the ground and prayed that if possible the hour might pass from him. "Abba, Father," he said, "everything is possible for you. Take this cup from me. Yet not what I will, but what you will." Then he returned to his disciples and found them sleeping. "Simon," he said to Peter, "are you asleep? Could you not keep watch for one hour? Watch and pray so that you will not fall into temptation. The spirit is willing, but the body is weak." Once more he went away and prayed the same thing. When he came back, he again found them sleeping, because their eyes were heavy. They did not know what to say to him. Returning the third time, he said to them, "Are you still sleeping and resting? Enough! The hour has come. Look, the Son of Man is betrayed into the hands of sinners. Rise! Let us go! Here comes my betrayer!" (Adapted from Mark 14:32-42 KJV)

116   In the Garden

Now upon the first day of the week … they told all these things unto the eleven,
and to all the rest — Luke 24:1-9 KJV

1. I come to the gar-den a - lone,
2. He speaks, and the sound of His voice
3. I'd stay in the gar-den with Him

While the
Is so
Tho the

dew is still on the ros - es; And the voice I hear, fall-ing
sweet the birds hush their sing - ing; And the mel - o - dy that He
night a-round me be fall - ing; But He bids me go – thru the

on my ear, The Son of God dis - clos - es.
gave to me With - in my heart is ring - ing. And He
voice of woe, His voice to me is call - ing.

Refrain

walks with me, and He talks with me, And He tells me I am His own,

And the joy we share as we tar- ry there, None oth-er has ev-er known.

WORDS: C. Austin Miles
MUSIC: C. Austin Miles

GARDEN

Low in the Grave He Lay 117

For the grave cannot praise Thee — Isaiah 38:18 KJV

1. Low in the grave He lay – Je - sus my Sav - ior! Wait - ing the
2. Vain - ly they watch His bed – Je - sus my Sav - ior! Vain - ly they
3. Death can-not keep his prey – Je - sus my Sav - ior! He tore the

Refrain

com - ing day – Je - sus my Lord! Up from the grave He a -
seal the dead – Je - sus my Lord!
bars a - way – Je - sus my Lord!

rose, With a might - y tri-umph o'er His foes; He a -
He a-rose, He a-rose;

rose a Vic-tor from the dark do-main, And He lives for - ev - er with His

saints to reign. He a-rose! He a-rose! Hal-le-lu-jah! Christ a-rose!
He a-rose! He a-rose!

WORDS: Robert Lowry
MUSIC: Robert Lowry

CHRIST AROSE

118   **He Arose**

He is risen from the dead — Matthew 28:7

WORDS: African-American spiritual

MUSIC: African-American spiritual; arr. by Phillip V. S. Lindsley

ASCENSIUS

He Arose

1. They cru - ci - fied my Sav - ior and nailed Him to the cross,
2. And Jos - eph begged His bod - y and laid it in the tomb,
3. Sister Ma - ry, she came run - ning a - look - ing for my Lord,
4. An an - gel came from heav - en and rolled the stone a - way,

They cru - ci - fied my Sav - ior and nailed Him to the cross,
And Jos - eph begged His bod - y and laid it in the tomb,
Sister Ma - ry she came run - ning a - look - ing for my Lord,
An an - gel came from heav - en and rolled the stone a - way,

They cru - ci - fied my Sav - ior and nailed Him to the cross,
And Jos - eph begged His bod - y and laid it in the tomb,
Sister Ma - ry she came run - ning a - look - ing for my Lord,
An an - gel came from heav - en and rolled the stone a - way,

D.C.

And the Lord will bear my spir - it home.
And the Lord will bear my spir - it home.
And the Lord will bear my spir - it home.
And the Lord will bear my spir - it home.

119 He Lives

*And as they were afraid, and bowed down their faces to the earth, they said
unto them, "Why seek ye the living among the dead?"* — Luke 24:5 KJV

1. I serve a ris-en Sav-ior, He's in the world to-day;
2. In all the world a-round me I see His lov-ing care,
3. Re-joice, re-joice, O Chris-tian, lift up your voice and sing

I know that He is liv-ing, what-ev-er men may say;
And tho' my heart grows wea-ry I nev-er will de-spair;
E-ter-nal hal-le-lu-jahs to Je-sus Christ the King!

I see His hand of mer-cy, I hear His voice of cheer,
I know that He is lead-ing thru all the storm-y blast,
The hope of all who seek Him, the help of all who find,

And just the time I need Him He's al-ways near.
The day of His ap-pear-ing will come at last.
None oth-er is so lov-ing, so good and kind.

WORDS: Alfred H. Ackley
MUSIC: Alfred H. Ackley

ACKLEY

© 1933 Homer A. Rodeheaver. Renewed 1961 by The Rodeheaver Co. (a div. of Word Music, Inc.)

He Lives

120   Because He Lives

But that He loved us, and sent His Son to be the propitiation for our sins — 1 John 4:10 KJV

1. God sent His Son, _____ they called Him Je - sus; _____
2. How sweet to hold _____ a new-born ba - by, _____
3. And then one day _____ I'll cross the riv - er; _____

He came to love, _____ heal, and for - give; _____
And feel the pride _____ and joy he gives; _____
I'll fight life's fi - nal war with pain; _____

He lived and died _____ to buy my par - don. _____
But great - er still _____ the calm as - sur - ance, _____
And then as death _____ gives way to vic - t'ry, _____

An emp - ty grave is there to prove my Sav - ior lives. _____
This child can face un - cer - tain days be-cause He lives. _____
I'll see the lights of glo - ry and I'll know He lives. _____

WORDS: William J. Gaither and Gloria Gaither   RESURRECTION
MUSIC: William J. Gaither

© Copyright 1971 William J. Gaither, Inc. (ASCAP). All rights controlled by Gaither Copyright Management.
Used by permission.

Because He Lives

Be-cause He lives _____ I can face to - mor - row; _____

Be-cause He lives _____ all fear is gone; _____

Be - cause I know _____ He holds the fu - ture, _____

And life is worth the liv - ing just be-cause He lives. _____

121 Christ the Lord Is Risen Today

O death, where is thy sting? O grave, where is thy victory? — 1 Corinthians 15:55 KJV

1. Christ the Lord is ris'n to-day, Al - le - lu - ia!
2. Lives a-gain our glo-rious King, Al - le - lu - ia!
3. Love's re-deem-ing work is done, Al - le - lu - ia!
4. Soar we now where Christ has led, Al - le - lu - ia!

Sons of men and an-gels say: Al - le - lu - ia!
Where, O death, is now thy sting? Al - le - lu - ia!
Fought the fight, the bat-tle won, Al - le - lu - ia!
Fol-l'wing our ex-alt-ed Head, Al - le - lu - ia!

Raise your joys and tri-umphs high, Al - le - lu - ia!
Dy-ing once He all doth save, Al - le - lu - ia!
Death in vain for-bids Him rise, Al - le - lu - ia!
Made like Him, like Him we rise, Al - le - lu - ia!

Sing, ye heav'ns, and earth re-ply: Al - le - lu - ia!
Where thy vic-to-ry, O grave? Al - le - lu - ia!
Christ has o-pened Par-a-dise, Al - le - lu - ia!
Ours the cross, the grave, the skies, Al - le - lu - ia!

WORDS: Charles Wesley
MUSIC: From *Lyra Davidica*, 1708

EASTER HYMN

Behold the Lamb 122

Behold the Lamb of God which takes away the sin of the world — John 1:29 KJV

Be-hold the Lamb! __ Be - hold the Lamb! __ Slain from the foun-
da-tion of the world. For sin-ners cru - ci-fied, ___ Oh, Ho - ly
Sac - ri - fice __ Be-hold the Lamb of God! Be-hold the Lamb! ___
Crown Him, crown Him, wor - thy is the Lamb. ___
Praise Him, praise Him. Heav'n and earth re - sound. __ Be -

WORDS: Dottie Rambo
MUSIC: Dottie Rambo; arranged by W. Elmo Mercer

123 He Rose Triumphantly

It was impossible for death to keep its hold on Him — Acts 2:24 NIV

Andantino

1. Our bless-ed Lord was slain, (was slain,) The Christ who came to
2. They sor-rowed when He died, (He died,) Nor sought their tears to
3. The stone was rolled a-way, (a way,) For Christ was raised that

accel.

reign; (to reign;) And in a grave He lay, To wait the com-ing
hide; (to hide;) But soon their bit-ter pain Was turned to joy a-
day; (that day;) And now He lives a-bove To man-i-fest His

Refrain Animato

day.
gain   He rose tri-um-phant-ly, In pow'r and maj-es-ty,
love

The Sav-ior rose no more to die; O let us now pro-claim

The glo-ry of His name, And tell to all He lives to-day.

WORDS: Oswald J. Smith
MUSIC: B. D. Ackley

The Day of Resurrection

124

He is not here: for He is risen, as He said.
Come, see the place where the Lord lay — Matthew 28:6 KJV

1. The day of res-ur-rec-tion! Earth, tell it out a-broad –
2. Our hearts be pure from e-vil, That we may see a-right
3. Now let the heav'ns be joy-ful, Let earth her song be-gin,

The Pass-o-ver of glad-ness, The Pass-o-ver of God!
The Lord in rays e-ter-nal Of res-ur-rec-tion light;
Let the round world keep tri-umph And all that is there-in;

From death to life e-ter-nal, From this world to the sky,
And, lis-t'ning to His ac-cents, May hear, so calm and plain,
Let all things seen and un-seen Their notes in glad-ness blend,

Our Christ hath brough us o-ver With hymns of vic-to-ry!
His own "All hail!" and, hear-ing, May raise the vic-tor strain.
For Christ the Lord hath ris-en, Our Joy that hath no end!

WORDS: John of Damascus (early 8th cent.); trans. by John Mason Neale
MUSIC: Arr. from Johann Michael Haydn

GREENLAND

125 Crown Him

As I live, saith the Lord, every knee shall bow to me,
and every tongue shall confess to God — Romans 14:11 KJV

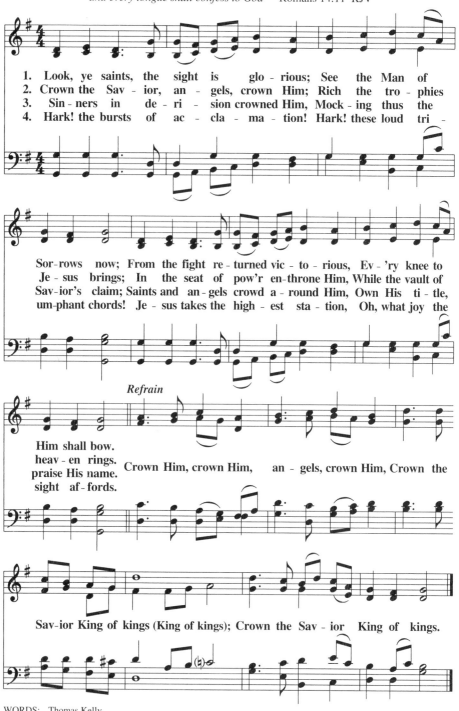

1. Look, ye saints, the sight is glo-rious; See the Man of
2. Crown the Sav-ior, an-gels, crown Him; Rich the tro-phies
3. Sin-ners in de-ri-sion crowned Him, Mock-ing thus the
4. Hark! the bursts of ac-cla-ma-tion! Hark! these loud tri-

Sor-rows now; From the fight re-turned vic-to-rious, Ev-'ry knee to
Je-sus brings; In the seat of pow'r en-throne Him, While the vault of
Sav-ior's claim; Saints and an-gels crowd a-round Him, Own His ti-tle,
um-phant chords! Je-sus takes the high-est sta-tion, Oh, what joy the

Refrain

Him shall bow.
heav-en rings.
praise His name. Crown Him, crown Him, an-gels, crown Him, Crown the
sight af-fords.

Sav-ior King of kings (King of kings); Crown the Sav-ior King of kings.

WORDS: Thomas Kelly
MUSIC: Welsh melody; arranged by B. B. McKinney

Breathe on Me

126

He breathed on them, and saith unto them, "Receive the Holy Spirit" — John 20:22 KJV

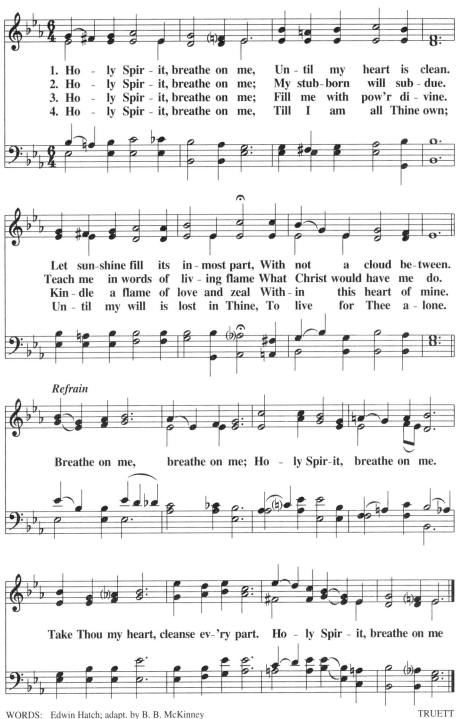

1. Ho - ly Spir - it, breathe on me, Un - til my heart is clean.
2. Ho - ly Spir - it, breathe on me; My stub - born will sub - due.
3. Ho - ly Spir - it, breathe on me; Fill me with pow'r di - vine.
4. Ho - ly Spir - it, breathe on me, Till I am all Thine own;

Let sun - shine fill its in - most part, With not a cloud be - tween.
Teach me in words of liv - ing flame What Christ would have me do.
Kin - dle a flame of love and zeal With - in this heart of mine.
Un - til my will is lost in Thine, To live for Thee a - lone.

Refrain

Breathe on me, breathe on me; Ho - ly Spir - it, breathe on me.

Take Thou my heart, cleanse ev - 'ry part. Ho - ly Spir - it, breathe on me

WORDS: Edwin Hatch; adapt. by B. B. McKinney
MUSIC: B. B. McKinney

TRUETT

127 Sweet, Sweet Spirit

In whom also after that ye believed,
ye were also sealed with that holy Spirit of promise — Ephesians 1:13 KJV

1. There's a sweet, sweet spir-it in this place, _____ And I
2. There are bless-ings you can-not re-ceive _____ till you
3. If you say He saved you from your sin, _____ now you're

know that it's the Spir-it of the Lord. _____ There are
know Him in His full-ness and be-lieve. _____ You're the
weak, you're bound, and can-not en-ter in, _____ you can

sweet ex-pres-sions on each face, _____ And I
one to pro-fit when you say, _____ "I am
make it right if you will yield; _____ you'll en-

know that it's the pres-ence of the Lord. _____
going to walk with Je-sus all the way." _____
joy the Ho-ly Spir-it that we feel. _____

WORDS: Doris Akers
MUSIC: Doris Akers

MANNA

Sweet, Sweet Spirit

Sweet Ho-ly Spir-it, Sweet Heav'n-ly Dove,

Stay right here with us Fill-ing us with Your

love. And for these bless-ings We lift our hearts in

praise; With-out a doubt we'll know that we have

been re-vived, when we shall leave this place. _____

128   Let It Breathe on Me

There came a sound from heaven …
and they were filled with the Holy Ghost — Acts 2:2-4 KJV

Refrain

Slow with feeling

Let it breathe on me, Let it breathe on me, Let the

breath of the Lord, now, breathe on me, Let it

breathe on me, Let it breathe on me, Let the

Fine

breath of the Lord, now, breathe on me.
1. While I'm work - ing,
2. When the path - way,

Lord, in your vine - yard here, I can do naught if
Lord, I can - not see, When the way is dark, Lord,

WORDS: Magnolia Lewis-Butts
MUSIC: Magnolia Lewis-Butts; arr. by W. O. Hoyle
© 1941 by Bowles Music House. Used by permission.

Let It Breathe on Me

Thou aren't near, Oh, come, bless-ed Lord, just so close to
breathe on me, Give me grace to know when Thou art

D.C.

me That I may feel You breathe on me.
near; Oh, I pray Thee, Lord, please breathe on me.

Surely the Presence of the Lord 129

In Thy presence is fullness of joy;
at Thy right hand there are pleasures for evermore — Psalm 16:11 KJV

Sure-ly the pres-ence of the Lord is in this place, I can feel His might-y

pow-er and His grace. ___ I can hear the brush of an-gel's wings, I see

glo - ry on each face; sure-ly the pres-ence of the Lord is in this place.

WORDS: Lanny Wolfe
MUSIC: Lanny Wolfe
WOLFE

130 Blessed Quietness

And the work of righteousness shall be peace; and the effect of
righteousness quietness and assurance — Isaiah 32:17 KJV

1. Joys are flow - ing like a riv - er Since the
2. Bring-ing life and health and glad - ness All a -
3. Like the rain that falls from heav - en, Like the
4. See, a fruit - ful field is grow - ing, Bless - ed
5. What a won - der - ful sal - va - tion, Where we

Com - fort - er has come; He a - bides with us for -
round, this heav-'nly Guest Ban-ished un - be - lief and
sun - light from the sky. So the Ho - ly Ghost is
fruit of right-eous - ness; And the streams of life are
al - ways see His face! What a per - fect hab - i -

Refrain

ev - er, Makes the trust - ing heart His home.
sad - ness, Changed our wea - ri - ness to rest.
giv - en, Com - ing on us from on high.
flow - ing In the lone - ly wil - der - ness.
ta - tion, What a qui - et rest - ing place!

Bless-ed

qui - et-ness, ho - ly qui - et-ness – What as - sur - ance in my soul! On the

WORDS: Manie P. Ferguson
MUSIC: W. S. Marshall; adapt. by James M Kirk

Blessed Quietness

storm-y sea   He speaks peace to me – How the   bil-lows   cease to   roll!

Holy Ghost, with Light Divine   131

Now the end of the commandment is charity out of a pure heart,
and of a good conscience, and of faith unfeigned — 1 Timothy 1:5 KJV

1. Ho - ly   Ghost, with   light   di - vine,   Shine   up -
2. Ho - ly   Ghost, with   pow'r   di - vine,   Cleanse   this
3. Ho - ly   Ghost, with   joy   di - vine,   Cheer   this
4. Ho - ly   Spir - it,   all   di - vine,   Dwell   with -

on   this   heart   of   mine;   Chase   the   shades   of
guilt - y   heart   of   mine;   Long   hath   sin   with -
sad - dened   heart   of   mine;   Bid   my   man - y
in   this   heart   of   mine;   Cast   down   ev - 'ry

night   a - way,   Turn   my   dark - ness   in - to   day.
out   con - trol,   Held   do - min - ion   o'er   my   soul.
woes   de - part,   Heal   my   wound - ed, bleed - ing   heart.
i - dol   throne,   Reign   su - preme, and reign   a - lone.

WORDS: Andrew Reed
MUSIC: Louis M. Gottschalk; adapt. by Edwin P. Parker

MERCY

132 The Comforter Has Come

But when the Comforter is come … He shall testify of me — John 15:26 KJV

1. Oh, spread the tid-ings 'round; wher-ev-er man is found,
2. The long, long night is past; the morn-ing breaks at last;
3. Lo, the great King of kings, with heal-ing in His wings,
4. Oh, bound-less love di-vine! How shall this tongue of mine

Wher-ev-er hu-man hearts and hu-man woes a-bound;
And hushed the dread-ful wail and fu-ry of the blast,
To ev-'ry cap-tive soul a full de-liv-'rance brings;
To won-d'ring mor-tals tell the match-less grace di-vine –

Let ev-'ry Chris-tian tongue pro-claim the joy-ful sound:
As o'er the gold-en hills the day ad-vanc-es fast!
And thru the va-cant cells the song of tri-umph rings:
That I, a child of hell, should in His im-age shine!

Refrain

The Com-fort-er has come! The Com-fort-er has come!

The Com-fort-er has come! The Ho-ly Ghost from heav'n,

WORDS: Frank Bottome
MUSIC: William J. Kirkpatrick

COMFORTER

The Comforter Has Come

The Fa - ther's prom-ise giv'n! Oh, spread the tid-ings 'round,
wher - ev - er man is found: The Com - fort - er has come!

Spirit of the Living God — 133

But with the Spirit of the living God; not in tables of stone,
but in fleshy tables of the heart — 2 Corinthians 3:3 KJV

Spir - it of the liv - ing God, fall fresh on me; Spir - it of the
liv - ing God, fall fresh on me. Break me, melt me, mold me,
fill me. Spir - it of the liv - ing God, fall fresh on me.

WORDS: Daniel Iverson
MUSIC: Daniel Iverson; arr. by B. B. McKinney

LIVING GOD

134 I'm Gonna Sing

O come, let us sing unto the Lord — Psalm 95:1 KJV

I'm gon-na sing when the Spir-it says sing, I'm gon-na
sing when the Spir-it says sing; I'm gon-na sing when the Spir-it says
sing And o - bey the Spir - it of the Lord.

2. shout 3. preach 4. pray 5. sing

WORDS: African-American spiritual
MUSIC: African-American spiritual

I'M GONNA SING

135 Breathe on Me, Breath of God

And [God] breathed into his nostrils the breath of life; and man became a living soul — Genesis 2:7 KJV

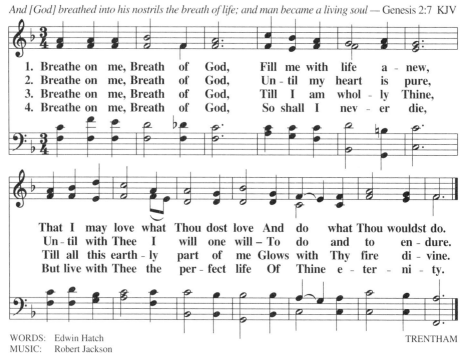

1. Breathe on me, Breath of God, Fill me with life a - new,
2. Breathe on me, Breath of God, Un - til my heart is pure,
3. Breathe on me, Breath of God, Till I am whol - ly Thine,
4. Breathe on me, Breath of God, So shall I nev - er die,

That I may love what Thou dost love And do what Thou wouldst do.
Un - til with Thee I will one will – To do and to en - dure.
Till all this earth - ly part of me Glows with Thy fire di - vine.
But live with Thee the per - fect life Of Thine e - ter - ni - ty.

WORDS: Edwin Hatch
MUSIC: Robert Jackson

TRENTHAM

Glory to His Name

136

The blood of Jesus Christ His Son cleanseth us from all sin — 1 John 1:7 KJV

1. Down at the cross where my Sav - ior died,
2. I am so won - drous - ly saved from sin,
3. Oh, pre - cious foun - tain that saves from sin,
4. Come to this foun - tain so rich and sweet,

Down where for cleans - ing from sin I cried,
Je - sus so sweet - ly a - bides with - in;
I am so glad I have en - tered in;
Cast thy poor soul at the Sav - ior's feet;

There to my heart was the blood ap - plied – Glo - ry to His name.
There at the cross where He took me in – Glo - ry to His name.
There Je-sus saves me and keeps me clean – Glo - ry to His name.
Plunge in to - day, and be made com - plete – Glo - ry to His name.

Refrain

Glo - ry to His name, Glo - ry to His name;

There to my heart was the blood ap - plied – Glo - ry to His name.

WORDS: Elisha A. Hoffman
MUSIC: John H. Stockton

GLORY TO HIS NAME

137   At the Cross

And He, bearing His cross, went forth into a place called the place of a skull — John 19:17 KJV

1. A - las! and did my Sav - ior bleed? And did my Sov-'reign die?
2. Was it for crimes that I have done He groaned up - on the tree?
3. Well might the sun in dark-ness hide And shut his glo - ries in,
4. But drops of grief can ne'er re - pay The debt of love I owe:

Would He de - vote that sa - cred head For such a worm as I?
A - maz - ing pit - y! grace un-known! And love be - yond de - gree!
When Christ, the might-y Mak - er, died For man the crea-ture's sin.
Here, Lord, I give my - self a - way – 'Tis all that I can do!

Refrain

At the cross, at the cross where I first saw the light, And the

bur - den of my heart rolled a - way
rolled a - way –
It was

there by faith I re-ceived my sight, And now I am hap-py all the day!

WORDS: Isaac Watts; refrain by Ralph E. Hudson   HUDSON
MUSIC: Ralph E. Hudson

Jesus Paid It All

138

They … washed their robes,
and made them white in the blood of the Lamb — Revelation 7:14 KJV

1. I hear the Sav-ior say, "Thy strength in-deed is small!
2. Lord, now in-deed I find Thy pow'r, and Thine a-lone,
3. For noth-ing good have I Where-by Thy grace to claim –
4. And when be-fore the throne I stand in Him com-plete,

Child of weak-ness, watch and pray, Find in Me thine all in all."
Can change the lep-er's spots And melt the heart of stone.
I'll wash my gar-ments white In the blood of Cal-v'ry's Lamb.
"Je-sus died my soul to save," My lips shall still re-peat.

Refrain

Je - sus paid it all, All to Him I owe;

Sin had left a crim-son stain – He washed it white as snow.

WORDS: Elvina M. Hall
MUSIC: John T. Grape

ALL TO CHRIST

139 Calvary Covers It All

And when they were come to the place, which is called Calvary ...
they crucified Him — Luke 23:33 KJV

1. Far dear-er than all that the world can im-part
2. The stripes that He bore and the thorns that He wore
3. How match-less the grace, when I looked in the face
4. How bless-ed the thought, that my soul by Him bought,

Was the mes-sage that came to my heart (to my heart);
Told His mer-cy and love ev-er-more (ev-er-more);
Of this Je-sus, my cru-ci-fied Lord (of my Lord);
Shall be His in the glo-ry on high (His on high),

How that Je-sus a-lone for my sin did a-tone,
And my heart bowed in shame as I called on His name,
My re-demp-tion com-plete I then found at His feet,
Where with glad-ness and song I'll be one of the throng,

And Cal-va-ry cov-ers it all.
And Cal-va-ry cov-ers it all.
And Cal-va-ry cov-ers it all.
And Cal-va-ry cov-ers it all.
1. cov-ers it all.

WORDS: Mrs. Walter G. Taylor
MUSIC: Mrs. Walter G. Taylor

CALVARY COVERS IT

Calvary Covers It All

Cal - va-ry cov - ers it all, My past with its sin and stain; My guilt and de - spair Je - sus took on Him there, And Cal - va-ry cov - ers it all.

When the soldiers crucified Jesus, they took his clothes, dividing them into four shares, one for each of them, with the undergarment remaining. This garment was seamless, woven in one piece from top to bottom. "Let's not tear it, "they said to one another. "Let's decide by lot who will get it. "This happened that the scripture might be fulfilled which said, "They divided my garments among them and cast lots for my clothing." So this is what the soldiers did. Near the cross of Jesus stood his mother, his mother's sister, Mary the wife of Clopas, and Mary Magdalene. When Jesus saw his mother there, and the disciple whom he loved standing nearby, he said to his mother, "Dear woman, here is your son," and to the disciple, "Here is your mother." From that time on, this disciple took her into his home. Later, knowing that all was now completed, and so that the Scripture would be fulfilled, Jesus said, "I am thirsty." A jar of wine vinegar was there, so they soaked a sponge in it, put the sponge on a stalk of the hyssop plant, and lifted it to Jesus' lips. When he had received the drink, Jesus said, "It is finished." With that, he bowed his head and gave up his spirit. (Adapted from John 19:23-30 KJV)

140   Are You Washed in the Blood

They overcame Him by the blood of the Lamb — Revelation 12:11 KJV

1. Have you been to Je - sus for the cleans - ing pow'r? Are you
2. Are you walk - ing dai - ly by the Sav - ior's side? Are you
3. When the Bride-groom com - eth will your robes be white? Are you
4. Lay a - side the gar - ments that are stained with sin And be

washed in the blood of the Lamb? Are you ful - ly trust - ing in His
washed in the blood of the Lamb? Do you rest each mo - ment in the
washed in the blood of the Lamb? Will your soul be read - y for the
washed in the blood of the Lamb; There's a foun - tain flow - ing for the

grace this hour? Are you washed in the blood of the Lamb?
Cru - ci - fied? Are you washed in the blood of the Lamb?
man - sions bright And be washed in the blood of the Lamb?
soul un - clean, O be washed in the blood of the Lamb!

Refrain

Are you washed in the blood, In the
Are you washed in the blood,

soul-cleans-ing blood of the Lamb? Are your gar-ments spot-less?
of the Lamb?

WORDS: Elisha A. Hoffman
MUSIC: Elisha A. Hoffman

WASHED IN THE BLOOD

Are You Washed in the Blood

Are they white as snow? Are you washed in the blood of the Lamb?

Nothing But the Blood 141

And the blood of Jesus Christ His Son cleanseth us from all sin — 1 John 1:7 KJV

1. What can wash a-way my sin? Noth-ing but the blood of Je-sus;
2. For my par-don this I see – Noth-ing but the blood of Je-sus;
3. Noth-ing can for sin a-tone – Noth-ing but the blood of Je-sus;
4. This is all my hope and peace – Noth-ing but the blood of Je-sus;

What can make me whole a-gain? Noth-ing but the blood of Je-sus.
For my cleans-ing, this my plea – Noth-ing but the blood of Je-sus.
Naught of good that I have done – Noth-ing but the blood of Je-sus.
This is all my right-eous-ness – Noth-ing but the blood of Je-sus.

Refrain

Oh! pre-cious is the flow That makes me white as snow;

No oth-er fount I know, Noth-ing but the blood of Je-sus.

WORDS: Robert Lowry
MUSIC: Robert Lowry

PLAINFIELD

142   There Is a Fountain

I will give unto him that is athirst of the fountain
of the water of life freely — Revelation 21:6 KJV

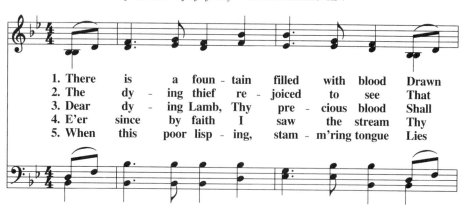

1. There is a foun - tain filled with blood Drawn
2. The dy - ing thief re - joiced to see That
3. Dear dy - ing Lamb, Thy pre - cious blood Shall
4. E'er since by faith I saw the stream Thy
5. When this poor lisp - ing, stam - m'ring tongue Lies

from Im - man - uel's veins, And sin - ners plunged be -
foun - tain in his day, And there may I, though
nev - er lose its pow'r, Till all the ran - somed
flow - ing wounds sup - ply, Re - deem - ing love has
si - lent in the grave, Then in a no - bler,

neath that flood Lose all their guilt - y - stains:
vile as he, Wash all my sins a - way:
Church of God Be saved to sin no more:
been my theme And shall be till I die:
sweet - er song, I'll sing Thy pow'r to save:

WORDS: William Cowper
MUSIC: Early American melody

CLEANSING FOUNTAIN

There Is a Fountain

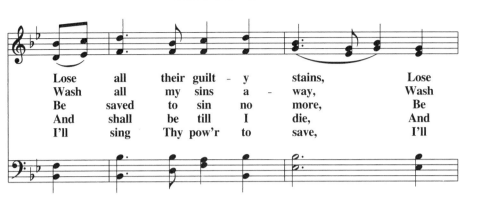

Lose	all	their	guilt	-	y	stains,	Lose
Wash	all	my	sins	a	-	way,	Wash
Be	saved	to	sin	no		more,	Be
And	shall	be	till	I		die,	And
I'll	sing	Thy	pow'r	to		save,	I'll

all	their	guilt	-	y	stains;	And	sin	-	ners	plunged	be	-
all	my	sins	a	-	way;	And	there	may	I,	though
saved	to	sin	no		more;	Till	all	the	ran - somed
shall	be	till	I		die;	Re	-	deem	-	ing	love	has
sing	Thy	pow'r	to		save;	Then	in	a	no - bler,

neath	that	flood	Lose	all	their	guilt	-	y	stains.
vile	as	he,	Wash	all	my	sins	a	-	way.
Church	of	God	Be	saved	to	sin	no		more.
been	my	theme	And	shall	be	till	I		die.
sweet	-	er	song,	I'll	sing	Thy	pow'r	to		save.

143   Victory in Jesus

He gives us the victory through our Lord Jesus Christ — 1 Corinthians 15:57 NIV

1. I heard an old, old sto-ry, how a Sav-ior came from glo-ry, How He gave His life on Cal-va-ry to save a wretch like me: I heard a-bout His groan-ing, of His pre-cious blood's a-ton-ing, Then
2. I heard a-bout His heal-ing, of His cleans-ing pow'r re-veal-ing, How He made the lame to walk a-gain and caused the blind to see; And then I cried, "Dear Je-sus, come and heal my bro-ken spir-it," And
3. I heard a-bout a man-sion He has built for me in glo-ry, And I heard a-bout the streets of gold be-yond the crys-tal sea; A-bout the an-gels sing-ing and the old re-demp-tion sto-ry, And

WORDS: Eugene M. Bartlett
MUSIC: Eugene M. Bartlett

HARTFORD

Victory in Jesus

I re-pent-ed of my sins and won the vic-to-ry.
some-how Je-sus came and brought to me the vic-to-ry.
some sweet day I'll sing up there the song of vic-to-ry.

Refrain

O vic-to-ry in Je-sus, my Sav-ior, for-ev-er!

He sought me and bought me with His re-deem-ing blood;

He loved me ere I knew Him, and all my love is due Him —

He plunged me to vic-to-ry be-neath the cleans-ing flood.

144 At Calvary

And when they were come to the place,
which is called Calvary, there they crucified Him — Luke 23:33 KJV

1. Years I spent in van - i - ty and pride,
2. By God's Word at last my sin I learned —
3. Now I've giv'n to Je - sus ev - 'ry - thing,
4. O, the love that drew sal - va - tion's plan!

Car - ing not my Lord was cru - ci - fied,
Then I trem - bled at the law I'd spurned,
Now I glad - ly own Him as my King,
O, the grace that brought it down to man!

Know - ing not it was for me He died On Cal - va - ry.
Till my guilt - y soul im - plor - ing turned To Cal - va - ry.
Now my rap - tured soul can on - ly sing Of Cal - va - ry.
O, the might - y gulf that God did span At Cal - va - ry!

Refrain

Mer - cy there was great, and grace was free, Par - don there was mul - ti -

plied to me, There my bur - dened soul found lib - er - ty — At Cal - va - ry.

WORDS: William R. Newell
MUSIC: Daniel B. Towner

CALVARY

There Is Power in the Blood 145

That I may know Him, and the power of His resurrection — Phillipians 3:10 KJV

1. Would you be free from the bur-den of sin? There's pow'r in the blood,
2. Would you be free from your pas-sion and pride? There's pow'r in the blood,
3. Would you be whit-er, much whit-er than snow? There's pow'r in the blood,
4. Would you do ser-vice for Je-sus your King? There's pow'r in the blood,

pow'r in the blood; Would you o'er e-vil a vic-to-ry win?
pow'r in the blood; Come for a cleans-ing to Cal-va-ry's tide –
pow'r in the blood; Sin-stains are lost in its life-giv-ing flow –
pow'r in the blood; Would you live dai-ly His prais-es to sing?

Refrain

There's won-der-ful pow'r in the blood. There is pow'r, pow'r,
there is

won-der-work-ing pow'r In the blood of the Lamb; There is
In the blood of the Lamb;

pow'r, pow'r, won-der-work-ing pow'r In the pre-cious blood of the Lamb.
there is

WORDS: Lewis E. Jones
MUSIC: Lewis E. Jones

POWER IN THE BLOOD

146 The Blood Will Never Lose Its Power

Through the blood of the everlasting covenenat — Hebrews 13:20 KJV

1. The blood that Je - sus shed for me
2. It soothes my doubts and calms my fears,

'way back on Cal - va - ry, The
And it dries all my tears; The

blood that gives me strength from day to day,
blood that gives me strength from day to day,

It will nev - er lose its pow'r. _____
It will nev - er lose its pow'r. _____

WORDS: Andraé Crouch
MUSIC: Andraé Crouch

THE BLOOD

The Blood Will Never Lose Its Power

147 He Touched Me

Jesus put forth His hand, and touched him, saying,
"I will; be thou clean" — Matthew 8:3 KJV

1. Shack-led by a heav-y bur-den, ___ 'Neath a load of
2. Since I met this bless-ed Sav-ior, ___ Since He cleansed and

guilt and shame, __ Then the hand of Je-sus touched me, ___ And
made me whole, __ I will nev-er cease to praise Him, __ I'll

Refrain

now I am no long-er the same. __ He touched me, O He
shout it while e-ter-ni-ty rolls. __

touched me, ___ And oh, the joy that floods my soul; ___ Some-thing

hap-pened, and now I know, He touched me and made me whole. _

WORDS: William J. Gaither
MUSIC: William J. Gaither

My Faith Has Found a Resting Place 148

Rest in the Lord — Psalm 37:7 KJV

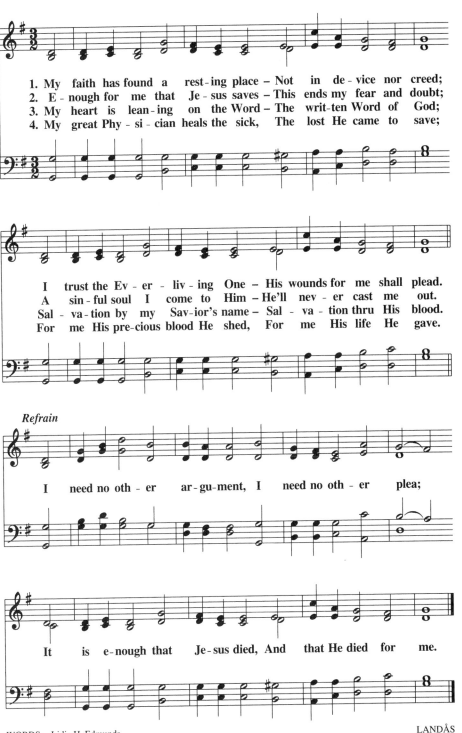

1. My faith has found a rest-ing place – Not in de - vice nor creed;
2. E - nough for me that Je - sus saves – This ends my fear and doubt;
3. My heart is lean-ing on the Word – The writ-ten Word of God;
4. My great Phy - si - cian heals the sick, The lost He came to save;

I trust the Ev - er - liv - ing One – His wounds for me shall plead.
A sin - ful soul I come to Him – He'll nev - er cast me out.
Sal - va-tion by my Sav-ior's name – Sal - va - tion thru His blood.
For me His pre-cious blood He shed, For me His life He gave.

Refrain

I need no oth - er ar - gu-ment, I need no oth - er plea;

It is e-nough that Je-sus died, And that He died for me.

WORDS: Lidie H. Edmunds
MUSIC: Norwegian melody; arr. by William J. Kirkpatrick

LANDÅS

149 He Will Remember Me

And he said unto Jesus, "Lord, remember me
when thou comest into Thy kingdom" — Luke 23:42 KJV

1. When on the cross of Cal-v'ry The Lord was cru-ci-fied;
2. O, what a shame to kill Him There on that rug-ged cross;
3. At His dear feet I'm kneel-ing, My sins I now con-fess;

The mob stood 'round a-bout Him And mocked un-til He died.
But such a death was need-ed To res-cue all the lost.
I bow in deep re-pent-ance, My soul He'll sure-ly bless.

Two thieves were nailed be-side Him To share the ag-o-ny,
His blood was made a ran-som To set the cap-tives free,
My blind-ed eyes He o-pens So that the light I see,

But one of them cried out to Him, "O Lord, re-mem-ber me."
I know that I'm in-clud-ed, and He will re-mem-ber me.
And when I reach the pearl-y gates, He will re-mem-ber me.

WORDS: Eugene M. Bartlett
MUSIC: Eugene M. Bartlett

He Will Remember Me

150   Hallelujah for the Cross!

And, having made peace through the blood of His cross — Colossians 1:20 KJV

1. The cross it stand-eth fast — Hal-le-lu - jah, hal-le-lu - jah!
2. It is the old cross still — Hal-le-lu - jah, hal-le-lu - jah!
3. 'Twas here the debt was paid — Hal-le-lu - jah, hal-le-lu - jah!

De - fy - ing ev - 'ry blast — Hal-le-lu - jah, hal-le-lu - jah!
Its tri - umph let us tell — Hal-le-lu - jah, hal-le-lu - jah!
Our sins on Je - sus laid — Hal-le-lu - jah, hal-le-lu - jah!

The winds of hell have blown, The world its hate hath shown,
The grace of God here shone Thru Christ, the bless-ed Son,
So round the cross we sing Of Christ, our of - fer - ing,

Yet it is not o - ver-thrown — Hal-le-lu - jah for the cross!
Who did for sin a - tone — Hal-le-lu - jah for the cross!
Of Christ, our liv - ing King — Hal-le-lu - jah for the cross!

WORDS: Horatius Bonar
MUSIC: James McGranahan

Hallelujah for the Cross!

Old Time Religion 151

When I call to remembrance the unfeigned faith that is in Thee — 2 Timothy 1:5 KJV

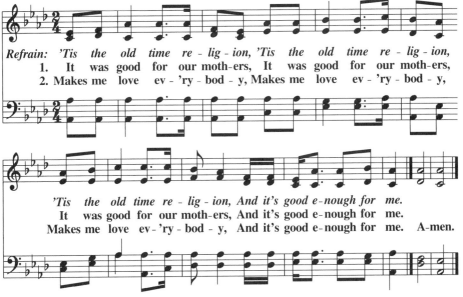

3. It has saved our fathers,
   And it's good enough for me.

4. It was good for the prophet Daniel,
   And it's good enough for me.

5. It was good for the Hebrew children,
   And it's good enough for me.

6. It was tried in the fiery furnace,
   And it's good enough for me.

7. It was good for Paul and Silas,
   And it's good enough for me.

8. It will do when I am dying,
   And it's good enough for me.

WORDS: African-American spiritual
MUSIC: African-American spiritual

YARMOUTH

152 Heaven Came Down

Hereafter ye shall see heaven open, and the angels of God ascending
and descending upon the Son of man — John 1:51 KJV

1. O what a won-der-ful, won-der-ful day – Day I will nev-er for-get;
   After I'd wan-dered in dark-ness a-way, Je-sus my Sav-ior I met.
   O what a ten-der, com-pas-sion-ate friend – He met the need of my heart;
   Shad-ows dis-pel-ling, with joy I am tell-ing, He made all the

2. Born of the Spir-it with life from a-bove In-to God's fam-'ly di-vine;
   Jus-ti-fied ful-ly thru Cal-va-ry's love, O what a stand-ing is mine!
   And the trans-ac-tion so quick-ly was made When as a sin-ner I came,
   Took of the of-fer of grace He did prof-fer – He saved me, O

3. Now I've a hope that will sure-ly en-dure Af-ter the pass-ing of time;
   I have a fu-ture in heav-en for sure, There in those man-sions sub-lime.
   And it's be-cause of that won-der-ful day When at the cross I be-lieved;
   Rich-es e-ter-nal and bless-ings su-per-nal From His pre-cious

WORDS: John W. Peterson
MUSIC: John W. Peterson

Heaven Came Down

153 Though Your Sins Be as Scarlet

Though your sins be as scarlet, they shall be as white as snow — Isaiah 1:18 KJV

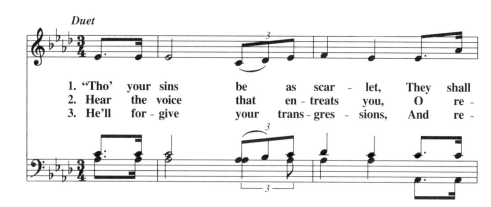

Duet

1. "Tho' your sins be as scar - let, They shall
2. Hear the voice that en - treats you, O re -
3. He'll for - give your trans - gres - sions, And re -

be as white as snow; Tho' your sins be as
turn ye un - to God! Hear the voice that en -
mem - ber them no more; He'll for give - your trans-

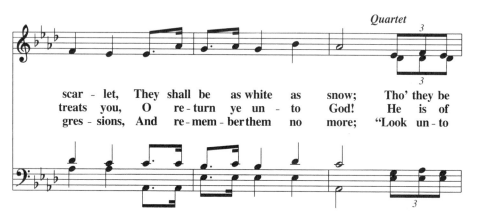

Quartet

scar - let, They shall be as white as snow; Tho' they be
treats you, O re - turn ye un - to God! He is of
gres - sions, And re - mem - ber them no more; "Look un - to

WORDS: Fanny J. Crosby
MUSIC: William H. Doane

Though Your Sins Be as Scarlet

154 By Grace Are Ye Saved

It is the gift of God — Ephesians 2:8 KJV

1. In grace the ho-ly God Did full sal-va-tion plan, E-lect-ing in His sov-'reign grace To save re-bel-lious man.
2. This grace of God ap-pears In Je-sus Christ His Son; He lift-ed on the cross of shame, The grace of God makes known.
3. To all who do be-lieve In God, thru Christ re-vealed By grace, they full sal-va-tion have, And "Sons of God" are sealed.

Refrain

By grace are ye saved thru faith, Thru faith, thru faith, Thru faith, thru faith, Thru faith, and that not of your-selves; Thru faith, and that not of your-

WORDS: Major Whittle
MUSIC: James McGranahan

By Grace Are Ye Saved

155   It Took a Miracle

Hallelujah! For our Lord God omnipotent reigns — Revelation 19:6 KJV

1. My Fa - ther is om - nip - o - tent, And that you can't de -
2. Though here His glo - ry has been shown, We still can't ful - ly
3. The Bi - ble tells us of His pow'r And wis - dom all way

ny; A God of might and mir - a - cles – 'Tis writ-ten in the
see The won-ders of His might, His throne – 'Twill take e - ter - ni -
through, And ev - 'ry lit - tle bird and flow'r Are tes - ti - mo-nies

Refrain

sky.
ty.   It took a mir-a-cle to put the stars in place, It took a
too.

mir - a - cle to hang the world in space; But when He saved my soul,

Cleansed and made me whole, It took a mir - a-cle of love and grace!

WORDS: John W. Peterson
MUSIC: John W. Peterson

MONTROSE

Lord, I Want to Be a Christian 156

Let this mind be in you, which was also in Christ Jesus — Phillipians 2:5 KJV

1. Lord, I want to be a Chris-tian In a my heart, in a my heart;
2. Lord, I want to be more lov - ing In a my heart, in a my heart;
3. Lord, I want to be more ho - ly In a my heart, in a my heart;
4. I don't want to be like Ju - das In a my heart, in a my heart;
5. Lord, I want to be like Je - sus In a my heart, in a my heart;

Lord, I want to be a Chris-tian In a my heart. _____
Lord, I want to be more lov - ing In a my heart. _____
Lord, I want to be more ho - ly In a my heart. _____
I don't want to be like Ju - das In a my heart. _____
Lord, I want to be like Je - sus In a my heart. _____

Refrain

In a my heart, _____ In a my heart, _____
In a my heart, In a my heart,

Lord, I want to be a Chris-tian In a my heart. _____

157 Nailed to the Cross

Behold the Lamb of God, which taketh away the sin of the world — John 1:29 KJV

Duet or Two-part

1. There was One who was will-ing to die in my stead, That a
2. He is ten - der and lov-ing and pa - tient with me, While He
3. I will cling to my Sav-ior and nev - er de-part - I will

soul so un-wor-thy might live, And the path to the cross He was
cleans-es my heart of its dross; But "there's no con-dem-na-tion," I
joy-ful-ly jour-ney each day With a song on my lips and a

will - ing to tread, All the sins of my life to for-give.
know I am free, For my sins are all nailed to the cross.
song in my heart, That my sins have been tak - en a - way.

Refrain (parts)

pp

They are nailed to the cross, They are nailed to the cross, O how

WORDS: Mrs. Frank A. Breck
MUSIC: Grant Colfax Tullar

Nailed to the Cross

much He was will-ing to bear! With what an-guish and loss,

Je - sus went to the cross! But He car-ried my sins with Him there.

rit.

For God So Loved the World   158

While we were yet sinners, Christ died for us — Romans 5:8 KJV

For God so loved the world He gave His on-ly
Some day He's com-ing back — What glo - ry that will

1 Son To die on Cal-v'ry's tree, From sin to set me free;

2 be! Won - der-ful His love to me.

WORDS: Frances Townsend, based on John 3:16
MUSIC: Alfred B. Smith

159 Wonderful Grace of Jesus

My grace is sufficient for thee — 2 Corinthians 12:9 KJV

1. Won-der-ful grace of Je - sus, Great-er than all my sin;
2. Won-der-ful grace of Je - sus, Reach-ing to all the lost,
3. Won-der-ful grace of Je - sus, Reach-ing the most de - filed,

How shall my tongue de - scribe it, Where shall its praise be - gin?
By it I have been par-doned, Saved to the ut - ter - most;
By its trans-form-ing pow - er Mak - ing him God's dear child,

Tak - ing a - way my bur - den, Set - ting my spir - it free,
Chains have been torn a - sun - der, Giv - ing me lib - er - ty,
Pur - chas-ing peace and heav - en For all e - ter - ni - ty –

For the won-der-ful grace of Je - sus reach - es me.
For the won-der-ful grace of Je - sus reach - es me.
And the won-der-ful grace of Je - sus reach - es me.

Refrain

Won - der-ful the match - less grace, the match - less grace of Je - sus,
Won - der-ful the match - less grace of Je - sus,

WORDS: Haldor Lillenas
MUSIC: Haldor Lillenas

Wonderful Grace of Jesus

160   The Cross Is Not Greater

Nay, in all these things we are more than conquerors
through Him that loved us — Romans 8:37 KJV

(The stanzas may be sung as a Solo)

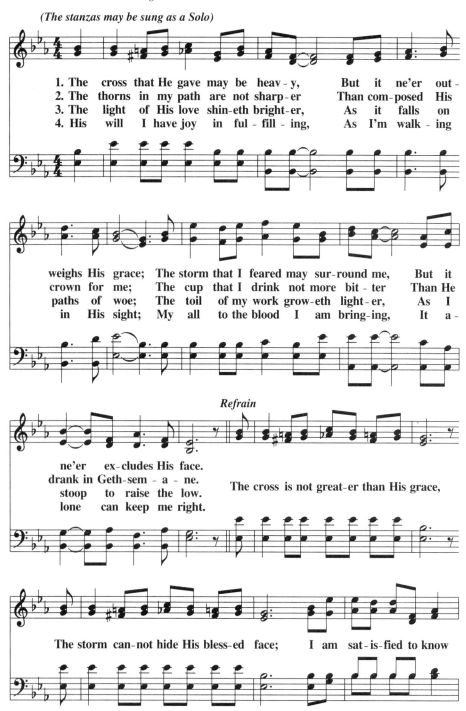

1. The cross that He gave may be heav-y,
2. The thorns in my path are not sharp-er
3. The light of His love shin-eth bright-er,
4. His will I have joy in ful-fill-ing,

But it ne'er out-
Than com-posed His
As it falls on
As I'm walk-ing

weighs His grace; The storm that I feared may sur-round me, But it
crown for me; The cup that I drink not more bit-ter Than He
paths of woe; The toil of my work grow-eth light-er, As I
in His sight; My all to the blood I am bring-ing, It a-

Refrain

ne'er ex-cludes His face.
drank in Geth-sem-a-ne.
stoop to raise the low.
lone can keep me right.

The cross is not great-er than His grace,

The storm can-not hide His bless-ed face; I am sat-is-fied to know

WORDS: Ballington Booth
MUSIC: Ballington Booth

The Cross is Not Greater

That with Je-sus here be-low, I can con-quer ev - 'ry foe. A - men.

Amazing Grace 161

For by grace are ye saved through faith;
and that not of yourselves — Ephesians 2:8 KJV

1. A - maz - ing grace – how sweet the sound – That saved a
2. 'Twas grace that taught my heart to fear, And grace my
3. Thru man - y dan - gers, toils, and snares I have al -
4. When we've been there ten thou - sand years, Bright shin - ing

wretch like me! _____ I once was lost, but
fears re - lieved; _____ How pre - cious did that
read - y come; _____ 'Tis grace hath brought me
as the sun, _____ We've no less days to

now am found, Was blind, but now I see. _____
grace ap - pear The hour I first be - lieved! _____
safe thus far, And grace will lead me home. _____
sing God's praise Than when we first be - gun. _____

WORDS: John Newton   McINTOSH
MUSIC: American melody from Carrell & Clayton's *Virginia Harmony*, 1831

162 He Looked Beyond My Fault

Where the Spirit of the Lord is, there is liberty — 2 Corinthians 3:17 KJV

A-maz-ing grace shall al-ways be my song of praise, . For it was grace that bought my lib-er-ty; _____ I do not know just why He came to love me so, ____ He looked be-yond by fault and saw my need. ____

I shall for-ev-er lift mine eyes to Cal-va-ry, __ To view the cross where Je-sus died for me; _____ How mar-vel-ous the grace that caught my

WORDS: Dottie Rambo
MUSIC: Adapted from *Londonderry Aire*

LONDONDERRY AIRE

He Looked Beyond My Fault

fall-ing soul, __ He looked be - yond my fault and saw my need. __

Amazing Grace 163

Being justified freely by His grace through the redemption
that is in Christ Jesus — Romans 3:24 KJV

1. A - maz - ing grace – how sweet the sound – That
2. 'Twas grace that taught my heart to fear, And
3. Thru man - y dan - gers, toils, and snares I
4. When we've been there ten thou - sand years, Bright

saved a wretch like me! I once was lost but
grace my fears re - lieved; How pre - cious did that
have al - read - y come; 'Tis grace hath brought me
shin - ing as the sun, We've no less days to

now am found Was blind, but now I see.
grace ap - pear The hour I first be - lieved!
safe thus far, And grace will lead me home.
sing God's praise Than when we'd first be - gun.

MUSIC: John Newton   MARTYRDOM
MUSIC: Hugh Wilson

164 He Giveth More Grace

Let us therefore come boldly unto the throne of grace — Hebrews 4:16 KJV

1. He giv-eth more grace when the
2. When we have ex-haust-ed our

bur-dens grow great-er; He send-eth more strength when the
store of en-dur-ance, When our strength has failed ere the

la-bors in-crease. To add-ed af-flic-tion He
day is half done, When we reach the end of our

add-ed His mer-cy; To mul-ti-plied tri-als, His
hoard-ed re-sourc-es, Our Fa-ther's full giv-ing is

mul-ti-plied peace.
on-ly be-gun.

Refrain

Oo loo loo, Oo loo loo,
His love has no lim-it; His grace has no meas-ure; His

He Giveth More Grace

poco rall.

accel.

Ah. _____ For out of His in - fi-nite
pow'r has no boun-da-ry known un - to men.

rall e cresc. **ff** *mp*

rich - es in Je - sus, He giv - eth, and giv - eth, and giv - eth a - gain!

Note: Cue-size notes are for last time

Depth of Mercy   165

I have trusted in Thy mercy — Psalm 13:5 KJV

1. Depth of mer - cy! can there be   Mer - cy still re - served for me?
2. I   have long with-stood His grace, Long pro-voked Him to   His face,
3. Now in - cline me to   re - pent, Let me now my sins   la - ment;
4. There for me my Sav - ior stands, Hold - ing forth His wound-ed hands;

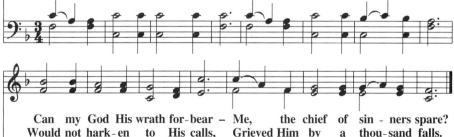

Can my God His wrath for - bear – Me,   the chief of sin - ners spare?
Would not hark - en to His calls, Grieved Him by   a thou-sand falls.
Now my foul re - volt de - plore, Weep, be - lieve, and sin   no more.
God is love! I know, I feel, Je -   sus weeps and loves me still.

WORDS: Charles Wesley   ALETTA
MUSIC: William B. Bradbury

166 Come, Thou Fount of Every Blessing

For with Thee is the fountain of life: in Thy light shall we see light — Psalm 36:9 KJV

1. Come, Thou Fount of ev-'ry bless-ing, Tune my heart to sing Thy
2. Here I raise mine *Eb - e - ne - zer; Hith - er by Thy help I'm
3. O to grace how great a debt - or Dai - ly I'm con-strained to

grace; Streams of mer - cy, nev - er ceas - ing, Call for
come; And I hope, by Thy good pleas - ure, Safe - ly
be! Let Thy grace, Lord, like a fet - ter, Bind my

songs of loud - est praise: Teach me some me - lo - dious
to ar - rive at home: Je - sus sought me when a
wan - d'ring heart to Thee: Prone to wan - der, Lord, I

son - net, Sung by flam - ing tongues a - bove; Praise the
stran - ger, Wan - d'ring from the fold of God; He, to
feel it, Prone to leave the God I love; Here's my

mount! I'm fixed up - on it, Mount of Thy re - deem-ing love.
res - cue me from dan - ger, In - ter-posed His pre-cious blood.
heart, Lord, take and seal it, Seal it for Thy courts a - bove.

*1 Samuel 7:12

WORDS: Robert Robinson
MUSIC: John Wyeth

NETTLETON

Just As I Am

167

That Christ Jesus came into the world to save sinners;
of whom I am chief — 1 Timothy 1:15 KJV

1. Just as I am, with-out one plea, But
2. Just as I am, and wait - ing not To
3. Just as I am, though tossed a - bout, With
4. Just as I am – poor, wretch - ed, blind, Sight,
5. Just as I am – Thou wilt re - ceive, Wilt

that Thy blood was shed for me, And that Thou bidst me
rid my soul of one dark blot, To Thee whose blood can
man - y a con - flict, many a doubt, Fight - ings and fears with -
rich - es, heal - ing of the mind, Yea, all I need in
wel - come, par - don, cleanse, re - lieve, Be - cause Thy prom - ise

come to Thee, O Lamb of God, I come! I come!
cleanse each spot, O Lamb of God, I come! I come!
in with - out, O Lamb of God, I come! I come!
Thee to find, O Lamb of God, I come! I come!
I be - lieve, O Lamb of God, I come! I come!

WORDS: Charlotte Elliott
MUSIC: William B. Bradbury

WOODWORTH

168   Softly and Tenderly

Who hath saved us, and called us with an holy calling — 2 Timothy 1:9 KJV

1. Soft - ly and ten - der - ly Je - sus is call - ing, Call - ing for
2. Why should we tar - ry when Je - sus is plead - ing, Plead - ing for
3. Time is now fleet - ing, the mo - ments are pass - ing, Pass - ing from
4. O for the won - der - ful love He has prom - ised, Prom - ised for

you and for me; See, on the por - tals He's wait - ing and watch-ing,
you and for me? Why should we lin - ger and heed not His mer - cies,
you and from me; Shad - ows are gath - er - ing, death-beds are com - ing,
you and for me; Tho we have sinned He has mer - cy and par - don,

Refrain

Watch-ing for you and for me.   Come home,   come home,
Mer - cies for you and for me?   Come home,   come home,
Com - ing for you and for me.
Par - don for you and for me.

Ye who are wea - ry, come home;   Ear - nest-ly, ten - der - ly,

Je - sus is call - ing – Call-ing, "O sin - ner, come home!"

WORDS: Will L. Thompson
MUSIC: Will L. Thompson

THOMPSON

The Lord is Speaking

169

And when we were all fallen to the earth,
I heard a voice speaking unto me — Acts 26:14 KJV

1. The Lord is speak - ing to
2. He speaks thru an earth - quake and thru a

you, to you; The Lord is
storm - tossed sea; He speaks thru a

Refrain

speak - ing to you, to you. Can't you
si - lent night so sweet, and quiet - ly.

hear what He's say - ing? Why are you wait - ing? The

Lord is speak - ing to you.

WORDS: Margaret Pleasant Douroux
MUSIC: Margaret Pleasant Douroux

170 Somebody's Knocking at Your Door

Behold, I stand at the door, and knock — Revelation 3:20 KJV

Some-bod - y's knock-ing at your door, Some-bod - y's

knock-ing at your door; O sin - ner, why don't you

an - swer? Some-bod - y's knock-ing at your door.

1. Knocks like Je - sus, Some-bod - y's knock-ing at your door;
2. Can't you hear Him? Some-bod - y's knock-ing at your door;
3. An - swer Je - sus, Some-bod - y's knock-ing at your door;
4. Je - sus calls you, Some-bod - y's knock-ing at your door;
5. Can't you trust Him? Some-bod - y's knock-ing at your door;

Knocks like Je - sus, Some-bod - y's knock-ing at your door;
Can't you hear Him? Some-bod - y's knock-ing at your door;
An - swer Je - sus, Some-bod - y's knock-ing at your door;
Je - sus calls you, Some-bod - y's knock-ing at your door;
Can't you trust Him? Some-bod - y's knock-ing at your door;

WORDS: African-American spiritual
MUSIC: African-American spiritual; arr. by Frederick J. Work and John W. Work, Jr.

SOMEBODY'S KNOCKING

Jesus Is Calling

171

Let us therefore fear...lest any man fall after the same example of unbelief — Hebrews 4:1, 11 KJV

1. Je-sus is ten-der-ly call-ing thee home – Call-ing to-day,
2. Je-sus is call-ing the wea-ry to rest – Call-ing to-day,
3. Je-sus is wait-ing, O come to Him now – Wait-ing to-day,
4. Je-sus is plead-ing, O list to His voice – Hear Him to-day,

call-ing to-day; Why from the sun-shine of love wilt thou roam
call-ing to-day; Bring Him thy bur-den and thou shalt be blest –
wait-ing to-day; Come with thy sins, at His feet low-ly bow –
hear Him to-day; They who be-lieve on His name shall re-joice –

Refrain

Far-ther and far-ther a-way.
He will not turn thee a-way. Call - ing to -
Come, and no long-er de-lay. Call - ing, call-ing to -
Quick-ly a-rise and a-way.

day, Call - ing to - day,
day, to - day, Call - ing, call-ing to - day, to - day,

Je - sus is call - ing, Is ten-der-ly call-ing to - day.
Je-sus is ten-der-ly call-ing to-day, Is

WORDS: Fanny J. Crosby
MUSIC: George C. Stebbins

CALLING TODAY

172 Do You Need a Friend?

Looking unto Jesus the author and finisher of our faith — Hebrews 12:2 KJV

1. Do you need a friend to keep you till the end?
2. He will un-der-stand, just take Him by the hand,

Well, then, may I rec-om-mend the Lord; (the Lord;)
You are part of what He's planned to-day; (to-day;)

He will sat-is-fy, He'll nev-er pass you by, Tell me
Look to Him a-lone, He'll not for-sake His own, Soon your

now, why don't you try the Lord? _____ He will make for
trou-bles will be gone a-way. _____ He your soul will

you a way, and see you through, For, this road He, too, has
bless, but sin you must con-fess, This true hap-pi-ness af-

WORDS: W. Elmo Mercer
MUSIC: W. Elmo Mercer

Do You Need a Friend?

trod; _____ Bro - ken lives He'll mend, Peace and strength He'll
fords; _____ Do you need a friend to keep you till the

send, Trust Him now to be your Friend, your God. _____
end? Well, then, may I rec-om - mend the Lord. _____

Come to Jesus 173

Draw nigh to God, and He will draw nigh to you — James 4:8 KJV

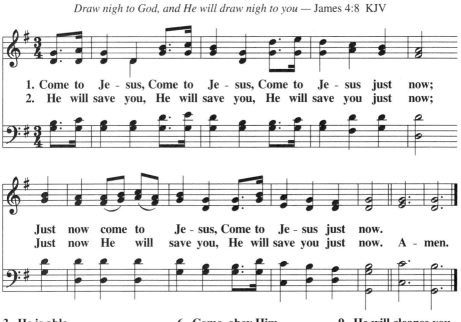

1. Come to Je - sus, Come to Je - sus, Come to Je - sus just now;
2. He will save you, He will save you, He will save you just now;

Just now come to Je - sus, Come to Je - sus just now.
Just now He will save you, He will save you just now. A - men.

3. He is able,
4. He is willing,
5. Come, confess Him,

6. Come, obey Him,
7. He will hear you,
8. He'll forgive you,

9. He will cleanse you,
10. Jesus loves you,
11. Only trust Him,

WORDS: Traditional
MUSIC: Traditional

174 Jesus, I Come

Being then made free from sin,
ye became the servants of righteousness — Romans 6:18 KJV

1. Out of my bond-age, sor-row and night, Je-sus, I come,
2. Out of my shame-ful fail-ure and loss, Je-sus, I come,
3. Out of un-rest and ar-ro-gant pride, Je-sus, I come,
4. Out of the fear and dread of the tomb, Je-sus, I come,

Je-sus, I come; In-to Thy free-dom, glad-ness and light,
Je-sus, I come; In-to the glo-rious gain of Thy cross,
Je-sus, I come; In-to Thy bless-ed will to a-bide,
Je-sus, I come; In-to the joy and light of Thy home,

Je-sus, I come to Thee; Out of my sick-ness
Je-sus, I come to Thee; Out of earth's sor-rows
Je-sus, I come to Thee; Out of my-self to
Je-sus, I come to Thee; Out of the depths of

in-to Thy health, Out of my want and in-to Thy wealth,
in-to Thy balm, Out of life's storms and in-to Thy calm,
dwell in Thy love, Out of de-spair in-to rap-tures a-bove,
ru-in un-told, In-to the peace of Thy shel-ter-ing fold,

WORDS: William T. Sleeper
MUSIC: George C. Stebbins

JESUS, I COME

Jesus, I Come

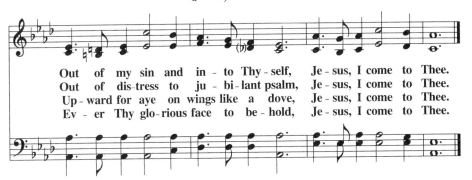

Out of my sin and in-to Thy-self, Je-sus, I come to Thee.
Out of dis-tress to ju-bi-lant psalm, Je-sus, I come to Thee.
Up-ward for aye on wings like a dove, Je-sus, I come to Thee.
Ev-er Thy glo-rious face to be-hold, Je-sus, I come to Thee.

Have You Tried Jesus?   175

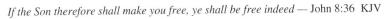

If the Son therefore shall make you free, ye shall be free indeed — John 8:36 KJV

Unison

1. Have you tried Je-sus _ in all your search-ing? _ Have you tried Je-sus _
2. Have you tried Je-sus _ as Lord and Sav-ior? _ Have you tried Je-sus _
3. Have you tried Je-sus _ as Lord and Sav-ior? _ Will you try Je-sus _

_ for peace with-in? _____ If you want an-swers _____ to your life's
_ to free you with-in? _____ To find the an-swers _____ to your life's
_ to free you from sin? ____ You'll find the an-swers _____ to your life's

prob-lems, _ Have you tried Je - sus _____ to set you free? _____
prob-lems, _ Have you tried Je - sus _____ to set you free? _____
prob-lems, _ Will you try Je - sus _____ to set you free? _____

WORDS: Phil Perkins
MUSIC: Phil Perkins

176 The Nail-Scarred Hand

Put my finger into the print of the nails — John 20:25 KJV

1. Have you failed in your plan of your storm-tossed life? Place your
2. Are you walk-ing a-lone thru the shad-ows dim? Place your
3. Would you fol-low the will of the ris-en Lord? Place your
4. Is your soul bur-dened down with its load of sin? Place your

hand in the nail-scarred hand; Are you wea-ry and worn from its
hand in the nail-scarred hand; Christ will com-fort your heart, put your
hand in the nail-scarred hand; Would you live in the light of His
hand in the nail-scarred hand; Throw your heart o-pen wide, let the

toil and strife?
trust in Him,
bless-ed Word? Place your hand in the nail-scarred hand.
Sav-ior in,

Refrain

Place your hand in the nail-scarred hand,

Place your hand in the nail-scarred hand. He will keep to the end, He's your

WORDS: B. B. McKinney
MUSIC: B. B. McKinney
LUBBOCK

The Nail-Scarred Hand

dear - est friend, Place your hand in the nail - scarred hand.

Tread Softly 177

Be silent, O all flesh, before the Lord — Zechariah 2:13 KJV

1. Be si - lent, be si - lent, A whis - per is heard, Be si - lent, and
2. Be si - lent, be si - lent, For ho - ly this place, This al - tar that
3. Be si - lent, be si - lent, Breathe hum - bly our prayer, A fore-taste of
4. Be si - lent, be si - lent, His mer - cy re - cord, Be si - lent, be

Refrain

lis - ten, O treas-ure each word!
ech - oes The mes-sage of grace.   Tread soft - ly, tread soft - ly, The
E - den This mo-ment we share.   Tread soft-ly here, tread soft-ly here,
si - lent And wait on the Lord.

Mas - ter is here, Tread soft - ly, tread soft - ly, He bids us draw near.
Tread soft-ly here, tread soft-ly here,

WORDS: Fanny J. Crosby
MUSIC: William H. Doane

178 Try Jesus, He Satisfies

Come unto Me, all ye that labour and are heavy laden,
and I will give you rest — Matthew 11:28 KJV

Unison

1. Come un-to Je-sus, all ye that la-bor, All that are wea-ry,
2. Come un-to Je-sus, don't waste a mo-ment; Your time so pre-cious
3. Come un-to Je-sus, Sav-ior and broth-er, Sure-ly you need Him

worn and de-filed. Bring Him your bur-dens, seek now His fa-vor,
is fleet-ing by, All your trans-gres-sions, free-ly con-fess-ing,
tru-est and best. Dear-er than fa-ther, fond-er than moth-er.

Tell Him your sor-rows, in Him con-fide.
He in His mer-cy, safe-ly will hide. *Refrain* He sat-is-fies, He sat-is-
Come un-to Je-sus, He'll give you rest.

fies, O will you let Him in your heart a-bide? He'll keep your

soul, what-ev-er be-tide. Won't you try Je-sus, He sat-is-fies.

WORDS: Roberta Martin
MUSIC: Roberta Martin; arr. by Aletha Robinson

Don't Stay Away

179

There is still room — Luke 14:22 KJV

1. Broth - ers, don't stay a - way, Broth - ers, don't
2. Mourn - ers, don't stay a - way, Mourn - ers, don't
3. Gam - bler, don't stay a - way, Gam - bler, don't
4. Sis - ter, don't stay a - way, Sis - ter, don't

stay a - way, Broth - ers, don't stay a - way,
stay a - way, Mourn - ers, don't stay a - way,
stay a - way, Gam - bler, don't stay a - way,
stay a - way, Sis - ter, don't stay a - way,

don't stay a - way, For my Lord says there's
don't stay a - way, For the Bi - ble says there's
don't stay a - way, For the an - gels say there's
don't stay a - way, For Je - sus says there's

room e - nough, room e - nough in the heav-ens for us all,

My Lord says there's room e - nough, Don't stay a - way.

WORDS: African-American spiritual
MUSIC: African-American spiritual; arr. by Phillip V. S. Lindsley

180   What Will You Do with Jesus?

Behold, I stand at the door and knock — Revelation 3:20 KJV

Unison or Solo

1. Je - sus is stand-ing at your heart's door, Stand-ing and
2. At your sad heart He is knock - ing still, Long-ing to
3. Oh, will you leave Him a - lone, out - side? Or will you
4. Will you now an - swer His ten - der call? Will you o -

knock - ing, He's knocked be - fore; This is the ques-tion you
en - ter, your soul to thrill; You must ac - cept or re -
choose Him what - e'er be - tide? This is the ques-tion you
bey Him what - e'er be - fall? Fol - low Him dai - ly as

Refrain, in Harmony

face once more: What will you do with Je - sus?
ject His will: What will you do with Je - sus?
must de - cide: What will you do with Je - sus?   What will you do with
Lord of all? What will you do with Je - sus?

Je - sus? Neu-tral you can - not be; Some-day your

WORDS: Sts. 1-4: B. B. McKinney; refrain: anonymous
MUSIC: B. B. McKinney

What Will You Do with Jesus?

heart will be ask - ing: "What will He do with me?"

Pass Me Not   181

Hear my cry, O God; attend unto my prayer — Psalm 61:1 KJV

1. Pass me not, O gen - tle Sav - ior, Hear my hum-ble cry,
2. Let me at a throne of mer - cy Find a sweet re - lief;
3. Trust-ing on - ly in Thy mer - it, Would I seek Thy face;
4. Thou the Spring of all my com - fort, More than life to me,

While on oth - ers Thou art call - ing, Do not pass me by.
Kneel-ing there in deep con - tri - tion, Help my un - be - lief.
Heal my wound-ed, bro-ken spir - it, Save me by Thy grace.
Whom have I on earth be - side Thee? Whom in heav'n but Thee?

Refrain

Sav - ior, Sav - ior, Hear my hum - ble cry;

While on oth-ers Thou art call - ing, Do not pass me by.

WORDS: Fanny J. Crosby
MUSIC: William H. Doane

182   Room at the Cross for You

In this was manifested the love of God toward us...that we might live through Him — 1 John 4:9 KJV

1. The cross up-on which Je-sus died Is a
2. Tho mil-lions have found Him a friend And have
3. The hand of my Sav-ior is strong, And the

shel-ter in which we can hide; And its grace so free
turned from the sins they have sinned, The Sav-ior still waits
love of my Sav-ior is long; Thru sun-shine or rain,

is suf-fi-cient for me, And deep is its foun-tain – as
to o-pen the gates And wel-come a sin-ner be-
thru loss or in gain, The blood flows from Cal-v'ry to

Refrain

wide as the sea.
fore it's too late. There's room at the cross for you, There's
cleanse ev-'ry stain.

room at the cross for you; Tho mil-lions have come, There's

WORDS: Ira F. Stanphill
MUSIC: Ira F. Stanphill

STANPHILL

Room at the Cross

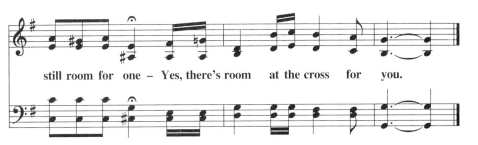

still room for one – Yes, there's room   at the cross   for   you.

Jesus Calls Us   183

Thou shalt have treasure in heaven ... come, follow me — Luke 18:22 KJV

1. Je - sus calls us,   o'er the   tu - mult   Of our
2. Je - sus calls us   from the   wor - ship   Of the
3. In our   joys and   in our   sor - rows, Days of
4. Je - sus calls us;   by Thy   mer - cies, Sav - ior,

life's   wild, rest - less sea,   Day by   day   His sweet voice
vain   world's gold - en store, From each i - dol that would
toil   and hours of ease, Still He calls, in cares and
may   we hear Thy call, Give our hearts to Thy o -

sound - eth, Say - ing, "Chris - tian, fol - low Me."
keep us,   Say - ing, "Chris - tian, love Me more."
pleas - ures, "Chris - tian, love Me more than these."
be - dience, Serve and love Thee best of all.

WORDS: Cecil F. Alexander   GALILEE
MUSIC: William H. Jude

184 Oh, Why Not Tonight?

For whosoever shall call upon the name of the Lord
shall be saved — Romans 10:13 KJV

1. Oh, do not let the word de-part, And close thine
2. To - mor-row's sun may nev - er rise, To bless thy
3. Our Lord in pit - y lin - gers still, And wilt thou
4. Our bless - ed Lord re - fus - es none Who would to

eyes a - gainst the light; Poor sin - ner, hard - en not your
long de - lud - ed sight; This is the time, oh, then be
thus His love re - quite? Re - nounce at once thy stub - born
Him their souls u - nite; Be - lieve, o - bey, the work is

Refrain

heart, Be saved oh, to - night. Oh, why not to -
wise, Be saved oh, to - night. Oh, why not to-night?
will, Be saved oh, to - night.
done, Be saved oh, to - night.

night? Oh, why not to-night? Wilt
Why not to-night? Why not to-night? Why not to-night? Wilt

WORDS: Elizabeth Reed
MUSIC: J. Calvin Bushey

Oh, Why Not Tonight?

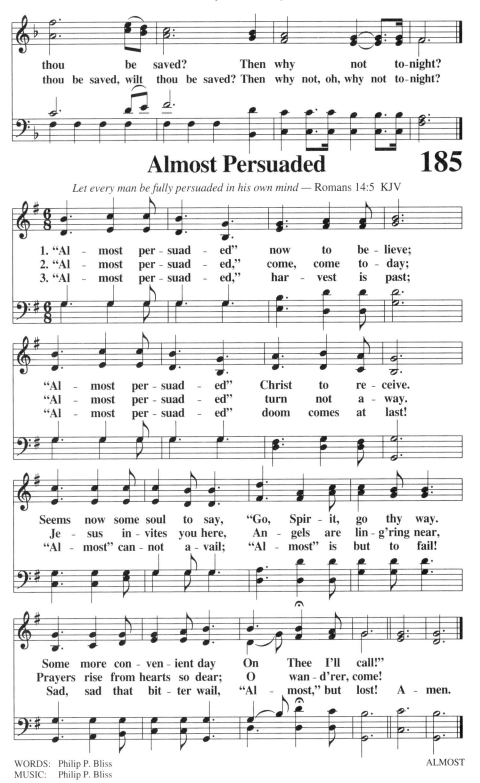

thou be saved? Then why not to-night?
thou be saved, wilt thou be saved? Then why not, oh, why not to-night?

Almost Persuaded   185

Let every man be fully persuaded in his own mind — Romans 14:5 KJV

1. "Al - most per - suad - ed" now to be - lieve;
2. "Al - most per - suad - ed," come, come to - day;
3. "Al - most per - suad - ed," har - vest is past;

"Al - most per - suad - ed" Christ to re - ceive.
"Al - most per - suad - ed" turn not a - way.
"Al - most per - suad - ed" doom comes at last!

Seems now some soul to say, "Go, Spir - it, go thy way.
Je - sus in - vites you here, An - gels are lin - g'ring near,
"Al - most" can - not a - vail; "Al - most" is but to fail!

Some more con - ven - ient day On Thee I'll call!"
Prayers rise from hearts so dear; O wan - d'rer, come!
Sad, sad that bit - ter wail, "Al - most," but lost! A - men.

WORDS: Philip P. Bliss
MUSIC: Philip P. Bliss

ALMOST

186   Kneel Down at the Altar

I will call upon the Lord, who is worthy to be praised — Psalm 18:3 KJV

1. When you're tired _____ and you're wound - ed,
2. A - bout bur - dens, a - bout sor - rows,
3. A - bout tri - als and tribu - la - tions,

bring Him your soul that's in need. _____
a - bout friends so un - kind. _____
a - bout cry - ing thru a smile. _____

He is a - ble to pro - tect you,
A - bout loved ones who are need - ing
A - bout need - ing Him to guide you,

your hun-gry soul _____ He'll feed. _____
just a bit of life's sun - shine. _____
as you walk the last mile. _____

WORDS: William Austin
MUSIC: William Austin; arr. by Roberta Martin
Arr. © 1958 by Roberta Martin. Used by permission.

Kneel Down at the Altar

187   Leave It There

Cast thy burden upon the Lord, and He shall sustain thee — Psalm 55:22 KJV

1. If the world from you with-hold of its sil - ver and its gold,
2. If your bod - y suf - fers pain and your health you can't re - gain,
3. When your en - e - mies as - sail and your heart be - gins to fail,
4. When your youth - ful days are gone and old age is steal-ing on,

And you have to get a - long with mea - ger fare,
And your soul is al - most sink - ing in de - spair,
Don't for - get that God in heav - en an - swers prayer;
And your bod - y bends be - neath the weight of care,

Just re - mem - ber, in His Word, how He feeds the lit - tle bird –
Je - sus knows the pain you feel, He can save and He can heal –
He will make a way for you and will lead you safe - ly thru –
He will nev - er leave you then, He'll go with you to the end –

Take your bur - den to the Lord and leave it there.
Take your bur - den to the Lord and leave it there.
Take your bur - den to the Lord and leave it there.
Take your bur - den to the Lord and leave it there.

WORDS: Charles A. Tindley
MUSIC: Charles A. Tindley

LEAVE IT THERE

Leave It There

188 Burdens Are Lifted at Calvary

The Lord hath laid on Him the iniquity of us all — Isaiah 53:6 KJV

1. Days are filled with sor-row and care, Hearts are lone - ly and drear;
2. Cast your care on Je - sus to - day, Leave your wor - ry and fear;
3. Trou-bled soul, the Sav-ior can see Ev - 'ry heart-ache and tear;

Bur-dens are lift - ed at Cal - va - ry – Je - sus is ver - y near.
Bur-dens are lift - ed at Cal - va - ry – Je - sus is ver - y near.
Bur-dens are lift - ed at Cal - va - ry – Je - sus is ver - y near.

Refrain

Bur-dens are lift - ed at Cal - va - ry, Cal - va - ry, Cal - va - ry;

Bur-dens are lift - ed at Cal - va - ry – Je - sus is ver - y near.

WORDS: John M. Moore
MUSIC: John M. Moore
BURDENS LIFTED

Let Jesus Come into Your Heart   189

And we will come unto Him, and make our abode with Him — John 14:23 KJV

1. If you are tired of the load of your sin, Let
2. If 'tis for pu - ri - ty now that you sigh, Let
3. If there's a tem - pest your voice can - not still, Let
4. If you would join the glad songs of the blest, Let

Je - sus come in - to your heart; If you de - sire a new
Je - sus come in - to your heart; Foun - tains for cleans - ing are
Je - sus come in - to your heart; If there's a void this world
Je - sus come in - to your heart; If you would en - ter the

life to be - gin, Let Je - sus come in - to your heart.
flow - ing near - by, Let Je - sus come in - to your heart.
nev - er can fill, Let Je - sus come in - to your heart.
man - sions of rest, Let Je - sus come in - to your heart.

Refrain

Just now your doubt-ings give o'er, Just now re - ject Him no more;

Just now throw o - pen the door – Let Je - sus come in - to your heart.

WORDS: Lelia N. Morris
MUSIC: Lelia N. Morris

McCONNELSVILLE

190 He's Only a Prayer Away

I have heard thy prayer — Isaiah 38:5 KJV

1. There's Some-one who loves ev-'ry sin-ner, _____ He's call-ing O
2. Though friends may de-ride and for-sake you, _____ And leave you a-
3. When oth-ers for-sake and de-sert you, _____ And you're in the

hear Him to-day; _____ 'Tis Je-sus, our bless-ed Re-deem-er _____
lone in the way, _____ Re-mem-ber the prom-ise of Je-sus _____
depth of de-spair, _____ Let God share your bur-den and sor-row _____

Refrain

He's on-ly a prayer a-way. _____
He's on-ly a prayer a-way. _____ He's on-ly a prayer a-
Just seek Him and He'll be there. _____

way, _____ He's on-ly a prayer a-way; _____ God will be

with you when-ev-er you pray – He's on-ly a prayer a-way. _____

WORDS: Johnny Lange and Harold L. Graham
MUSIC: Johnny Lange and Harold L. Graham

Tell Jesus All

Praying always with all prayer and supplication — Ephesians 6:18 KJV

1. Are you bur - dened, worn and wea - ry, Heed - ing
2. Would you have your past for - giv - en, And be
3. Are you need - ing one to guide you, Shel - ter

still the temp-ter's call? Is your life each day more drear - y?
lift - ed, if you fall? Trust the Friend whose side was riv - en,
when the storms ap - pall, Some-one who would stay be - side you?

Refrain

Just tell Je - sus, tell Him all. Just tell Je - sus, tell Him

all, Tri - als great and tri - als small; He will

share them, free - ly bear them, Just tell Je - sus, tell Him all.

WORDS: James Rowe
MUSIC: J. M. Henson

192 The Savior is Waiting

For Thou wilt light my candle:
the Lord my God will enlighten my darkness — Psalm 18:28 KJV

1. The Sav - ior is wait - ing to en - ter your heart, Why don't you
2. If you'll take one step toward the Sav-ior, my friend, You'll find His

let Him come in? __ There's noth - ing in this world to keep you a - part,
arms o - pen wide, _ Re - ceive Him and all of your dark-ness will end,

Refrain

What is your an - swer to Him? __
With-in your heart He'll a - bide. __
Time af-ter time He has

wait-ed be-fore, And now He is wait-ing a - gain, __ To see if you're

will-ing to o-pen the door, Oh, how he wants to come in. __

WORDS: Ralph Carmichael
MUSIC: Ralph Carmichael

Only Trust Him

193

Behold, your God will come with vengeance, even God with
a recompence; He will come and save you — Isaiah 35:4 KJV

1. Come, ev - 'ry soul by sin op-pressed – There's
2. For Je - sus shed His pre - cious blood Rich
3. Yes, Je - sus is the Truth, the Way, That

mer - cy with the Lord, And He will sure - ly
bless - ings to be - stow; Plunge now in - to the
leads you in - to rest; Be - lieve in Him with -

give you rest By trust - ing in His word.
crim - son flood That wash - es white as snow.
out de - lay And you are ful - ly blest.

Refrain

On - ly trust Him, on - ly trust Him, on - ly trust Him now;

He will save you, He will save you, He will save you now.

WORDS: John H. Stockton
MUSIC: John H. Stockton

STOCKTON

194   Why Do You Wait?

Behold, I stand at the door, and knock...I will come in to him,
and will sup with him, and he with Me — Revelation 3:20 KJV

1. Why do you wait, dear broth-er,   O   why do you tar-ry so
2. What do you hope, dear broth-er,   To   gain by a   fur-ther de -
3. Do you not feel, dear broth-er,   His   Spir-it now striv-ing with -
4. Why do you wait, dear broth-er?   The   har-vest is pass-ing a -

long?   Your Sav-ior is wait-ing to   give   you   A
lay?   There's no one to save you but   Je - sus,   There's
in?   O   why not ac-cept His sal - va - tion   And
way;   Your Sav-ior is long-ing to   bless   you,   There's

Refrain

place in His sanc-ti-fied throng.
no oth-er way but His way.
throw off your bur-den of   sin?   Why not, why not, Why not come to Him
dan-ger and death in de - lay.

now?   Why   not,   why   not,   Why not come to Him now?

WORDS: George F. Root
MUSIC: George F. Root

Turn Your Eyes upon Jesus 195

Looking unto Jesus the author and finisher of our faith — Hebrews 12:2 KJV

1. O soul, are you wea-ry and trou - bled? No light in the
2. Thru death in - to life ev - er - last - ing He passed, and we
3. His word shall not fail you – He prom - ised; Be - lieve Him, and

dark-ness you see? ____ There's light for a look at the Sav - ior, And
fol - low Him there; ____ O- ver us sin no more hath do - min - ion – For
all will be well: ____ Then go to a world that is dy - ing, His

Refrain

life more a - bun - dant and free! ____
more than con-q'rors we are. ____ Turn your eyes up-on Je -
per - fect sal - va - tion to tell! ____

sus, Look full in His won-der-ful face, ____ And the things of
won-der-ful face,

earth will grow strange-ly dim In the light of His glo-ry and grace. ____

WORDS: Helen H. Lemmel
MUSIC: Helen H. Lemmel

LEMMEL

196 Come Just As You Are

*Then Peter said unto them, "Repent, and be baptized every
one of you in the name of Jesus Christ" — Acts 2:38 KJV*

1. Ye who are trou-bled and bur-dened by sin, Come just as you
2. Deep in your heart sin has writ-ten its scar; Come just as you
3. Sin-ful and guilt-y, heart-bro-ken and lost, Come just as you
4. Naught of your good-ness for sin can a-tone; Come just as you
5. Come with your heart-ache, your sor-row and pain; Come just as you

are.   Come to the Sav-ior, a new life be-gin. Oh,
are.   Though from your Fa-ther you've wan-dered a-far, Oh,
are.   Think what your ran-som on Cal-va-ry cost! Oh,
are.   Trust in the mer-it of Je-sus a-lone, And
are.   No one has come to the Sav-ior in vain. Oh,

Refrain

come just as you are! Come just as you are. Oh, come just as you are!

Turn from your sin, let the Sav-ior come in, and come just as you are.

WORDS: Haldor Lillenas
MUSIC: Haldor Lillenas

Kneel at the Cross

197

*And that He might reconcile both unto God in one body by the
cross, having slain the enmity thereby — Ephesians 2:16 KJV*

1. Kneel at the cross, Christ will meet you there, Come while He waits for
2. Kneel at the cross, There is room for all Who would His glo - ry
3. Kneel at the cross, Give your i - dols up, Look un - to realms a -

you; List to His voice, Leave with Him your care
share; Bliss there a - waits, Harm can ne'er be - fall
bove; Turn not a - way To life's spark-ling cup;

Refrain

And be - gin life a - new.
Those who are an-chored there. Kneel at the cross,
Trust on - ly in His love. Kneel at the cross, Kneel at the cross,

Leave ev - 'ry care; Kneel at the
Leave ev - 'ry care, Leave, ev - 'ry care; Kneel at the cross,

cross, Je-sus will meet you there.
Kneel at the cross, there, meet you there.

WORDS: Charles E. Moody
MUSIC: Charles E. Moody

198   I Surrender All

We have forsaken all, and followed Thee — Matthew 19:27 KJV

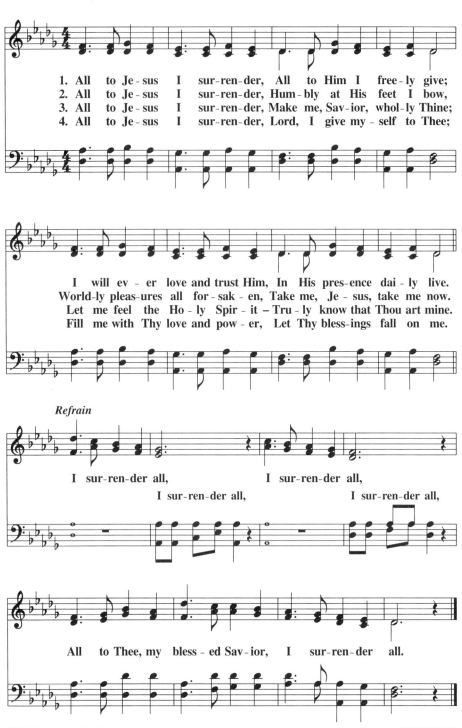

1. All to Je-sus I sur-ren-der, All to Him I free-ly give;
2. All to Je-sus I sur-ren-der, Hum-bly at His feet I bow,
3. All to Je-sus I sur-ren-der, Make me, Sav-ior, whol-ly Thine;
4. All to Je-sus I sur-ren-der, Lord, I give my-self to Thee;

I will ev-er love and trust Him, In His pres-ence dai-ly live.
World-ly pleas-ures all for-sak-en, Take me, Je-sus, take me now.
Let me feel the Ho-ly Spir-it – Tru-ly know that Thou art mine.
Fill me with Thy love and pow-er, Let Thy bless-ings fall on me.

Refrain

I sur-ren-der all,   I sur-ren-der all,
I sur-ren-der all,   I sur-ren-der all,

All to Thee, my bless-ed Sav-ior, I sur-ren-der all.

WORDS: Judson W. Van DeVenter
MUSIC: Winfield S. Weeden

SURRENDER

Wherever He Leads, I'll Go 199

Master, I will follow Thee whithersoever Thou goest — Matthew 8:19 KJV

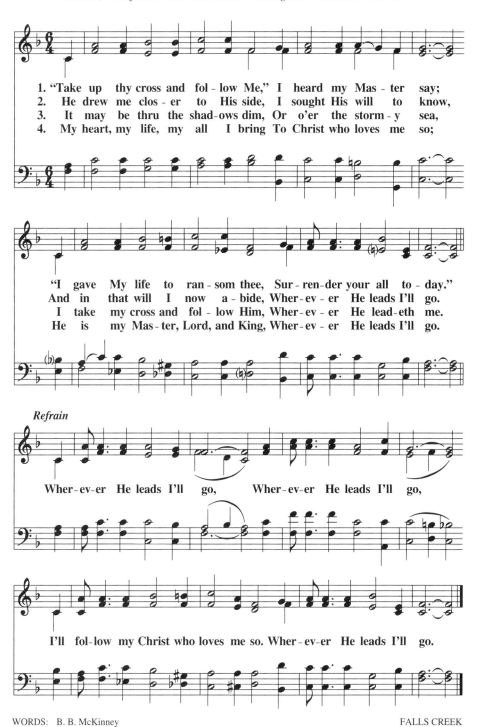

1. "Take up thy cross and fol-low Me," I heard my Mas-ter say;
2. He drew me clos-er to His side, I sought His will to know,
3. It may be thru the shad-ows dim, Or o'er the storm-y sea,
4. My heart, my life, my all I bring To Christ who loves me so;

"I gave My life to ran-som thee, Sur-ren-der your all to-day."
And in that will I now a-bide, Wher-ev-er He leads I'll go.
I take my cross and fol-low Him, Wher-ev-er He lead-eth me.
He is my Mas-ter, Lord, and King, Wher-ev-er He leads I'll go.

Refrain

Wher-ev-er He leads I'll go, Wher-ev-er He leads I'll go,

I'll fol-low my Christ who loves me so. Wher-ev-er He leads I'll go.

WORDS: B. B. McKinney
MUSIC: B. B. McKinney
FALLS CREEK

200 Thy Way, O Lord

Teach me Thy way, O Lord — Psalm 86:11 KJV

1. Thy way, O Lord, not mine, Thy will be done, not mine; Since Thou for me didst bleed, And now doth inter- cede, Each day I sim - ply plead, Thy will be done.

2. Thy way, O Lord, not mine, Let glo - ry all be Thine; Keep me, lest I may stray, Near Thee from day to day; Teach me to watch and pray, Thy will be done.

3. Hide me from self, O Lord, May I at - tend Thy word; Send pride be - yond re - call, Let each as - sail - er fall, Be Thou my all in all, Thy will be done.

4. Sub - mis - sive - ly I bow; With strength and grace en - dow This wea - ry, sin - ful heart; Shield from each cru - el dart; May I from Thee ne'er part, Thy will be done.

Refrain

Thy will, Thy will be done, Thy will, Thy will be done;

Thy will be done, Thy will be done,

In - cline my heart each day to say, "Thy will be done." A - men.

WORDS: Nina B. Jackson
MUSIC: E. C. Deas

Touch Me, Lord Jesus

201

And He touched her hand — Matthew 8:15 KJV

1. Touch me, Lord Je - sus, With Thy hand of mer - cy,
2. Mold me, dear Mas - ter; As I bow be - fore Thee,
3. Feed me, dear Je - sus, From Thy ho - ly ta - ble,
4. Guide me, Je - ho - vah, Thru this vale of sor - row,

Make each throb-bing heart-beat Feel Thy pow'r di - vine.
Pros - trate and help - less, Make my heart Thy throne.
Rain bread from heav - en, Let my cup o'er - flow.
I am safe for - ev - er, Trust-ing in Thy love.

Take my will for - ev - er, I will doubt Thee nev - er,
Purge my dross with his - sop; Burn me with Thy fire;
Na - ked, sick and hun - gry; Poor and weak and lone-ly,
Bear me thru the cur - rent; O'er the chil - ly Jor - dan,

Cleanse me, dear Sav - ior, Make me whol - ly Thine.
Lord, make and use me; Ev - er all Thine own.
Feed me, Lord Je - sus Till I want no more.
Lead me, dear Mas - ter To my home a - bove.

WORDS: Lucie E. Campbell
MUSIC: Lucie E. Campbell

202 I Am Thine, O Lord

If I be lifted up…will draw all men unto me — John 12:32 KJV

1. I am Thine, O Lord, I have heard Thy voice, And it
2. Con - se - crate me now to Thy ser - vice, Lord, By the
3. O the pure de - light of a sin - gle hour That be -
4. There are depths of love that I can - not know Till I

told Thy love to me; But I long to rise in the
pow'r of grace di - vine; Let my soul look up with a
fore Thy throne I spend, When I kneel in prayer, and with
cross the nar - row sea; There are heights of joy that I

arms of faith, And be clos - er drawn to Thee.
stead - fast hope, And my will be lost in Thine.
Thee, my God, I com - mune as friend with friend!
may not reach Till I rest in peace with Thee.

Refrain

Draw me near - er, near - er, bless-ed Lord, To the
near - er near - er,

WORDS: Fanny J. Crosby
MUSIC: William H. Doane

I AM THINE

I Am Thine, O Lord

cross where Thou hast died; Draw me near - er, near - er,

near - er, bless - ed Lord, To Thy pre - cious, bleed - ing side.

Sanctuary 203

Lord, who shall abide in thy Tabernacle? He that walketh uprightly — Psalm 15:1-2 KJV

Lord, pre - pare me to be a sanc-tu - ar - y, pure and

ho - ly, tried and true; With thanks-giv - ing, I'll be a

liv - ing sanc-tu - ar - y for You.

WORDS: John Thompson and Randy Scruggs
MUSIC: John Thompson and Randy Scruggs

204 I'll Go Where You Want Me to Go

I delight to do Thy will, O my God — Psalm 40:8 KJV

1. It may not be on the moun - tain's height Or
2. Per - haps to - day there are lov - ing words Which
3. There's sure - ly some - where a low - ly place In

o - ver the storm - y sea, It may not be at the
Je - sus would have me speak, There may be now, in the
earth's har - vest fields so wide, Where I may la - bor thru

bat - tle's front My Lord will have need of me; But
paths of sin, Some wan - d'rer whom I should seek; O
life's short day For Je - sus the Cru - ci - fied; So,

if by a still, small voice He calls To paths I do not
Sav - ior, if Thou wilt be my Guide, Tho dark and rug-ged the
trust - ing my all un - to Thy care – I know Thou lov - est

WORDS: St. 1: Mary Brown; sts. 2-3: Charles E. Prior
MUSIC: Carrie E. Rounsefell

I'll Go Where You Want Me to Go

205 Living for Jesus

I live by the faith of the Son of God — Galatians 2:20 KJV

1. Liv-ing for Je-sus a life that is true, Striv-ing to please Him in
2. Liv-ing for Je-sus who died in my place, Bear-ing on Cal - v'ry my
3. Liv-ing for Je-sus thru earth's lit - tle while, My dear-est treas - ure the

all that I do, Yield-ing al - le - giance, glad-heart-ed and free.
sin and dis-grace, Such love con-strains me to an-swer His call.
light of His smile, Seek-ing the lost ones He died to re - deem.

Refrain

This is the path-way of bless-ing for me.
Fol - low His lead - ing and give Him my all. O Je-sus, Lord and
Bring-ing the wea - ry to find rest in Him.

Sav-ior, I give my-self to Thee; For Thou, in Thine a - tone-ment, Didst

give Thy-self for me; I own no oth-er Mas-ter, My heart shall be Thy

WORDS: Thomas O. Chisholm
MUSIC: C. Harold Lowden

LIVING

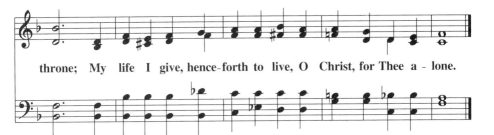

throne; My life I give, hence-forth to live, O Christ, for Thee a - lone.

Have Thine Own Way, Lord 206

*The way of the Lord is strength to the upright: but destruction
shall be to the workers of iniquity — Proverbs 10:29 KJV*

1. Have Thine own way, Lord! Have Thine own way! Thou art the
2. Have Thine own way, Lord! Have Thine own way! Search me and
3. Have Thine own way, Lord! Have Thine own way! Wound-ed and
4. Have Thine own way, Lord! Have Thine own way! Hold o'er my

Pot - ter, I am the clay: Mold me and make me Af - ter Thy
try me, Mas-ter, to - day! Whit-er than snow, Lord, Wash me just
wea - ry, Help me, I pray! Pow-er, all pow - er, Sure-ly is
be - ing Ab - so-lute sway! Fill with Thy Spir - it Till all shall

will, While I am wait - ing, Yield-ed and still.
now, As in Thy pres - ence Hum-bly I bow.
Thine! Touch me and heal me, Sav-ior di - vine!
see Christ on - ly, al - ways, Liv-ing in me!

WORDS: Adelaide A. Pollard
MUSIC: George C. Stebbins

ADELAIDE

207 Out of the Depths

Out of the depths have I cried — Psalm 130:1 KJV

Unison or Duet

1. Out of the depths of my soul I cry, Je - sus draw nigh,
2. Lord, let my life con - se - crat - ed be, Hid - den in Thee,
3. Out of the depths of my soul I plead, Je - sus hear me,

Je - sus draw nigh, Lord, lend an ear to my ear - nest plea.
Hid - den in Thee, Let me for - ev - er Thy word o - bey.
Je - sus hear me, Let me stead - fast in Thy word e'er be. That

Je - sus draw near - er to me. _____
Lord, draw me clos - er each day. _____
no sin might be seen in me. _____

WORDS: Thelma Gross
MUSIC: Thelma Gross; arr. by Calvin Burrell

Out of the Depths

O, Lord, hear Thou my plead - ing, speak to my soul,
O, Lord, I want to la - bor, faith-ful each day,
In - crease Thou my faith, Lord, deep-er in Thee,

Cleanse and make whole, let me for - ev - er in Thee a - bide,
In this true way, tell-ing the world what a Sav-ior I've found,
Let me e'er be so that no sin might be found in me,

Lord, let me walk by Thy side. _____
spread-ing the Gos - pel a - round. _____
Lord, draw me clos - er to Thee. _____

208 Love Is Surrender

*By this we know that we love the children of God,
when we love God, and keep His commandments* — 1 John 5:2 KJV

Unison

1. Talk a-bout love, __ how it makes __ life com - plete; __
2. Sing a-bout love __ and the strength __ it can give; __
3. Shout a-bout love __ and the wars __ will all end; __

__ You can talk __ all you want, __ make it sound __
__ You can sing __ how you're read - y to face __
__ You can shout __ we're all broth - ers and e -

__ nice and sweet; __ But the words __ have an emp-ty ring, __
__ life and live; __ But you know __ as the days go by __
__ ven pre - tend, __ But you can't __ cov-er up the past, __

__ and they don't __ real - ly mean a thing, __
__ that no mat - ter how hard you try, __ With - out
__ just pre - tend - ing - 'll nev - er - last, __

Him love is not to be found, not to be found. __

WORDS: Ralph Carmichael
MUSIC: Ralph Carmichael
© 1968 Bud John Songs, Inc. (ASCAP)

Love Is Surrender

For love is sur - ren-der, Love is sur - ren-der to His will, _____ Love is sur - ren-der to His will. _

In My Life, Lord, Be Glorified   209

O sing unto the Lord a new song — Psalm 98:1 KJV

1. In my life, Lord, be glo-ri-fied, be glo-ri-fied,
2. In my song, Lord, be glo-ri-fied, be glo-ri-fied,
3. In Your Church, Lord, be glo-ri-fied, be glo-ri-fied,

In my life, Lord, be glo-ri-fied to - day.
In my song, Lord, be glo-ri-fied to - day.
In Your Church, Lord, be glo-fi-fied to - day.

WORDS: Bob Kilpatrick
MUSIC: Bob Kilpatrick

210 O Love That Wilt Not Let Me Go

God commendeth His love toward us — Romans 5:8 KJV

1. O Love that wilt not let me go, I rest my wea-ry soul in Thee, I give Thee back the life I owe, That in Thine o-cean depths its flow May rich-er, full-er be.

2. O Light that fol-l'west all my way, I yield my flick-'ring torch to Thee; My heart re-stores its bor-rowed ray, That in Thy sun-shine's glow its day May bright-er, fair-er be.

3. O Joy that seek-est me thru pain, I can-not close my heart to Thee; I trace the rain-bow thru the rain, And feel the prom-ise is not vain That morn shall tear-less be.

4. O Cross that lift-est up my head, I dare not ask to hide from Thee: I lay in dust life's glo-ry dead, And from the ground there blos-soms red Life that shall end-less be. A - men.

WORDS: George Matheson
MUSIC: Albert L. Peace

ST. MARGARET

Speak to My Heart

211

Oh that God would speak — Job 11:5 KJV

1. Speak to my heart, Lord Je - sus, Speak that my soul may hear;
2. Speak to my heart, Lord Je - sus, Purge me from ev - 'ry sin;
3. Speak to my heart, Lord Je - sus, It is no long - er mine;

Speak to my heart, Lord Je - sus, Calm ev - 'ry doubt and fear.
Speak to my heart, Lord Je - sus, Help me the lost to win.
Speak to my heart, Lord Je - sus, I would be whol - ly Thine.

Refrain

Speak to my heart, oh, speak to my heart, Speak to my heart, I pray;

Yield - ed and still, seek - ing Thy will, Oh, speak to my heart to - day.

WORDS: B. B. McKinney
MUSIC: B. B. McKinney

HOLCOMB

212   Oh, to Be Kept by Jesus

Whoso putteth his trust in the Lord shall be safe — Proverbs 29:25 KJV

1. Oh to be kept by Je - sus, kept by the
2. Oh to be kept by Je - sus, kept by His
3. Kept by His ho - ly Spir - it, to me this

pow - er of God. Kept from the world un -
pow - er di - vine. Kept thru toil and
is best of all. I'm safe in His ho - ly

spot - ted, tread-ing where Je - sus trod.
tri - als, kept by His hand in mine.
keep - ing, He'll ev - er hear my call.

Refrain

Oh, to be kept by Je - sus; Lord at Thy

feet I fall; I would be noth-ing,

WORDS: Thurston G. Frazier
MUSIC: Thurston G. Frazier; arr. by K. Morris

Oh, to Be Kept by Jesus

noth-ing, noth-ing, Thou shalt be all and all.

Take My Life, and Let It Be 213

Consecrate yourselves today to the Lord — Exodus 32:29 KJV

1. Take my life, and let it be Con - se - crat - ed,
2. Take my voice, and let me sing, Al - ways, on - ly,
3. Take my will, and make it Thine; It shall be no
4. Take my love; my Lord, I pour At Thy feet its

Lord, to Thee. Take my mo - ments and my days; Let them flow in
for my King. Take my lips, and let them be Filled with mes-sag -
long - er mine. Take my heart, it is Thine own; It shall be Thy
trea - sure store. Take my - self, and I will be Ev - er, on - ly,

cease - less praise, Let them flow in cease-less praise.
es from Thee, Filled with mes - sag - es from Thee.
roy - al throne, It shall be Thy roy - al throne.
all for Thee, Ev - er, on - ly, all for Thee. A - men.

WORDS: Frances Ridley Havergal HENDON
MUSIC: Henri A. César Malan; arr. by Lowell Mason

214 More Love to Thee

I pray, that your love may abound yet more and more — Philippians 1:9 KJV

1. More love to Thee, O Christ, More love to Thee!
2. Once earth-ly joy I craved, Sought peace and rest;
3. Then shall my lat - est breath Whis - per Thy praise;

Hear Thou the prayer I make On bend - ed knee;
Now Thee a - lone I seek, Give what is best;
This be the part - ing cry My heart shall raise;

This is my earn - est plea: More love, O Christ, to Thee,
This all my prayer shall be; More love, O Christ, to Thee,
This still its prayer shall be; More love, O Christ, to Thee,

More love to Thee, More love to Thee!
More love to Thee, More love to Thee!
More love to Thee, More love to Thee!

WORDS: Elizabeth Prentiss
MUSIC: William H. Doane

MORE LOVE TO THEE

Footsteps of Jesus

215

If any man serve Me, let him follow Me — John 12:26 KJV

1. Sweet - ly, Lord, have we heard Thee call - ing, "Come, fol - low Me!"
2. Though they lead o'er the cold, dark moun-tains, Seek - ing His sheep,
3. If they lead through the tem - ple ho - ly, Preach-ing the Word,
4. Then at last, when on high He sees us, Our jour-ney done,

And we see where Thy foot-prints fall - ing Lead us to Thee.
Or a - long by Si - lo - am's foun-tains, Help - ing the weak:
Or in homes of the poor and low - ly, Serv - ing the Lord:
We will rest where the steps of Je - sus End at His throne.

Refrain

Foot - prints of Je - sus, that make the path-way glow!

We will fol - low the steps of Je - sus wher - e'er they go.

WORDS: Mary B. C. Slade
MUSIC: Asa B. Everett

FOOTSTEPS

216   Only Believe

All things are possible to him that believeth — Mark 9:23 KJV

1. Fear not, lit-tle flock, from the cross to the throne, From
2. Fear not, lit-tle flock, He go-eth a-head, Your-
3. Fear not, lit-tle flock, what-ev-er your lot, He

death in-to life He went for His own; All pow-er in
Shep-herd se-lect-eth the path you must tread; The wa-ters of
en-ters all rooms, "the doors be-ing shut;" He nev-er for-

earth, all pow-er a-bove, Is giv-en to Him for the
Ma-rah He'll sweet-en for thee, He drank all the bit-ter in
sakes, He nev-er is gone, So count on His pres-ence in

Refrain

flock of His love.
Geth-sem-a-ne.   On - ly be-lieve,   on - ly be-lieve;
dark-ness and dawn.

All things are pos-si-ble, on-ly be-lieve; On - ly be-lieve,

WORDS: Paul Rader
MUSIC: Paul Rader

Only Believe

on - ly be-lieve; All things are pos-si-ble, on - ly be-lieve.

We Are Climbing Jacob's Ladder 217

And behold a ladder set up on the earth — Genesis 28:12 KJV

1. We are climb-ing Ja-cob's lad - der, We are
2. Ev - 'ry round goes high - er, high - er, Ev - 'ry
3. Sin - ner, do you love my Je - sus? Sin - ner,
4. If you love Him, why not serve Him? If you
5. We are climb-ing high - er, high - er, We are

climb - ing Ja-cob's lad - der, We are climb - ing
round goes high - er, high - er, Ev - 'ry round goes
do you love my Je - sus? Sin - ner, do you
love Him, why not serve Him? If you love Him,
climb - ing high - er, high - er, We are climb - ing

Ja-cob's lad - der, Sol-diers of the cross.
high - er, high - er, Sol-diers of the cross.
love my Je - sus? Sol-diers of the cross.
why not serve Him? Sol-diers of the cross.
high - er, high - er, Sol-diers of the cross. A - men.

WORDS: African-American spiritual
MUSIC: African-American spiritual

JACOB'S LADDER

218 Open My Eyes, That I May See

That I may see the good of Thy chosen — Psalm 106:5 KJV

1. O-pen my eyes, that I may see Glimps-es of truth Thou
2. O-pen my ears, that I may hear Voic-es of truth Thou
3. O-pen my mouth, and let me bear Glad-ly the warm truth

hast for me; Place in my hands the won-der-ful key
send-est clear; And while the wave-notes fall on my ear,
ev-'ry-where; O-pen my heart, and let me pre-pare

That shall un-clasp, and set me free. Si-lent-ly now I
Ev-'ry-thing false will dis-ap-pear. Si-lent-ly now I
Love with Thy chil-dren thus to share. Si-lent-ly now I

wait for Thee, Read-y, my God, Thy will to see;
wait for Thee, Read-y, my God, Thy will to see;
wait for Thee, Read-y, my God, Thy will to see;

WORDS: Clara H. Scott
MUSIC: Clara H. Scott

Open My Eyes, That I May See

O- pen my eyes, il - lu - mine me, Spir - it di - vine!
O- pen my ears, il - lu - mine me, Spir - it di - vine!
O- pen my heart, il - lu - mine me, Spir - it di - vine! A - men.

Yes, Lord, Yes   219

My soul shall be joyful in the Lord — Psalm 35:9 KJV

I'll say yes, Lord, yes, to Your will and to Your way. _

_ I'll say yes, Lord, yes; I will trust You and o - bey. _

_ When Your Spir-it speaks to me, _ With my whole heart

I'll a-gree, _ And my an-swer will be yes, Lord, yes. (Lord, yes.)

WORDS: Lynn Keesecker   YES, LORD, YES
MUSIC: Lynn Keesecker

220   Is Your All on the Altar?

Casting all your care upon Him; for He careth for you — 1 Peter 5:7 KJV

1. You have longed for sweet peace and for faith to in-crease, And have
2. Would you walk with the Lord in the light of His Word, And have
3. O we nev-er can know what the Lord will be-stow Of the
4. Who can tell all the love He will send from a-bove, And how

earn-est-ly, fer-vent-ly prayed; __ But you can-not have rest
peace and con-tent-ment al - way? __ You must do His sweet will
bless-ings for which we have prayed, __ Till our bod-y and soul
hap - py our hearts will be made, __ Of the fel-low-ship sweet

or be per-fect-ly blest Un - til all on the al - tar is laid. __
to be free from all ill – On the al - tar your all you must lay. __
He doth ful - ly con-trol, And our all on the al - tar is laid. __
we shall share at His feet When our all on the al - tar is laid! __

Refrain

Is your all on the al - tar of sac - ri - fice laid? Your heart does the

WORDS: Elisha A. Hoffman
MUSIC: Elisha A. Hoffman

Is Your All on the Altar?

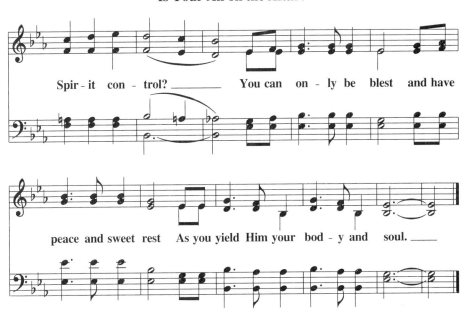

Spir - it con - trol? _____ You can on - ly be blest and have

peace and sweet rest As you yield Him your bod - y and soul. ____

Must Jesus Bear the Cross Alone? 221

If any man will come after Me, let him deny himself,
and take up his cross, and follow Me — Matthew 16:24 KJV

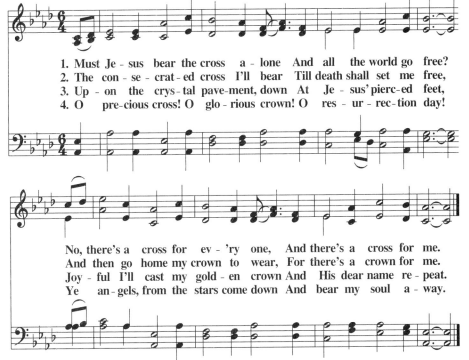

1. Must Je - sus bear the cross a - lone And all the world go free?
2. The con - se - crat - ed cross I'll bear Till death shall set me free,
3. Up - on the crys - tal pave-ment, down At Je - sus' pierc-ed feet,
4. O pre-cious cross! O glo - rious crown! O res - ur - rec-tion day!

No, there's a cross for ev - 'ry one, And there's a cross for me.
And then go home my crown to wear, For there's a crown for me.
Joy - ful I'll cast my gold - en crown And His dear name re - peat.
Ye an - gels, from the stars come down And bear my soul a - way.

WORDS: Thomas Shepherd
MUSIC: George N. Allen

MAITLAND

222 Higher Ground

[The Lord] set my feet upon a rock — Psalm 40:2 KJV

1. I'm press-ing on the up-ward way, New heights I'm
2. My heart has no de-sire to stay Where doubts a -
3. I want to live a-bove the world, Tho' Sa - tan's
4. I want to scale the ut-most height, And catch a

gain - ing ev-'ry-day; Still pray-ing as I on - ward
rise and fears dis-may; Tho' some may dwell where these a -
darts at me are hurled; For faith has caught a joy - ful
gleam of glo-ry bright; But still I'll pray till heav'n I've

Refrain

bound, "Lord, plant my feet on high - er ground."
bound, My pray'r, my aim is high - er ground.
sound, The song of saints on high - er ground.
found, "Lord, lead me on to high - er ground."

Lord, lift me

up, and I shall stand By faith, on heav - en's ta-ble-land; A high-er

plane than I have found, Lord, plant my feet on high - er ground.

WORDS: Johnson Oatman, Jr.
MUSIC: Charles H. Gabriel

HIGHER GROUND

"Are Ye Able," Said the Master 223

Whosoever will come after Me, let him deny himself,
and take up his cross, and follow Me — Mark 8:34 KJV

1. "Are ye a - ble," said the Mas - ter, "To be cru - ci - fied with
2. "Are ye a - ble" to re - mem - ber, When a thief lifts up his
3. "Are ye a - ble," when the shad - ows Close a - round you with the
4. "Are ye a - ble?" still the Mas - ter Whis - pers down e - ter - ni -

me?" "Yea," the stur - dy dream - ers an - swered, "To the
eyes, That his par - doned soul is wor - thy Of a
sod, To be - lieve that spir - it tri - umphs, To com -
ty, And he - ro - ic spir - its an - swer, Now, as

Refrain

death we fol - low Thee:"
place in par - a - dise?
mend your soul to God? "Lord, we are a - ble" – our spir - its are Thine;
then in Gal - i - lee:

Re - mold them – make us like Thee, di - vine: Thy guid - ing ra - diance a -

bove us shall be A bea - con to God, to love and loy - al - ty.

WORDS: Earl Marlatt
MUSIC: Harry S. Mason

BEACON HILL

224 Satisfied with Jesus

A good man shall be satisfied from himself — Proverbs 14:14 KJV

Unison Slowly

1. I am sat-is-fied with Je-sus, He has done so much for me,
2. He is with me in my tri-als, Best of friends of all is He;
3. I can hear the voice of Je-sus Call-ing out so plead-ing-ly,
4. When my work on earth is end-ed, And I cross the mys-tic sea,

He has suf-fered to re - deem me, He has died to set me
I can al-ways count on Je - sus, Can He al-ways count on
"Go and win the lost and stray - ing;" Is He sat-is-fied with
Oh, that I would hear Him say - ing, "I am sat-is-fied with

Refrain (parts)

free.
me?
me?
thee."

I am sat-is-fied, I am sat-is-fied,

I am sat-is-fied with Je - sus, But the ques-tion comes to me, As I

WORDS: B. B. McKinney
MUSIC: B. B. McKinney
ROUTH

Satisfied with Jesus

think of Cal - va - ry, Is my Mas-ter sat - is -fied with me?

I Have Decided to Follow Jesus 225

No man, having put his hand to the plow and looking back,
is fit for the kingdom of God — Luke 9:62 KJV

1. I have de - cid - ed ____ to fol - low Je - sus, ____ I have de -
2. Tho' no join with me, ____ still I will fol - low, ____ Tho' no one
3. The world be - hind me, ____ the cross be - fore me, ____ The world be -

cid - ed ____ to fol - low Je - sus, ____ I have de - cid - ed ____
join me, ____ still I will fol - low, ____ Tho' no one join me, ____
hind me, ____ the cross be - fore me, ____ The world be hind - me, ____

__ to fol - low Je - sus, ____ No turn-ing back, ____ no turn-ing back! _
__ still I will fol - low, ____ No turn-ing back, ____ no turn-ing back! _
__ the cross be-fore me, ____ No turn-ing back, ____ no turn-ing back! _

WORDS: Attributed to an Indian prince, as sung in Garo, Assam   ASSAM
MUSIC: Indian folk melody

226   Do You Really Care?

He was moved with compassion on them — Matthew 9:36 KJV

1. I look a-round in the place that I live; I see peo-ple with
2. I see peo-ple just long-ing to know What they can live for and

so much to give; Yet there are those who are dy-ing to know
where they can go; We have the hope and the pur-pose to share,

Just that some-bod-y cares. Do you real - ly care?
But, do we real-ly care? Will you take the dare?

Do you know how to share With peo - ple
Spread Good News ev - 'ry-where? The cross of

ev - 'ry-where? Do you real - ly care?
Christ to bear? Do you real - ly   care?

WORDS: Bill Cates
MUSIC: Bill Cates

CATES

Do You Really Care?

Peo-ple grope in dark-ness, Search-ing for a way,

D.S. al Fine

Don't you know of some-one You can help to - day?

I'll Live for Him 227

[Jesus] died for us, that, whether we wake or sleep,
we should live together with Him — 1 Thessalonians 5:10 KJV

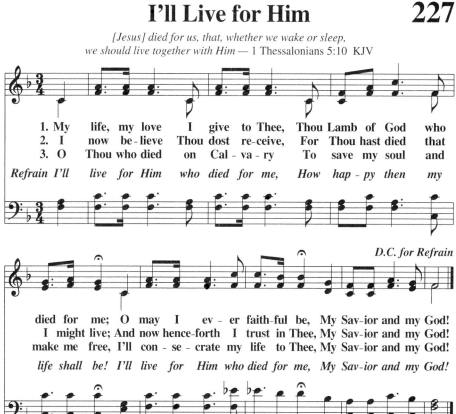

1. My life, my love I give to Thee, Thou Lamb of God who
2. I now be-lieve Thou dost re-ceive, For Thou hast died that
3. O Thou who died on Cal - va - ry To save my soul and

Refrain I'll live for Him who died for me, How hap - py then my

D.C. for Refrain

died for me; O may I ev - er faith-ful be, My Sav-ior and my God!
I might live; And now hence-forth I trust in Thee, My Sav-ior and my God!
make me free, I'll con - se - crate my life to Thee, My Sav-ior and my God!

life shall be! I'll live for Him who died for me, My Sav-ior and my God!

WORDS: Ralph E. Hudson
MUSIC: C. R. Dunbar

DUNBAR

228   Lead Me to Calvary

And when they were come to the place, which is called Calvary,
there they crucified Him — Luke 23:33 KJV

1. King of my life I crown Thee now – Thine shall the glo - ry
2. Show me the tomb where Thou wast laid, Ten - der - ly mourned and
3. Let me like Ma - ry, thru the gloom, Come with a gift to
4. May I be will - ing, Lord, to bear Dai - ly my cross for

be; Lest I for - get Thy thorn-crowned brow,
wept; An - gels in robes of light ar - rayed
Thee; Show to me now the emp - ty tomb –
Thee; E - ven Thy cup of grief to share –

Refrain

Lead me to Cal - va - ry.
Guard - ed Thee whilst Thou slept.
Lead me to Cal - va - ry.
Thou hast borne all for me.

Lest I for-get Geth -

sem - a - ne, Lest I for-get Thine ag - o - ny,

Lest I for-get Thy love for me, Lead me to Cal - va - ry.

WORDS: Jennie Evelyn Hussey
MUSIC: William J. Kirkpatrick

DUNCANNON

Where He Leads Me   229

And He calleth His own sheep by name, and leadeth them out — John 10:3 KJV

1. I can hear my Sav - ior call - ing,
2. I'll go with Him thru the gar - den,
3. I'll go with Him thru the judg - ment,
4. He will give me grace and glo - ry,

Refrain: Where He leads me I will fol - low,

I can
I'll go
I'll go
He will
Where He

hear my Sav - ior call - ing,
with Him thru the gar - den,
with Him thru the judg - ment,
give me grace and glo - ry,
leads me I will fol - low,

I can hear my Sav - ior
I'll go with Him thru the
I'll go with Him thru the
He will give me grace and
Where He leads me I will

D.C. for Refrain

call - ing,   "Take thy cross and fol - low, fol - low Me."
gar - den,   I'll go with Him, with Him all the way.
judg - ment,   I'll go with Him, with Him all the way.
glo - ry,   And go with me, with me all the way.
fol - low —   I'll go with Him, with Him all the way.

WORDS: E. W. Blandy
MUSIC: John S. Norris

NORRIS

230   Footprints of Jesus

And said, I cried by reason of mine affliction unto the Lord, and He heard me — Jonah 2:2 KJV

Refrain

Foot-prints of Je - sus, lead - ing the way,

Foot-prints of Je - sus, by night and by day;

Sure if I fol - low, life will be sweet!

Saved by the prints of His wound-ed feet.

With religious fervor

1. They led to Beth-a - ny, _____ there's where He
2. Once I was lost and _____ He heard my
3. Dan - i - el saw in Him _____ a great roll - ing
4. That's how I know Him, _____ that's why I

Effective as a solo

WORDS: Lucie E. Campbell
MUSIC: Lucie E. Campbell

Footprints of Jesus

stayed; _____ They led to Geth-sem - a - ne _____
cry; _____ He left His Fa - ther's _____
stone; _____ I - sa - iah saw Him tread _____
say, _____ Je - sus is lead-ing me, _____

_ there's where He prayed; _____ They led to
_ man - sion on high; _____ He took my
_ the wine-press a - lone; _____ If we some
_ all the way; _____ I shall reach

Cal-va-ry, _____ sal - va-tion com - plete, _____ Saved by the
bur - den, _____ and now I can sing _____ "Glo - ry to
day our _____ dear Sav-ior would meet, _____ Fol-low the
Heav-en's _____ _ por-tals so sweet, _____ Led by the

prints of His wound-ed feet. _____
God, I'm a child of the King." _____
prints of His wound-ed feet. _____
prints of His wound-ed feet. _____

231 Let Others See Jesus in You

Sir, we would see Jesus — John 12:21 KJV

1. While pass-ing thru this world of sin, And oth-ers your
2. Your life's a book be-fore their eyes, They're read-ing it
3. What joy 'twill be at set of sun, In man-sions be
4. Then live for Christ both day and night, Be faith-ful, be

life shall view, Be clean and pure with-out, with-in,
thru and thru; Say, does it point them to the skies,
yond the blue, To find some souls that you have won;
brave and true, And lead the lost to life and light;

Refrain

Let oth-ers see Je-sus in you.
Do oth-ers see Je-sus in you?
Let oth-ers see Je-sus in you.
Let oth-ers see Je-sus in you.

Let oth-ers see Je-sus in

you, Let oth-ers see Je-sus in you; Keep tell-ing the
you, in you, you, in you;

sto-ry, be faith-ful and true, Let oth-ers see Je-sus in you.

WORDS: B. B. McKinney
MUSIC: B. B. McKinney

COLEMAN

Guide Me, O Thou Great Jehovah 232

The Lord shall guide thee continually — Isaiah 58:11 KJV

1. Guide Me, O Thou great Je - ho - vah, Pil - grim thru this bar - ren
2. O - pen now the crys - tal foun - tain Whence the heal - ing wat - ers
3. When I tread the verge of Jor - dan, Bid my anx - ious fears sub -

land; I am weak, but Thou art might - y, Hold me with Thy pow'r - ful
flow; Let the fi - ery, cloud - y pil - lar Lead me all my jour - ney
side; Bear me thru the swell - ing cur - rent, Land me safe on Ca - naan's

hand: Bread of Heav - en, Feed me till I want no
thru: Strong De - liv - erer, Be Thou still my strength and
side: Song of prais - es I will ev - er give to

more; Bread of Heav - en, Feed me till I want no more.
shield; Strong De - liv - erer, Be Thou still my strength and shield.
Thee; Song of prais - es I will ev - er give to Thee.

WORDS: William Williams
MUSIC: Thomas Hastings

ZION

233 Lead Me, Guide Me

For Thy name's sake lead me, and guide me — Psalm 31:3 KJV

1. I am weak and I need Thy strength and pow'r, To help me
2. Help me tread in the paths of right-eous-ness, Be my aid when
3. I am lost, if you take your hand from me, I am blind with-

o-ver my weak-est hour, Let me thru the dark-ness Thy face to
Sa-tan and sin op-press. I am put-ting all my trust in
out Thy Light to see, Lord, just al-ways let me Thy ser-vant

Refrain - reverently

see, Lead me, oh Lord, lead me.____ Lead me, guide me a-
Thee, Lead me, oh Lord, lead me.____
be, Lead me, oh Lord, lead me.____

long the way, For if you lead me I can-not stray,

Lord, let me walk each day with Thee, Lead me, oh Lord, lead me.

WORDS: Doris Akers
MUSIC: Doris Akers; arr. by Maxine Blackburn

Lead, Kindly Light

234

Now are ye light in the Lord — Ephesians 5:8 KJV

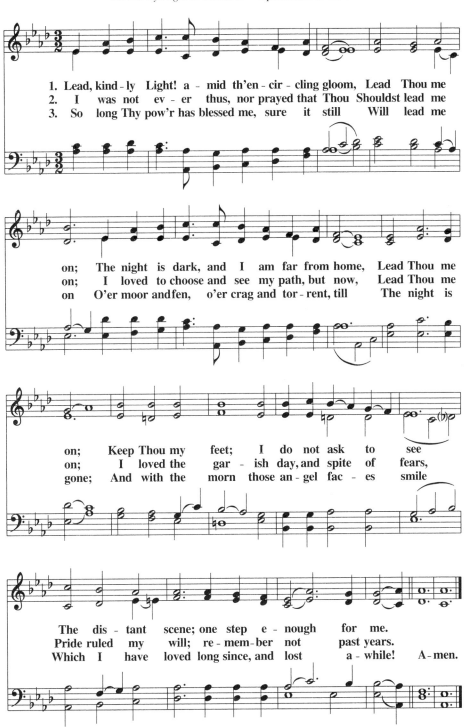

1. Lead, kind-ly Light! a - mid th'en - cir - cling gloom, Lead Thou me
2. I was not ev - er thus, nor prayed that Thou Shouldst lead me
3. So long Thy pow'r has blessed me, sure it still Will lead me

on; The night is dark, and I am far from home, Lead Thou me
on; I loved to choose and see my path, but now, Lead Thou me
on O'er moor and fen, o'er crag and tor - rent, till The night is

on; Keep Thou my feet; I do not ask to see
on; I loved the gar - ish day, and spite of fears,
gone; And with the morn those an - gel fac - es smile

The dis - tant scene; one step e - nough for me.
Pride ruled my will; re - mem - ber not past years.
Which I have loved long since, and lost a - while! A - men.

WORDS: John H. Newman
MUSIC: John B. Dykes

LUX BENIGNA

235 He Leadeth Me

He leadeth me beside still waters — Psalm 23:2 KJV

1. He lead - eth me! O bless - ed thought! O
2. Some - times 'mid scenes of deep - est gloom, Some -
3. Lord, I would clasp Thy hand in mine, Nor
4. And when my task on earth is done, When

words with heav'n - ly com - fort fraught! What - e'er I do, wher -
times where E - den's bow - ers bloom, By wa - ters still, o'er
ev - er mur - mur nor re - pine; Con - tent, what - ev - er
by Thy grace the vic - t'ry's won, E'en death's cold wave I

e'er I be, Still 'tis God's hand that lead - eth me.
trou - bled sea, Still 'tis His hand that lead - eth me!
lot I see, Since 'tis my God that lead - eth me!
will not flee, Since God thru Jor - dan lead - eth me.

Refrain

He lead-eth me, He lead-eth me, By His own hand He lead-eth me;

His faith-ful fol-l'wer I would be, For by His hand He lead-eth me.

WORDS: Joseph H. Gilmore
MUSIC: William B. Bradbury

HE LEADETH ME

All the Way My Savior Leads Me 236

He will be our guide even unto death — Psalm 48:14 KJV

1. All the way my Sav-ior leads me – What have I to ask be - side?
2. All the way my Sav-ior leads me – Cheers each wind - ing path I tread,
3. All the way my Sav-ior leads me – O the full - ness of His love!

Can I doubt His ten-der mer - cy, Who thru life has been my Guide?
Gives me grace for ev-'ry tri - al, Feeds me with the liv - ing bread.
Per - fect rest to me is prom-ised In my Fa - ther's house a - bove.

Heav'n-ly peace, di - vin - est com-fort, Here by faith in Him to dwell!
Tho' my wea - ry steps may fal - ter And my soul a - thirst may be,
When my spir - it, clothed im - mor - tal, Wings its flight to realms of day,

For I know, what-e'er be - fall me, Je-sus do - eth all things well;
Gush-ing from the Rock be - fore me, Lo! a spring of joy I see;
This my song thru end-less a - ges: Je-sus led me all the way;

For I know, what-e'er be - fall me, Je-sus do - eth all things well.
Gush-ing from the Rock be - fore me, Lo! a spring of joy I see.
This my song thru end-less a - ges: Je-sus led me all the way.

WORDS: Fanny J. Crosby
MUSIC: Robert Lowry

ALL THE WAY

237   The Lord Is My Shepherd

The Lord is my shepherd; I shall not want — Psalm 23:1 KJV

1. The Lord is my Shep-herd, I shall not want; By still wa-ters He lead-eth His sheep;___ Tho' the en-e-my gath-er and foes may op-press, Je-sus watch-es while His lit-tle ones sleep.___

2. He mak-eth me to lie down in pas-tures green, My cup with His bless-ings o-ver-flows;___ He a-noint-eth my head with oil from a-bove, For my Mas-ter has boun-ti-ful stores.___

3. He pre-par-eth a ta-ble in the midst of my foes, But His good-ness and mer-cy are there;___ At the end of death's val-ley, in the house of the Lord, There for-ev-er His good-ness we'll share.___

Effective as a solo.

WORDS: Lucie E. Campbell, based on Psalm 23
MUSIC: Lucie E. Campbell

The Lord Is My Shepherd

238 I Walk with the King

And I will walk among you, and will be your God,
and ye shall be my people — Leviticus 26:12 KJV

1. In sor-row I wan-dered, my spir-it op-pressed, But
2. For years in the fet-ters of sin I was bound, The
3. O soul near de-spair in the low-lands of strife, Look

now I am hap-py — se - cure-ly I rest; From
world could not help me — no com-fort I found; But
up and let Je - sus come in - to your life; The

morn - ing till eve-ning glad car - ols I sing, And
now like the birds and the sun-beams of Spring, I'm
joy of sal - va - tion to you He would bring; Come

this is the rea - son: I walk with the King.
free and re - joic-ing — I walk with the King.
in - to the sun-light and walk with the King.

WORDS: James Rowe
MUSIC: B. D. Ackley

I Walk with the King

Refrain

I walk with the King, hal - le - lu - jah! I

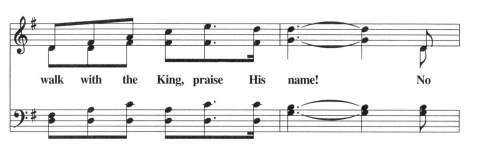

walk with the King, praise His name! No

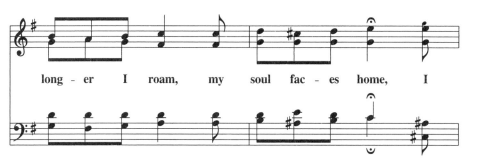

long - er I roam, my soul fac - es home, I

walk and I talk with the King.

239 Lead Me, Savior

Lead me into the land of uprightness — Psalm 143:10 KJV

1. Sav - ior, lead me, lest I stray,
2. Thou the ref - uge of my soul,
3. Sav - ior, lead me, then at last,

1. Sav - ior, lead me, lest I stray,

Gen - tly lead me all the way;
When life's storm - y bil - lows roll,
When the storm of life is past,

Gen - tly lead me all the way;

I am safe when by Thy side,
I am safe when Thou art nigh,
To the land of end - less day,

I am safe when by Thy side,

I would in Thy love a - bide.
All my hopes on Thee re - ly.
Where all tears are wiped a - way.

I would in Thy love a - bide.

WORDS: Frank M. Davis
MUSIC: Frank M. Davis

Lead Me, Savior

240   O I Want to See Him

When He shall appear, we shall be like Him, for we shall see Him as He is — 1 John 3:2 KJV

1. As I jour - ney thru the land sing - ing as I go,
2. When in ser - vice for my Lord dark may be the night,
3. When in val - leys low I look t'ward the moun-tain height,
4. When be-fore me bil - lows rise from the might - y deep,

Point - ing souls to Cal - va - ry – to the crim - son flow,
But I'll cling more close to Him, He will give me light;
And be-hold my Sav - ior there, lead - ing in the fight,
Then my Lord di - rects my bark; He doth safe - ly keep,

Man - y ar - rows pierce my soul from with - out, with-in;
Sa - tan's snares may vex my soul, turn my tho'ts a - side;
With a ten - der hand out-stretched t'ward the val - ley low,
And He leads me gen - tly on thru this world be-low;

But my Lord leads me on, thru Him I must win.
But my Lord goes a - head, leads what-e'er be - tide.
Guid-ing me, I can see, as I on - ward go.
He's a real friend to me, O I love Him so.

WORDS: R. H. Cornelius
MUSIC: R. H. Cornelius

O I Want to See Him

241 The Lord Is My Shepherd

The Lord is my shepherd; I shall not want — Psalm 23:1 KJV

1. The Lord is my Shep-herd, no want shall I know; I feed in green pas-tures, safe-fold-ed I rest; He lead-eth my soul where the still wa-ters flow, Re-stores me when wan-d'ring, re-deems when op-

2. Thru the val-ley and shad-ow of death tho' I stray, Since Thou art my Guard-ian, no e-vil I fear; Thy rod shall de-fend me, Thy staff be my stay; No harm can be-fall, with my Com-fort-er

3. In the midst of af-flic-tion my ta-ble is spread; With bless-ings un-meas-ured my cup run-neth o'er; With per-fume and oil Thou a-noint-est my head; O what shall I ask of Thy prov-i-dence

4. Let good-ness and mer-cy, my boun-ti-ful God, Still fol-low my steps till I meet Thee a-bove: I seek by the path which my fore-fa-thers trod, Thru the land of their so-journ, Thy king-dom of

WORDS: James Montgomery, based on Psalm 23
MUSIC: Thomas Koschat

The Lord Is My Shepherd

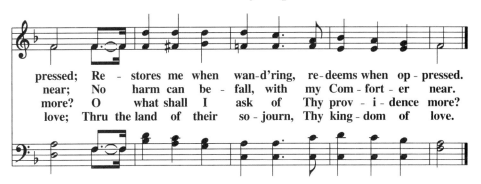

pressed; Re - stores me when wan-d'ring, re - deems when op - pressed.
near; No harm can be - fall, with my Com - fort - er near.
more? O what shall I ask of Thy prov - i - dence more?
love; Thru the land of their so - journ, Thy king - dom of love.

Father, Lead Me Day by Day 242

And lead me in the way everlasting — Psalm 139:24 KJV

1. Fa - ther, lead me day by day, Ev - er in Thine
2. When in dan - ger, make me brave, Make me know that
3. When I'm tempt - ed to do wrong, Make me stead - fast,
4. May I do the good I know, Serv - ing glad - ly

own good way; Teach me to be pure and
Thou canst save; Keep me safe - ly by Thy
wise, and strong; And when all a - lone I
here be - low; When at last go home to

true, Show me what I ought to do.
side; Let me in Thy love a - bide.
stand, Shield me with Thy might - y hand.
Thee, Ev - er - more Thine own to be. A - men.

WORDS: John P. Hopps
MUSIC: Pierre de Corbeil

243   Jesus, Savior, Pilot Me

In all thy ways acknowledge Him, and He shall direct thy paths — Proverbs 3:6 KJV

1. Je - sus, Sav - ior, pi - lot me   O - ver life's tem - pes-tuous
2. As a moth - er stills her child, Thou canst hush the o - cean
3. When at last I near the shore, And the fear - ful break-ers

sea: Un - known waves be - fore me roll,
wild;   Bois - t'rous waves o - bey Thy will
roar   'Twixt me and the peace - ful rest –

Hid - ing rocks and treach-'rous shoal;   Chart and
When Thou say'st to them, "Be still!"   Won - drous
Then, while lean - ing on Thy breast,   May I

com - pass come from Thee – Je - sus, Sav - ior, pi - lot me!
Sov - 'reign of the sea, Je - sus, Sav - ior, pi - lot me!
hear Thee say to me, "Fear not – I will pi - lot thee!"

WORDS: Edward Hopper
MUSIC: John E. Gould

PILOT

Yield Not to Temptation 244

Watch and pray, that ye enter not into temptation — Matthew 26:41 KJV

Unison

1. Yield not to temp-ta-tion, For yield-ing is sin; Each vic-t'ry will
2. Shun e-vil com-pan-ions, Bad lan-guage dis-dain; God's name hold in
3. To him that o'er-com-eth, God giv-eth a crown; Thru faith we will

help you Some oth-er to win; Fight man-ful-ly on-ward,
rev-'rence, Nor take it in vain; Be thought-ful and ear-nest,
con-quer, Tho' of-ten cast down; He who is our Sav-ior,

Dark pas-sions sub-due; Look ev-er to Je-sus, He'll car-ry you
Kind-heart-ed and true; Look ev-er to Je-sus, He'll car-ry you
Our strength will re-new; Look ev-er to Je-sus, He'll car-ry you

Refrain

through.
through. Ask the Sav-ior to help you, Com-fort, strength-en and
through.

keep you; He is will-ing to aid you, He will car-ry you through.

WORDS: Horatio R. Palmer
MUSIC: Horatio R. Palmer

245 I Know that My Redeemer Liveth

And this is the record, that God hath given to us eternal life,
and this life is in His Son — 1 John 5:11 KJV

1. I know that my Re-deem-er liv - eth And on the
2. I know His prom-ise nev-er fail - eth – The word He
3. I know my man-sion He pre-par - eth, That where He

earth a-gain shall stand; I know e-ter-nal life He
speaks, it can-not die; Tho' cru-el death my flesh as-
is there I may be; O won-drous tho't – for me He

giv - eth, That grace and pow'r are in His
sail - eth, Yet I shall see Him by and
car - eth! And He at last will come for

Refrain

hand.
by.   I know, I know   that Je - sus
me.   I know, I know

WORDS: Jessie B. Pounds
MUSIC: James H. Fillmore

HANNAH

I Know that My Redeemer Liveth

I know that my Redeemer lives, and that in the end he will stand upon the earth. And after my skin has been destroyed, yet in my flesh I will see God; I myself will see him with my own eyes — I, and not another. How my heart yearns within me. (Adapted from Job 19:25-27 KJV)

246   I Would Be True

A faithful man who can find? — Proverbs 20:6 KJV

1. I would be true, for there are those that trust me; I would be
2. I would be friend of all – the foe, the friend-less; I would be
3. I would be prayer - ful thru each bus - y mo - ment; I would be

pure, for there are those who care; I would be strong, for
giv - ing, and for - get the gift; I would be hum - ble, to
con - stant - ly in touch with God; I would be tuned to

there is much to suf - fer; I would be brave, for there is much to
for I know my weak-ness; I would look up, and laugh and love, and
hear the slight-est whis - per; I would have faith to keep the path Christ

dare, I would be brave, for there is much to dare.
lift, I would look up, and laugh, and love, and lift.
trod, I would have faith to keep the path Christ trod.

WORDS: Howard Arnold Walter
MUSIC: Joseph Yates Peek

PEEK

Abide with Me

247

Abide in me, and I in you — John 15:4 KJV

1. A - bide with me – fast falls the e - ven - tide,
2. Swift to its close ebbs out life's lit - tle day,
3. I need Thy pres - ence ev - 'ry pass - ing hour –
4. Hold Thou Thy word be - fore my clos - ing eyes,

The dark-ness deep - ens – Lord, with me a - bide;
Earth's joys grow dim, its glo - ries pass a - way;
What but Thy grace can foil the temp-ter's pow'r?
Shine thru the gloom and point me to the skies;

When oth - er help - ers fail and com-forts flee,
Change and de - cay in all a - round I see –
Who like Thy - self my guide and stay can be?
Heav'n's morn-ing breaks and earth's vain shad-ows flee –

Help of the help-less, O a - bide with me!
O Thou who chang-est not, a - bide with me!
Thru cloud and sun-shine, O a - bide with me!
In life, in death, O Lord, a - bide with me!

WORDS: Henry F. Lyte
MUSIC: William H. Monk

EVENTIDE

248 I Love You, Lord

I will love Thee, O Lord, my strength — Psalm 18:1 KJV

I love You, Lord, ___ and I lift my voice ___ to

wor - ship You, O my soul, re - joice! Take

joy, my King, ___ in what You hear; ___ may it be a

sweet, sweet sound in Your ear. ___

WORDS: Laurie Klein
MUSIC: Laurie Klein; arr. Eugene Thomas

I LOVE YOU, LORD

Blessed Assurance   249

Wherefore thou art no more a servant, but a son;
and if a son, then an heir of God through Christ – Galatians 4:7 KJV

1. Bless-ed as - sur - ance, Je - sus is mine!   O what a fore - taste of
2. Per - fect sub - mis - sion, per - fect de - light!   Vi - sions of rap - ture now
3. Per - fect sub - mis - sion – all is at rest,   I in my Sav - ior am

glo - ry di - vine!   Heir of sal - va - tion, pur - chase of God,
burst on my sight;   An - gels de - scend - ing bring from a - bove
hap - py and blest;   Watch-ing and wait - ing, look - ing a - bove,

Refrain

Born of His Spir - it, washed in His blood.   This is my sto - ry,
Ech - oes of mer - cy, whis-pers of love.
Filled with His good - ness, lost in His love.

this is my song, Prais-ing my Sav - ior all the day long; This is my

sto - ry, this is my song, Prais-ing my Sav - ior all the day long.

WORDS: Fanny J. Crosby
MUSIC: Phoebe P. Knapp

ASSURANCE

250 God Never Fails

Heaven and earth shall pass away, but My words shall not pass away — Matthew 24:35 KJV

WORDS: George Jordan
MUSIC: George Jordan; arr. by H. Pickard

God Never Fails

251 He Hideth My Soul

In the time of trouble He shall hide me — Psalm 27:5 KJV

1. A won-der-ful Sav-ior is Je-sus my Lord, A
2. A won-der-ful Sav-ior is Je-sus my Lord – He
3. With num-ber-less bless-ings each mo-ment He crowns, And,
4. When clothed in His bright-ness trans-port-ed I rise To

won-der-ful Sav-ior to me; He hid-eth my soul in the
tak-eth my bur-den a-way, He hold-eth me up and I
filled with His full-ness di-vine, I sing in my rap-ture, "O
meet Him in clouds of the sky, His per-fect sal-va-tion, His

cleft of the rock, Where riv-ers of pleas-ure I see.
shall not be moved, He giv-eth me strength as my day.
glo-ry to God For such a Re-deem-er as mine!"
won-der-ful love, I'll shout with the mil-lions on high.

Refrain

He hid-eth my soul in the cleft of the rock That shad-ows a dry, thirst-y

WORDS: Fanny J. Crosby
MUSIC: William J. Kirkpatrick

KIRKPATRICK

He Hideth My Soul

land; He hid-eth my life in the depths of His love, And cov-ers me
there with His hand, And cov-ers me there with His hand.

My Soul, Be on Thy Guard   252

Truly my soul waiteth upon God — Psalm 62:1 KJV

1. My soul, be on thy guard – Ten thou-sand foes a - rise;
2. O watch and fight and pray, The bat - tle ne'er give o'er;
3. Ne'er think the vic-t'ry won, Nor lay thine ar - mor down;
4. Fight on, my soul, till death Shall bring thee to thy God;

The hosts of sin are press-ing hard To draw thee from the skies.
Re - new it bold-ly ev - 'ry day, And help di - vine im - plore.
The work of faith will not be done Till thou ob - tain thy crown.
He'll take thee, at thy part-ing breath, To His di - vine a - bode.

WORDS: George Heath
MUSIC: Lowell Mason

LABAN

253 Does Jesus Care?

Casting all your care upon Him; for He careth for you — 1 Peter 5:7 KJV

1. Does Je-sus care when my heart is pained Too deep-ly for mirth and song; As the bur-dens press, and the cares dis-tress, And the way grows wea-ry and long?

2. Does Je-sus care when my way is dark With a name-less dread and fear? As the day-light fades in-to deep night shades, Does He care e-nough to be near?

3. Does Je-sus care when I've tried and failed To re-sist some temp-ta-tion strong; When for my deep grief I find no re-lief, Tho' my tears flow all the night long?

4. Does Je-sus care when I've said good-bye To the dear-est on earth to me, And my sad heart aches till it near-ly breaks— Is it aught to Him? Does He see?

Refrain

O yes, He cares — I know He cares! His heart is touched with my grief; When the

WORDS: Frank E. Graeff
MUSIC: J. Lincoln Hall

Does Jesus Care?

days are wea-ry, the long nights drear-y, I know my Sav-ior cares. (He cares.)

Rock of Ages
254

But one of the soldiers with a spear pierced His side, and
forthwith came there out blood and water — John 19:34 KJV

1. Rock of a - ges, cleft for me, Let me hide my - self in Thee;
2. Could my tears for - ev - er flow, Could my zeal no lan-guor know,
3. While I draw this fleet-ing breath, When my eyes shall close in death,

Let the wa - ter and the blood, From Thy wound-ed side which flowed,
These for sin could not a - tone – Thou must save, and Thou a - lone:
When I rise to worlds un-known And be - hold Thee on Thy throne,

Be of sin the dou-ble cure, Save from wrath and make me pure.
In my hand no price I bring, Sim - ply to Thy cross I cling.
Rock of A - ges, cleft for me, Let me hide my self in Thee.

WORDS: Augustus M. Toplady
MUSIC: Thomas Hastings

TOPLADY

255 It Is Well with My Soul

He hath delivered my soul in peace from the battle that was against me — Psalm 55:18

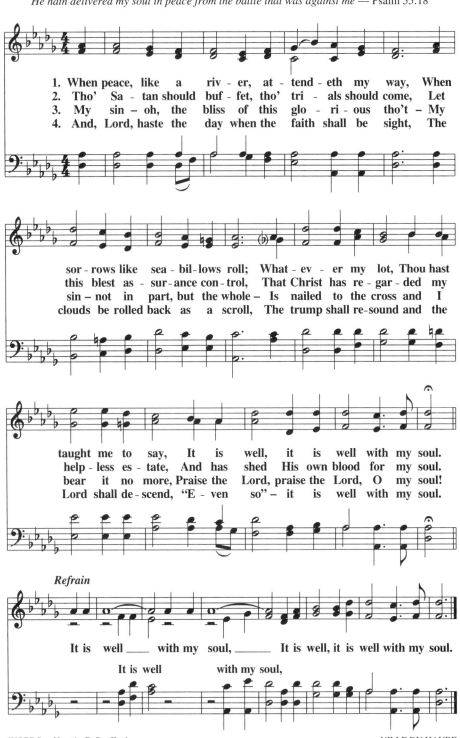

1. When peace, like a riv - er, at - tend - eth my way, When
2. Tho' Sa - tan should buf - fet, tho' tri - als should come, Let
3. My sin – oh, the bliss of this glo - ri - ous tho't – My
4. And, Lord, haste the day when the faith shall be sight, The

sor - rows like sea - bil-lows roll; What - ev - er my lot, Thou hast
this blest as - sur-ance con - trol, That Christ has re - gar - ded my
sin – not in part, but the whole – Is nailed to the cross and I
clouds be rolled back as a scroll, The trump shall re-sound and the

taught me to say, It is well, it is well with my soul.
help - less es - tate, And has shed His own blood for my soul.
bear it no more, Praise the Lord, praise the Lord, O my soul!
Lord shall de - scend, "E - ven so" – it is well with my soul.

Refrain

It is well ___ with my soul, ___ It is well, it is well with my soul.

It is well with my soul,

WORDS: Horatio G. Spafford
MUSIC: Philip P. Bliss

VILLE DU HAVRE

Jesus Is Always There

256

I am continually with thee — Psalm 73:23 KJV

1. Some-times our skies are cloud - y and drear - y,
2. When in the midst of life with its prob - lems,
3. When we are walk - ing thru the green pas - tures,
4. "Lo, I am with you al - way," is writ - ten,

Some-times our hearts are bur-dened with care; But we may know, what-
Bent with our toil and bur - dens we bear; Won-der - ful thought and
Or o - ver moun-tains rug - ged and bare; Pre-cious the thought and
God will not fail to an - swer our prayer; Trust-ing His word we

Refrain

e'er may be - fall us, Je-sus is al - ways there.
deep con-so - la - tion: Je-sus is al - ways there.
sweet the as - sur-ance, Je-sus is al - ways there.
rest in His prom-ise – Je-sus is al - ways there.

Nev-er a bur-den that

He doth not car - ry, Nev - er a sor-row that He doth not share;

Wheth-er the days may be sun-ny or drear-y, Je-sus is al - ways there.

WORDS: Bertha Mae Lillenas
MUSIC: Bertha Mae Lillenas

257 Standing on the Promises

For all the promises of God in Him are yea — 2 Corinthians 1:20 KJV

1. Standing on the promises of Christ my King,
Thru eternal ages let His praises ring;
Glory in the highest, I will shout and sing,
Standing on the promises of God.

2. Standing on the promises that cannot fail,
When the howling storms of doubt and fear assail,
By the living word of God I shall prevail,
Standing on the promises of God.

3. Standing on the promises of Christ the Lord,
Bound to Him eternally by love's strong cord,
Overcoming daily with the Spirit's sword,
Standing on the promises of God.

4. Standing on the promises I cannot fall,
List'ning ev'ry moment to the Spirit's call,
Resting in my Savior, as my all in all,
Standing on the promises of God.

WORDS: R. Kelso Carter
MUSIC: R. Kelso Carter

PROMISES

Standing on the Promises

258 Ask What You Will

Whatsoever ye shall ask in prayer, believing, ye shall receive — Matthew 21:22 KJV

Refrain

Ask what you will of the Sav-ior, And it shall not be in vain. _____ Call when you need His as-sis-tance, _____ He will hear when you call His name. _____

Fine

1. When two or three are gath-ered in His name,
2. He said that we should try Him and we should,
3. We wor-ry o-ver prob-lems and we know

Touch-ing and a-gree-ing up-on the same thing, He'll
He said that He would nev-er with-hold an-y good, If
We can get re-lief if in prayer we will go; He

WORDS: Doris Akers
MUSIC: Doris Akers

Ask What You Will

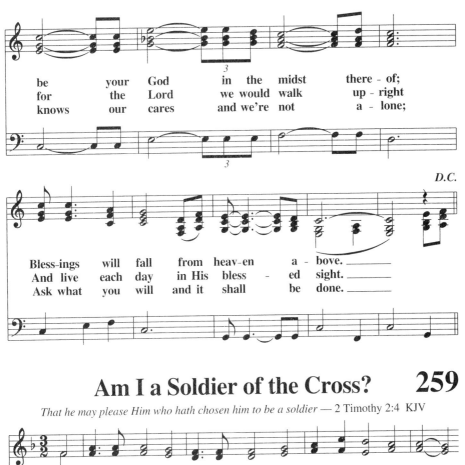

be your God in the midst there - of;
for the Lord we would walk up - right
knows our cares and we're not a - lone;

D.C.

Bless-ings will fall from heav-en a - bove. _____
And live each day in His bless - ed sight. _____
Ask what you will and it shall be done. _____

Am I a Soldier of the Cross?   259

That he may please Him who hath chosen him to be a soldier — 2 Timothy 2:4 KJV

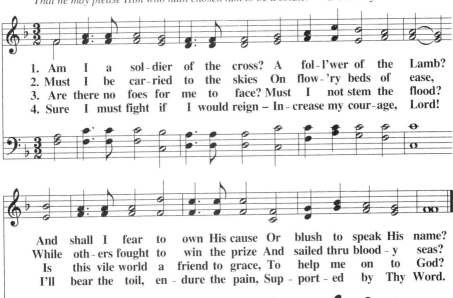

1. Am I a sol - dier of the cross? A fol - l'wer of the Lamb?
2. Must I be car - ried to the skies On flow - 'ry beds of ease,
3. Are there no foes for me to face? Must I not stem the flood?
4. Sure I must fight if I would reign – In - crease my cour - age, Lord!

And shall I fear to own His cause Or blush to speak His name?
While oth - ers fought to win the prize And sailed thru blood - y seas?
Is this vile world a friend to grace, To help me on to God?
I'll bear the toil, en - dure the pain, Sup - port - ed by Thy Word.

WORDS: Isaac Watts
MUSIC: Thomas A. Arne

ARLINGTON

260 Never Alone

Lo, I am with you always, even unto the end of the world — Matthew 28:20 KJV

1. I've seen the light - ning flash - ing And heard the
2. The world's fierce winds are blow - ing – Temp - ta - tion's
3. When in af - flic - tion's val - ley I tread the
4. He died on Cal - v'ry's moun - tain, For me they

thun - der roll, I've felt sin's break - ers dash - ing, Which
sharp and keen; I have a peace in know - ing My
road of care, My Sav - ior helps me car - ry The
pierced His side, For me He o-pened that foun - tain, The

tried to con-quer my soul; I've heard the voice of my
Sav - ior stands be - tween; He stands to shield me from
cross so heav-y to bear; Tho' all a - round me is
crim - son, cleans - ing tide; For me He's wait - ing in

Sav - ior, He bid me still fight on – He
dan - ger When all my friends are gone – He
dark - ness And earth - ly joys are flown, My
glo - ry Up - on His heav'n - ly throne – He

WORDS: Source unknown, 19th century
MUSIC: Source unknown, 19th century; arr. by Eldon Burkwall

Never Alone

261 God Leads Us Along

Lead me, O Lord, in Thy righteousness — Psalm 5:8 KJV

1. In shad-y, green pas-tures, so rich and so sweet, God
2. Some times on the mount where the sun shines so bright, God
3. Tho' sor-rows be-fall us and Sa-tan op-pose, God
4. A-way from the mire and a-way from the clay, God

leads His dear chil-dren a-long;
leads His dear chil-dren a-long;
leads His dear chil-dren a-long;
leads His dear chil-dren a-long;

Where the
Some
Thru
A-

wa-ter's cool flow bathes the wea-ry one's feet, God
times in the val-ley, in dark-est of night, God
grace we can con-quer, de-feat all our foes, God
way up in glo-ry, e-ter-ni-ty's day, God

leads His dear chil-dren a-long.
leads His dear chil-dren a-long.
leads His dear chil-dren a-long.
leads His dear chil-dren a-long.

WORDS: G. A. Young
MUSIC: G. A. Young

GOD LEADS US

God Leads Us Along

Refrain

Some thru the wa - ters, some thru the flood,

Some thru the fire, but all thru the blood;

Some thru great sor - row, but God gives a song,

In the night sea - son and all the day long.

262 Leaning on the Everlasting Arms

The eternal God is thy refuge,
and underneath are the everlasting arms — Deuteronomy 33:27 KJV

1. What a fel-low-ship, what a joy di-vine, Lean-ing on the ev-er-
2. O how sweet to walk in this pil-grim way, Lean-ing on the ev-er-
3. What have I to dread, what have I to fear, Lean-ing on the ev-er-

last-ing arms; What a bless-ed-ness, what a peace is mine,
last-ing arms; O how bright the path grows from day to day,
last-ing arms? I have bless-ed peace with my Lord so near,

Refrain

Lean-ing on the ev-er-last-ing arms.
Lean-ing on Je-sus,

Lean - ing

lean - ing, Safe and se-cure from all a-larms; Lean - ing,
lean-ing on Je-sus, Lean-ing on Je-sus,

lean - ing, Lean-ing on the ev-er-last-ing arms.
lean-ing on Je-sus,

WORDS: Elisha A. Hoffman
MUSIC: Anthony J. Showalter

SHOWALTER

Be Still, My Soul

263

Be still, and know that I am God — Psalm 46:10 KJV

1. Be still, my soul – the Lord is on thy side! _____ Bear pa-tient-
2. Be still, my soul – thy God doth un - der - take _____ To guide the
3. Be still, my soul – the hour is has-t'ning on _____ When we shall

ly the cross of grief or pain; _____ Leave to thy God to
fu - ture as He has the past; _____ Thy hope, thy con - fi -
be for - ev - er with the Lord, _____ When dis - ap - point - ment,

or - der and pro - vide _____ In ev - 'ry change He faith-ful will re -
dence let noth-ing shake _____ All now mys - te - rious shall be bright at
grief, and fear are gone, _____ Sor-row for - got, love's pur - est joys re -

main. _____ Be still, my soul – thy best, thy heav'n-ly Friend _____
last. _____ Be still, my soul – the waves and winds still know _____
stored. _____ Be still, my soul – when change and tears are past, _____

Thru thron - y ways leads to a joy - ful end. _____
His voice who ruled them while He dwelt be - low. _____
All safe and bless - ed we shall meet at last. _____

WORDS: Katharina von Schlegel; trans. by Jane L. Borthwick (Ps. 46:10)
MUSIC: Jean Sibelius; arr. from *The Hymnal*, 1933

FINLANDIA

264   Come, Ye Disconsolate

Let us therefore come boldly unto the throne of grace — Hebrews 4:16 KJV

1. Come, ye dis - con - so - late, wher - e'er ye lan - guish –
2. Joy of the des - o - late, light of the stray - ing,
3. Here see the Bread of Life, see wa - ters flow - ing

Come to the mer - cy seat, fer - vent - ly kneel;
Hope of the pen - i - tent, fade - less and pure!
Forth from the throne of God, pure from a - bove;

Here bring your wound - ed hearts, here tell your an - guish:
Here speaks the Com - fort - er, ten - der - ly say - ing,
Come to the feast of love – come ev - er know - ing

Earth has no sor - row that heav'n can - not heal.
"Earth has no sor - row that heav'n can - not cure."
Earth has no sor - row but heav'n can re - move.

WORDS: Sts. 1-2: Thomas Moore; st. 3: Thomas Hastings
MUSIC: Samuel Webbe

CONSOLATOR

I'd Rather Have Jesus

265

Then Peter said, "Silver and gold I do not have, but what I have I give you" — Acts 3:6 NIV

1. I'd rath-er have Je-sus than sil - ver or gold, I'd rath-er be
2. I'd rath-er have Je-sus than men's ap - plause, I'd rath-er be
3. He's fair - er than lil - ies of rar - est bloom, He's sweet-er than

His than have rich-es un - told; I'd rath-er have Je-sus than
faith-ful to His dear cause; I'd rath-er have Je-sus than
hon - ey from out the comb; He's all that my hun-ger-ing

hous-es or lands. I'd rath-er be led by His nail-pierced hand.
world-wide fame. I'd rath-er be true to His ho - ly name.
spir - it needs. I'd rath-er have Je-sus and let Him lead.

Refrain

Than to be the king of a vast do-main Or be held in sin's dread sway. _

I'd rath-er have Je-sus than an - y-thing This world af-fords to - day. _

WORDS: Rhea F. Miller
MUSIC: George Beverly Shea

I'D RATHER HAVE JESUS

266   In Times Like These

Behold, now is the accepted time; behold, now is the day of salvation — 2 Corinthians 6:2 KJV

1. In times like these you need a Sav - ior, In times like
2. In times like these you need the Bi - ble, In times like
3. In times like these I have a Sav - ior, In times like

these you need an an - chor; Be ver - y sure, be ver - y
these O be not i - dle; Be ver - y sure, be ver - y
these I have an an - chor; I'm ver - y sure, I'm ver - y

sure Your an-chor holds and grips the Sol - id
sure Your an-chor holds and grips the Sol - id
sure My an-chor holds and grips the Sol - id

Refrain

Rock!
Rock! This Rock is Je - sus, Yes, He's the One; This Rock is
Rock!

WORDS: Ruth Caye Jones   TIMES LIKE THESE
MUSIC: Ruth Caye Jones

In Times Like These

Je - sus, The on - ly One!
1., 2. Be ver - y sure, be ver - y
3. I'm ver - y sure, I'm ver - y

sure Your an-chor holds and grips the Sol-id Rock!
sure My an-chor holds and grips the Sol-id Rock!

But mark this: There will be terrible times in the last days. People will be lovers of themselves, lovers of money, boastful, proud, abusive, disobedient to their parents, ungrateful, unholy, without love, unforgiving, slanderous, without self-control, brutal, not lovers of the good, treacherous, rash, conceited, lovers of pleasure rather than lovers of God — having a form of godliness but denying its power. Have nothing to do with them. They are the kind who worm their way into homes and gain control over weak-willed women, who are loaded down with sins and are swayed by all kinds of evil desires, always learning but never able to acknowledge the truth. Just as Jannes and Jambres opposed Moses, so also these men oppose the truth — men of depraved minds, who, as far as the faith is concerned, are rejected. But they will not get very far because, as in the case of those men, their folly will be clear to everyone.
(Adapted from 2 Timothy 3:1-9 KJV)

267 A Shelter in the Time of Storm

The Lord is my Rock, and my Fortress, and my Deliverer — Psalm 18:2 KJV

1. The Lord's our Rock, in Him we hide – A shel-ter in the time of storm;
2. A shade by day, de - fense by night – A shel-ter in the time of storm;
3. The rag - ing storms may round us beat – A shel-ter in the time of storm;
4. O Rock di - vine, O Ref-uge dear – A shel-ter in the time of storm;

Se - cure what-ev - er ill be - tide – A shel-ter in the time of storm.
No fears a - larm, no foes af-fright – A shel-ter in the time of storm.
We'll nev - er leave our safe re-treat – A shel-ter in the time of storm.
Be Thou our help - er ev - er near – A shel-ter in the time of storm.

Refrain

O Je-sus is a Rock in a wea-ry land, A wea-ry land, a wea-ry land;

O Je-sus is a Rock in a wea-ry land – A shel-ter in the time of storm.

WORDS: Vernon J. Charlesworth
MUSIC: Ira D. Sankey

SHELTER

The Rock That Is Higher than I 268

Lead me to the Rock that is higher than I — Psalm 61:2 KJV

1. O some-times the shad-ows are deep, And rough seems the
2. O some-times how long seems the day, And some-times how
3. O near to the Rock let me keep, If bless-ings or

path to the goal; And sor-rows, some-times how they sweep Like
wea-ry my feet; But toil-ing in life's dust-y way, The
sor-rows pre-vail; Or climb-ing the moun-tain-way steep, Or

Refrain

tem-pests down o-ver the soul! O then to the Rock let me
Rock's bless-ed shad-ow, how sweet!
walk-ing the shad-ow-y vale.

fly, To the Rock that is high-er than I; O
let me fly, high-er, is high-er than I;

then to the Rock let me fly, To the Rock that is high-er than I!
let me fly,

WORDS: Erastus Johnson
MUSIC: William G. Fischer

ROCK OF REFUGE

269 Under His Wings

In the shadow of Thy wings will I rejoice — Psalm 63:7 KJV

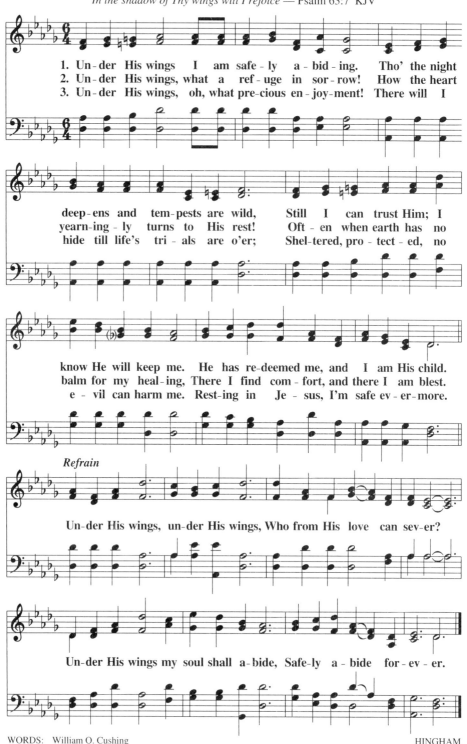

1. Un-der His wings I am safe-ly a-bid-ing. Tho' the night
2. Un-der His wings, what a ref-uge in sor-row! How the heart
3. Un-der His wings, oh, what pre-cious en-joy-ment! There will I

deep-ens and tem-pests are wild, Still I can trust Him; I
yearn-ing-ly turns to His rest! Oft-en when earth has no
hide till life's tri-als are o'er; Shel-tered, pro-tect-ed, no

know He will keep me. He has re-deemed me, and I am His child.
balm for my heal-ing, There I find com-fort, and there I am blest.
e-vil can harm me. Rest-ing in Je-sus, I'm safe ev-er-more.

Refrain

Un-der His wings, un-der His wings, Who from His love can sev-er?

Un-der His wings my soul shall a-bide, Safe-ly a-bide for-ev-er.

WORDS: William O. Cushing
MUSIC: Ira D. Sankey

HINGHAM

Jesus on the Mainline

Where is the wise? Where is the scribe? Where is the disputer of this world?
Hath not God made foolish the wisdom of this world? — 1 Corinthians 1:20 KJV

2. If you want your body healed, tell Him what you want.
3. If you want your soul revived, tell Him what you want.
4. Call Him up, call Him up, tell Him what you want.

WORDS: Traditional
MUSIC: Traditional

271 Some Day

We shall not all sleep, but we shall all be changed — 1 Corinthians 15:51 KJV

1. Beams of heav - en, as I go, Thru this wil - der-ness be -
2. Of - ten-times my sky is clear, Joy a - bounds with-out a
3. Hard - er yet may be the fight, Right may oft - en yield to
4. Bur - dens now may crush me down, Dis - ap - point - ments all a -

low, Guide my feet in peace - ful ways, Turn my
tear, Though a day so bright be - gun, Clouds may
might, Wick - ed - ness a - while may reign, Sa - tan's
round, Trou - bles speak in mourn-ful sigh, Sor - row

mid - nights in - to days; When in the dark - ness I would
hide to - mor - row's sun. There'll be a day that's al - ways
cause may seem to gain; There is a God that rules a -
through a tear-stained eye; There is a world where pleas-ure

grope, Faith al - ways sees a star of hope, And soon from
bright, A day that nev - er yields to night, And in its
bove, With hand of pow'r and heart of love, If I am
reigns, No mourn-ing soul shall roam its plains, And to that

WORDS: Charles Albert Tindley
MUSIC: Charles Albert Tindley; arr. by F. A. Clark

SOMEDAY

Some Day

all   life's grief and   dan - ger,   I shall be   free   some
light   the streets of   glo - ry,   I shall be - hold   some
right,   He'll fight my   bat - tle,   I shall have peace   some
land   of peace and   glo - ry   I want   to   go   some

Refrain

day.
day.   I do not know   how long 'twill be,   Nor what the
day.
day.

fu - ture holds for   me,   But this I   know,   if Je - sus

leads me,   I shall get   home   some   day.

272 Have Faith in God

O Lord my God, in Thee do I put my trust — Psalm 7:1 KJV

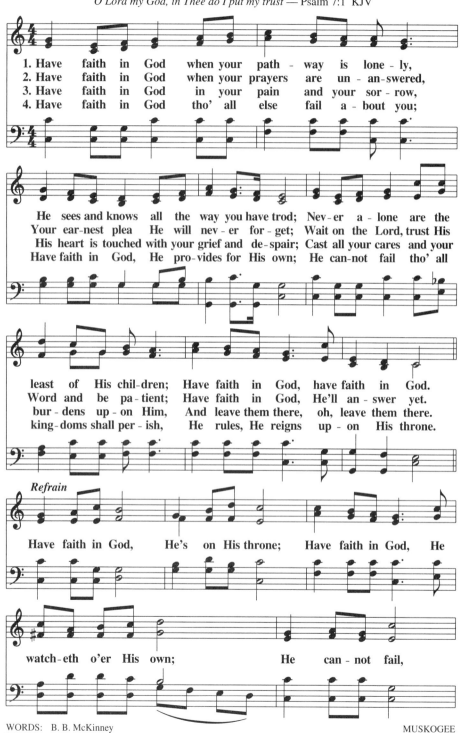

1. Have faith in God when your path - way is lone - ly,
2. Have faith in God when your prayers are un - an - swered,
3. Have faith in God in your pain and your sor - row,
4. Have faith in God tho' all else fail a - bout you;

He sees and knows all the way you have trod; Nev - er a - lone are the
Your ear - nest plea He will nev - er for - get; Wait on the Lord, trust His
His heart is touched with your grief and de - spair; Cast all your cares and your
Have faith in God, He pro - vides for His own; He can - not fail tho' all

least of His chil - dren; Have faith in God, have faith in God.
Word and be pa - tient; Have faith in God, He'll an - swer yet.
bur - dens up - on Him, And leave them there, oh, leave them there.
king - doms shall per - ish, He rules, He reigns up - on His throne.

Refrain

Have faith in God, He's on His throne; Have faith in God, He

watch - eth o'er His own; He can - not fail,

WORDS: B. B. McKinney
MUSIC: B. B. McKinney
MUSKOGEE

Have Faith in God

He must pre-vail; Have faith in God, have faith in God.

My Faith Looks Up to Thee 273

That Christ may dwell in your hearts by faith — Ephesians 3:17 KJV

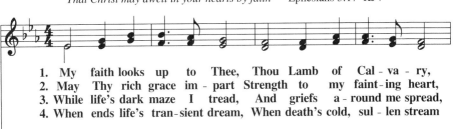

1. My faith looks up to Thee, Thou Lamb of Cal - va - ry,
2. May Thy rich grace im - part Strength to my faint-ing heart,
3. While life's dark maze I tread, And griefs a - round me spread,
4. When ends life's tran-sient dream, When death's cold, sul - len stream

Sav - ior di - vine! Now hear me while I pray, Take all my
My zeal in - spire; As Thou hast died for me, O may my
Be Thou my guide; Bid dark-ness turn to day, Wipe sor-row's
Shall o'er me roll; Blest Sav - ior, then, in love, Fear and dis -

guilt a - way, O let me from this day Be whol - ly Thine!
love to Thee Pure, warm and change-less be, A liv - ing fire.
tears a - way, Nor let me ev - er stray From Thee a - side.
trust re-move; O bear me safe a - bove, A ran-somed soul!

WORDS: Ray Palmer
MUSIC: Lowell Mason

OLIVET

274 The Solid Rock

He only is my rock and my salvation — Psalm 62:6 KJV

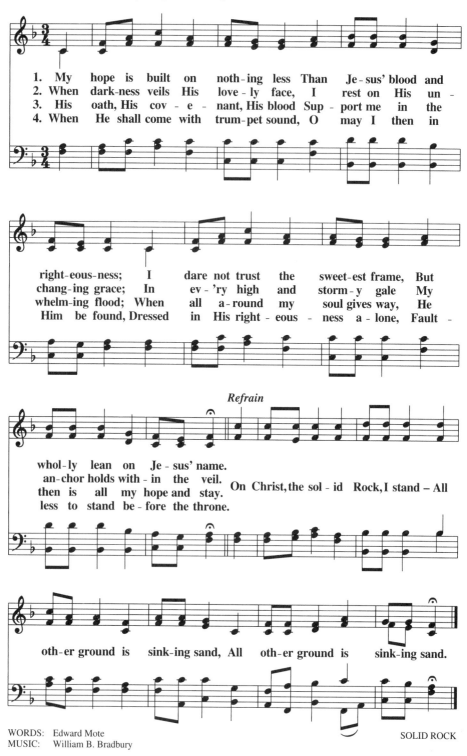

1. My hope is built on noth-ing less Than Je-sus' blood and
2. When dark-ness veils His love-ly face, I rest on His un-
3. His oath, His cov-e-nant, His blood Sup-port me in the
4. When He shall come with trum-pet sound, O may I then in

right-eous-ness; I dare not trust the sweet-est frame, But
chang-ing grace; In ev-'ry high and storm-y gale My
whelm-ing flood; When all a-round my soul gives way, He
Him be found, Dressed in His right-eous-ness a-lone, Fault-

Refrain

whol-ly lean on Je-sus' name.
an-chor holds with-in the veil.
then is all my hope and stay. On Christ, the sol-id Rock, I stand – All
less to stand be-fore the throne.

oth-er ground is sink-ing sand, All oth-er ground is sink-ing sand.

WORDS: Edward Mote
MUSIC: William B. Bradbury

SOLID ROCK

Faith of Our Mothers

275

And He said to the woman, "Thy faith hath saved thee" — Luke 7:50 KJV

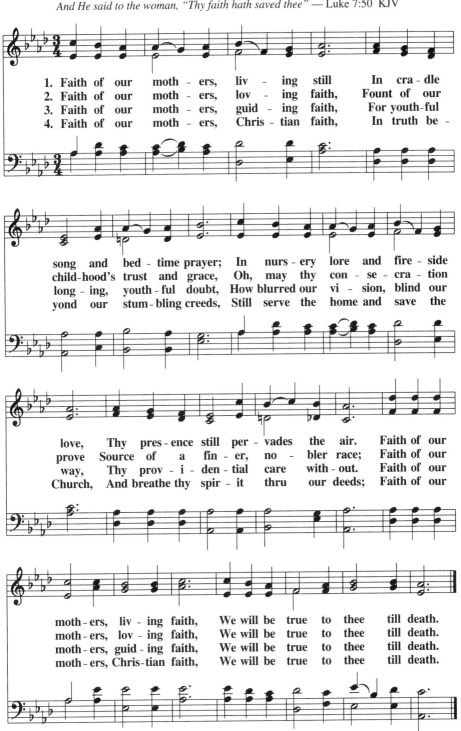

1. Faith of our moth - ers, liv - ing still In cra - dle
2. Faith of our moth - ers, lov - ing faith, Fount of our
3. Faith of our moth - ers, guid - ing faith, For youth-ful
4. Faith of our moth - ers, Chris - tian faith, In truth be -

song and bed - time prayer; In nurs - ery lore and fire - side
child-hood's trust and grace, Oh, may thy con - se - cra - tion
long - ing, youth - ful doubt, How blurred our vi - sion, blind our
yond our stum - bling creeds, Still serve the home and save the

love, Thy pres - ence still per - vades the air. Faith of our
prove Source of a fin - er, no - bler race; Faith of our
way, Thy prov - i - den - tial care with - out. Faith of our
Church, And breathe thy spir - it thru our deeds; Faith of our

moth - ers, liv - ing faith, We will be true to thee till death.
moth - ers, lov - ing faith, We will be true to thee till death.
moth - ers, guid - ing faith, We will be true to thee till death.
moth - ers, Chris-tian faith, We will be true to thee till death.

WORDS: A. B. Patten
MUSIC: Henri F. Hemy; arr. by James G. Walton

ST. CATHERINE

276 Keep on Believing

Believe in the Lord your God — 2 Chronicles 20:20 KJV

1. Some - times, the shad - ows gath - er, And mists ob - scure the way; Some - times, the clouds grow heav - y, And dark - en all the day. How pre-cious to re - mem - ber Our Fa - ther's lov - ing care, — That

2. Some - times, the way is drear - y, We seem to walk a - lone; For - get - ting that the Fa - ther Keeps watch a - bove His own. How man - y need-less sor - rows The faith - less have to bear, For

3. Some - times, our lov - ing serv - ice Seems des - tined but to fail; And e - vils that op - pose us, Seem cer - tain to pre - vail. How sweet the con - so - la - tion That God is ev - 'ry - where, — That

4. O soul, weighed down with sor - row, Be - neath a heav - y load, Re - mem - ber God will help you, How - ev - er rough the road. His grace is still suf - fi - cient For ev - 'ry load of care, — God

WORDS: Frank C. Huston
MUSIC: Frank C. Huston

Keep on Believing

He still loves His chil-dren, And He an - swers prayer.
God still loves His chil-dren, And He an - swers prayer.
He still loves His chil-dren, And He an - swers prayer.
ev - er loves His chil-dren, And He an - swers prayer.

Refrain

Keep on be - liev - ing, God will an - swer prayer;

Keep on be - liev - ing, nev - er de - spair; Tho'

you be heav - y la - den, And bur-dened down with care, Re -

mem-ber God still loves you, And He an - swers prayer.

277 Surely Goodness and Mercy

Surely goodness and mercy shall follow me — Psalm 23:6 KJV

1. A pil-grim was I, and a - wan - d'ring, ___ In the
2. He re-stor-eth my soul when I'm wea - ry, ___ He
3. When I walk thru the dark lone-some val - ley, ___ My

cold night of sin I did roam, ___ When Je - sus the kind Shep-herd
giv - eth me strength day by day; ___ He leads me be - side the still
Sav - ior will walk with me there; ___ And safe - ly His great hand will

found me, ___ And now I am on my way home. ___
wa - ters, ___ He guards me each step of the way. ___
lead me ___ To the man-sions He's gone to pre - pare. ___

Refrain

Sure-ly good-ness and mer - cy shall fol - low me All the

days, all the days of my life; ___ Sure-ly good-ness and

WORDS: John W. Peterson and Alfred B. Smith
MUSIC: John W. Peterson and Alfred B. Smith

GOODNESS

Surely Goodness and Mercy

278 God Is the Answer

He shall call upon Me and I will answer him — Psalm 91:15 KJV

God is the an - swer, God is the an - swer, God is the an-swer in the time of need. God is the an - swer, God is the an - swer, God is the an-swer in the time of need.

WORDS: R. H. Goodpasteur
MUSIC: R. H. Goodpasteur

God Is the Answer

1. One day   I was bur - dened,   my mind   was ill at
2. He pros - pers and pro - tects me   __ ev - 'ry-where I

ease,   I was search-ing   for an an - swer,   I
go,   Just   when I   need Him   most,   He

heard   it   in   the   trees,   And they whis-pered to   me:
makes   the bles - sings flow,   I'm so glad I   know that

"God   is the   an - swer,   God   is the   an - swer,
God   is the   an - swer,   God   is the   an - swer,

God   is the an - swer in the   time   of need."
God   is the an - swer in the   time   of need.

279 My Soul Shall Live with Jesus

We should live together with Him — 1 Thessalonians 5:10 KJV

1. I have heard of a man-sion That is bright-er than the
2. Oh some-time my way seems drear - y And I'm sink - ing in de -
3. Then some-time my load gets heav - y And I know not what to

sun, And some day I'm goin, to dwell there When my works on earth are
spair, But I call up - on my Sav - ior For I know He'll an-swer
do, But I think a - bout my Sav - ior And I'm sure - ly go - ing

done, For I know my time is not long In this sin - ful world of
prayer, Yes I know my Sav-ior liv - eth And He knows just what I
thru, For I know that He will guide me All a - long this pil-grim

pain, Then my soul shall rest with Je-sus, With the Sav - ior, He's the King.
do, And I'm go - ing home to Je-sus, I've got heav-en in my view.
way, I am go - ing home to glo-ry, I shall make the goal some day.

Refrain

O yes, my trou-bles will be o - ver When I reach the oth-er

WORDS: Louise King
MUSIC: Louise King
© 1933 by Louise King. Used by permission.

My Soul Shall Live with Jesus

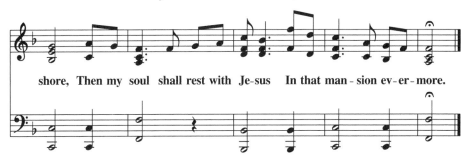

shore, Then my soul shall rest with Je-sus In that man - sion ev - er - more.

O for a Faith That Will Not Shrink 280

The trying of your faith worketh patience — James 1:3 KJV

1. O for a faith that will not shrink Tho'
2. That will not mur - mur nor com - plain Be -
3. A faith that shines more bright and clear When
4. Lord, give me such a faith as this, And

pressed by man - y a foe, That will not trem - ble
neath the chas - t'ning rod, But in the hour of
tem - pests rage with - out, That, when in dan - ger,
then, what - e'er may come, I'll taste e'en now the

on the brink Of an - y earth - ly woe;
grief or pain Will lean up - on its God;
knows no fear, In dark - ness feels no doubt.
hal - lowed bliss Of an e - ter - nal home.

WORDS: William H. Bathurst
MUSIC: William H. Havergal

EVAN

281 I Know Who Holds Tomorrow

*Take therefore no thought for the morrow: for the morrow
shall take thought for the things of itself — Matthew 6:34 KJV*

1. I don't know ____ a-bout to-mor-row, ____ I just live ____
2. Ev-'ry step ____ is get-ting bright-er, ____ As the gold -
3. I don't know ____ a.-bout to-mor-row, ____ It may bring __

____ from day to day. ____ I don't bor - row from its
____ en stairs I climb; ____ Ev-'ry bur - den's get-ting
____ me pov-er-ty; ____ But the one ____ who feeds the

sun - shine, ____ For its skies ____ may turn to gray. ____
light-er; ____ Ev-'ry cloud ____ is sil-ver lined. ____
spar-row, ____ Is the one ____ who stands by me. ____

____ I don't wor - ry o'er the fu-ture, ____ For I
____ There the sun ____ is al-ways shin-ing, ____ There no
____ And the path ____ that be my por-tion, ____ May be

WORDS: Ira F. Stanphill
MUSIC: Ira F. Stanphill
I KNOW

I Know Who Holds the Future

282   Faith of Our Fathers

Thy faith hath made thee whole — Mark 5:34 KJV

1. Faith of our fa - thers, liv - ing still   In spite of
2. Our fa - thers, chained in pris - ons dark,   Were still in
3. Faith of our fa - thers, we will love   Both friend and

dun - geon, fire and sword – O how our hearts beat high with
heart and con - science free; How sweet would be their chil - dren's
foe in all our strife; And preach Thee, too, as love knows

joy When-e'er we hear that glo - rious word! Faith of our
fate If they, like them, could die for thee! Faith of our
how, By kind - ly words and vir - tuous life. Faith of our

fa - thers, ho - ly faith, We will be true to thee till death!
fa - thers, ho - ly faith, We will be true to thee till death!
fa - thers, ho - ly faith, We will be true to thee till death!

WORDS: Frederick W. Faber
MUSIC: Henri F. Hemy; adapt. by James G. Walton

ST. CATHERINE

Jesus Is All the World to Me 283

For to me to live is Christ, and to die is gain — Philippians 1:21 KJV

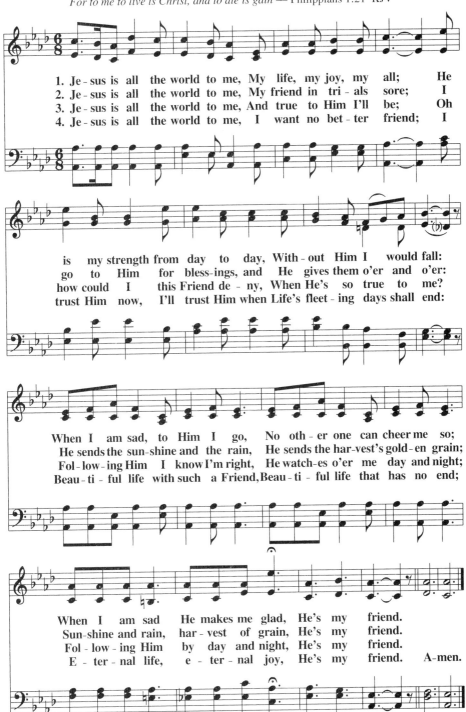

1. Je-sus is all the world to me, My life, my joy, my all; He
2. Je-sus is all the world to me, My friend in tri-als sore; I
3. Je-sus is all the world to me, And true to Him I'll be; Oh
4. Je-sus is all the world to me, I want no bet-ter friend; I

is my strength from day to day, With-out Him I would fall:
go to Him for bless-ings, and He gives them o'er and o'er:
how could I this Friend de-ny, When He's so true to me?
trust Him now, I'll trust Him when Life's fleet-ing days shall end:

When I am sad, to Him I go, No oth-er one can cheer me so;
He sends the sun-shine and the rain, He sends the har-vest's gold-en grain;
Fol-low-ing Him I know I'm right, He watch-es o'er me day and night;
Beau-ti-ful life with such a Friend, Beau-ti-ful life that has no end;

When I am sad He makes me glad, He's my friend.
Sun-shine and rain, har-vest of grain, He's my friend.
Fol-low-ing Him by day and night, He's my friend.
E-ter-nal life, e-ter-nal joy, He's my friend. A-men.

WORDS: Will L. Thompson
MUSIC: Will L. Thompson

ELIZABETH

284 The Love of God

God is love — 1 John 4:16 KJV

1. The love of God is great - er far Than tongue or
2. When hoar - y time shall pass a - way, And earth - ly
3. Could we with ink the o - cean fill, And were the

pen can ev - er tell; It goes be - yond the high - est
thrones and king - doms fall; When men who here re - fuse to
skies of parch - ment made; Were ev - 'ry stalk on earth a

star, And reach - es to the low - est hell; The guilt - y
pray, On rocks and hills and moun - tains call; God's love, so
quill, And ev - 'ry man a scribe by trade; To write the

pair, bowed down with care, God gave His Son to
sure, shall still en - dure, All meas - ure - less and
love of God a - bove Would drain the o - cean

WORDS: F. M. Lehman
MUSIC: F. M. Lehman; arr. by Claudia Lehman Mays

LOVE OF GOD

The Love of God

285 I Will Trust in the Lord

Trust in the Lord with all thine heart — Proverbs 3:5 KJV

Unison

1. I will trust in the Lord, I will trust in the Lord, I will trust in the Lord 'til I die. _____ I will trust in the Lord, I will
2. I'm going to watch, fight, and pray, I'm going to watch, fight, and pray, I'm going to watch, fight, and pray 'til I die. _____ I'm going to watch, fight, and pray, I'm going to
3. I'm going to treat ev-'ry-bod-y right I'm going to treat ev-'ry-bod-y right, I'm going to treat ev-'ry-bod-y right 'til I die. _____ I'm going to treat ev-'ry-bod-y right, I'm going to
4. I'm going to stay on my bend-ed knees, I'm going to stay on my bend-ed knees, I'm going to stay on my bend-ed knees 'til I die. _____ I'm going to stay on my bend-ed knees, I'm going to

WORDS: Traditional
MUSIC: Traditional; arr. by J. Jefferson Cleveland

I Will Trust in the Lord

trust	in	the	Lord,	I will
watch,	fight,	and	pray,	I'm going to
treat	ev - 'ry - bod - y	right,	I'm going to
stay	on my bend - ed	knees,	I'm going to

trust	in the	Lord	'til I die. _____
watch,	fight, and	pray	'til I die. _____
treat	ev-'ry-bod - y	right	'til I die. _____
stay	on my bend - ed	knees	'til I die. _____

And at midnight Paul and Silas prayed, and sang praises unto God: and the prisoners heard them. And suddenly there was a great earthquake, so that the foundations of the prison were shaken: and immediately all the doors were opened, and every one's bands were loosed. And the keeper of the prison awaking out of his sleep, and seeing the prison doors open, he drew out his sword, and would have killed himself, supposing that the prisoners had been fled. But Paul cried with a loud voice, saying, Do thyself no harm: for we are all here. Then he called for a light, and sprang in, and came trembling, and fell down before Paul and Silas, And brought them out, and said, Sirs, what must I do to be saved? And they said, Believe on the Lord Jesus Christ, and thou shalt be saved, and thy house. And they spake unto him the word of the Lord, and to all that were in his house. And he took them the same hour of the night, and washed their stripes; and was baptized, he and all his, straightway. And when he had brought them into his house, he set meat before them, and rejoiced, believing in God with all his house. (Acts 16:25-34 KJV)

286   Someday He'll Make It Plain

*Sufferings ... are not worthy to be compared with the glory
which shall be revealed — Romans 8:18 KJV*

1. I do not know why oft 'round me My hopes all shat - tered seem to be; God's per-fect plan I can - not see, But some-day I'll un der-stand.
2. I can-not tell the depth of love Which moves the Fa - ther's heart a - bove, My faith to test, my love to prove, But some-day I'll un-der-stand.
3. Tho' tri - als come thru pass - ing days, My life will still be filled with praise; For God will lead thru dark-ened ways, But some-day I'll un-der-stand.

Refrain (parts)

Some-day He'll make it plain to me, Some-day when I His face shall see;

WORDS: Lida Shivers Leech
MUSIC: Adam Geibel

Some Day He'll Make It Plain

Some-day from tears I shall be free, For some-day I shall un-der-stand.

I Am Trusting Thee, Lord Jesus 287

In Thee do I put my trust — Psalm 16:1 KJV

1. I am trust - ing Thee, Lord Je - sus —
2. I am trust - ing Thee to guide me —
3. I am trust - ing Thee for pow - er —
4. I am trust - ing Thee, Lord Je - sus —

Trust - ing on - ly Thee; Trust - ing Thee for
Thou a - lone shalt lead, Ev - 'ry day and
Thine can nev - er fail; Words which Thou Thy -
Nev - er let me fall; I am trust - ing

full sal - va - tion, Great _____ and free.
hour sup - ply - ing All _____ my need.
self shalt give me Must _____ pre - vail.
Thee for - ev - er, And _____ for all.

WORDS: Frances R. Havergal
MUSIC: Ethelbert W. Bullinger

BULLINGER

288 We'll Understand It Better By and By

The Lord give thee understanding in all things — 2 Timothy 2:7 KJV

1. We are oft - en tossed and driv'n on the rest - less sea of time,
2. We are oft - en des - ti - tute of the things that life de-mands,
3. Tri - als dark on ev - 'ry hand, and we can - not un - der-stand
4. Temp - ta - tions, hid - den snares oft - en take us un - a - wares,

Som - ber skies and howl - ing tem - pests oft suc -
Want of food and want of shel - ter — thirst - y
All the ways that God would lead us to that
And our hearts are made to bleed for man - y a

ceed a bright sun-shine, In that land of per - fect day,
hills and bar - ren lands, We are trust - ing in the Lord,
bless - ed Prom - ised Land; But He guides us with His eye,
thought-less word or deed, And we won - der why the test

when the mists have rolled a - way, We will
and ac - cord - ing to His word, We will
and we'll fol - low till we die. For we'll
when we try to do our best. But we'll

WORDS: Charles Albert Tindley
MUSIC: Charles Albert Tindley; arr. by F. A. Clark

BY AND BY

We'll Understand It Better By and By

289 Farther Along

Thou shalt make me to know wisdom — Psalm 51:6 KJV

1. Tempt - ed and tried we're oft made to won - der Why it should
2. When death has come and tak - en our loved ones, It leaves our
3. Faith - ful till death said our lov - ing Mas - ter, A few more
4. When we see Je - sus com-ing in glo - ry When He comes

be thus all the day long; While there are oth - ers liv - ing a -
home so lone - ly and drear; Then do we won - der why oth - ers
days to la - bor and wait; Toils of the road will then seem as
from His home in the sky; Then we shall meet Him in that bright

bout us, Nev - er mo - lest - ed tho' in the wrong.
pros - per, Liv - ing so wick - ed year aft - er year.
noth - ing, As we sweep thru the beau - ti - ful gate.
man - sion, We'll un - der - stand it all by and by.

Refrain

Far-ther a - long we'll know all a - bout it, Far-ther a -

WORDS: W. B. Stevens
MUSIC: W. B. Stevens; arr. by J. R. Baxter, Jr.

Farther Along

long we'll un-der-stand why; Cheer up my broth - er, live in the

sun - shine, We'll un - der - stand it all by and by.

Do not fret because of evil men or be envious of those who do wrong; for like the grass they will soon wither, like green plants they will soon die away. Trust in the Lord and do good; dwell in the land and enjoy safe pasture. Delight yourself in the Lord and he will give you the desires of your heart.Commit your way to the Lord; trust in him and he will do this: He will make your righteousness shine like the dawn, the justice of your cause like the noonday sun. Be still before the Lord and wait patiently for him; do not fret when men succeed in their ways, when they carry out their wicked schemes. Refrain from anger and turn from wrath; do not fret — it leads only to evil. For evil men will be cut off, but those who hope in the Lord will inherit the land. A little while, and the wicked will be no more; though you look for them, they will not be found. But the meek will inherit the land and enjoy great peace.
(Adapted from Psalm 37:1-11 KJV)

290 Some Bright Morning

For then would I fly away, and be at rest — Psalm 55:6 KJV

1. Be not a-wea-ry for la-bor will cease Some glad
2. Wea-ri-some bur-dens will all be laid down, Some glad
3. La-bor well done shall re-ceive its re-ward, Some glad
4. O what a time of re-joic-ing will come, Some glad
5. There with the loved ones who've gone on be-fore, Some glad

morn-ing.
morn-ing.
morn-ing.
morn-ing.
morn-ing.

Tur-moil will change in-to in-fi-nite peace,
Then shall our cross be ex-changed for a crown,
Thou who art faith-ful shall be with the Lord,
When all the ran-somed are gath-ered at home,
We shall sing praise to the Lamb ev-er-more,

Refrain

Some glad morn-ing. Some bright morn-ing, Some glad

morn-ing, When the sun is shin-ing in th'e-ter-nal sky;

Some bright morn-ing, Some glad morn-ing,

WORDS: Charlotte G. Homer
MUSIC: Charles H. Gabriel

Some Bright Morning

We shall see the Lord of Har - vest, by and by.

Jesus Never Fails   291

Heaven and earth shall pass away, but My words shall not pass away — Matthew 24:35 KJV

1. Earth-ly friends may prove un - true, Doubts and fears as - sail;
2. Tho' the sky be dark and drear, Fierce and strong the gale;
3. In life's dark and bit - ter hour Love will still pre - vail;

One still loves and cares for you, One who will not fail.
Just re - mem-ber He is near, And He will not fail.
Trust His ev - er - last-ing pow'r – Je - sus will not fail.

Refrain

Je - sus nev-er fails, Je - sus nev-er fails;

Heav'n and earth may pass a - way, But Je - sus nev-er fails.

WORDS: Arthur A. Luther   JESUS NEVER FAILS
MUSIC: Arthur A. Luther

292 'Tis So Sweet to Trust in Jesus

Trust in the Lord with all thine heart — Proverbs 3:5 KJV

1. 'Tis so sweet to trust in Je - sus, Just to take Him at His word, Just to rest up - on His prom - ise, Just to know, "Thus saith the Lord."
2. O how sweet to trust in Je - sus, Just to trust His cleans - ing blood, Just in sim - ple faith to plunge me 'Neath the heal - ing, cleans - ing flood!
3. Yes, 'tis sweet to trust in Je - sus, Just from sin and self to cease, Just from Je - sus sim - ply tak - ing Life and rest and joy and peace.
4. I'm so glad I learned to trust Thee, Pre - cious Je - sus, Sav - ior, Friend; And I know that Thou art with me, Wilt be with me to the end.

Refrain

Je - sus, Je - sus, how I trust Him! How I've proved Him o'er and o'er! Je - sus, Je - sus, pre - cious Je - sus! O for grace to trust Him more!

WORDS: Louisa M. R. Stead
MUSIC: William J. Kirkpatrick

TRUST IN JESUS

Wonderful Words of Life 293

Holding forth the word of life; that I may rejoice in the day of Christ — Philippians 2:16 KJV

1. Sing them o - ver a - gain to me – Won-der-ful words of Life;
2. Christ, the bless-ed One, gives to all Won-der-ful words of Life;
3. Sweet - ly ech - o the gos - pel call – Won-der-ful words of Life;

Let me more of their beau - ty see – Won-der-ful words of Life.
Sin - ner, list to the lov - ing call – Won-der-ful words of Life.
Of - fer par-don and peace to all – Won-der-ful words of Life.

Words of life and beau - ty, Teach me faith and du - ty:
All so free - ly giv - en, Woo - ing us to heav - en:
Je - sus, on - ly Sav - ior, Sanc - ti - fy for - ev - er:

Refrain

Beau-ti - ful words, won-der-ful words, Won-der-ful words of Life;

Beau-ti - ful words, won-der-ful words, Won-der-ful words of Life.

WORDS: Philip P. Bliss
MUSIC: Philip P. Bliss

WORDS OF LIFE

294 Holy Bible, Book Divine

Thou hast the words of eternal life — John 6:68 KJV

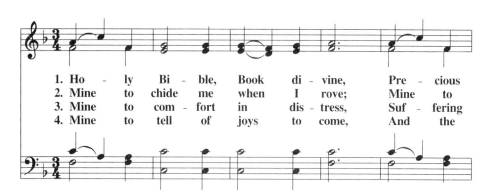

1. Ho - ly Bi - ble, Book di - vine, Pre - cious
2. Mine to chide me when I rove; Mine to
3. Mine to com - fort in dis - tress, Suf - fering
4. Mine to tell of joys to come, And the

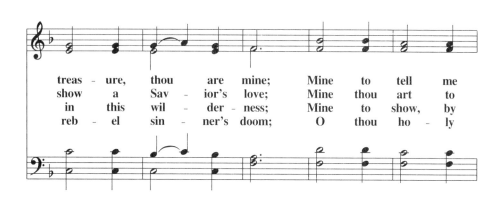

treas - ure, thou are mine; Mine to tell me
show a Sav - ior's love; Mine thou art to
in this wil - der - ness; Mine to show, by
reb - el sin - ner's doom; O thou ho - ly

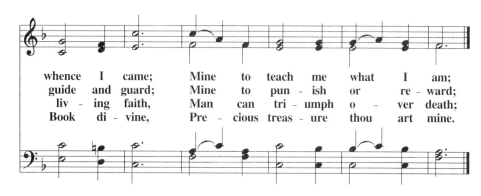

whence I came; Mine to teach me what I am;
guide and guard; Mine to pun - ish or re - ward;
liv - ing faith, Man can tri - umph o - ver death;
Book di - vine, Pre - cious treas - ure thou art mine.

WORDS: John Burton
MUSIC: William B. Bradbury

ALETTA

Break Thou the Bread of Life 295

And Jesus said unto them, "I am the Bread of Life" — John 6:35 KJV

1. Break Thou the Bread of Life, Dear Lord, to me,
2. Bless Thou the truth, dear Lord, To me, to me,
3. Thou art the bread of Life, O Lord, to me,
4. O send Thy Spir-it, Lord, Now un-to me,

As Thou didst break the loaves Be-side the sea;
As Thou didst bless the bread By Gal-i-lee;
Thy ho-ly Word the truth That sav-eth me;
That He may touch my eyes, And make me see:

Be-yond the sa-cred page I seek Thee, Lord;
Then shall all bond-age cease, All fet-ters fall,
Give me to eat and live With Thee a-bove,
Show me the truth con-cealed With-in Thy Word,

My spir-it pants for Thee, O liv-ing Word.
And I shall find my peace, My All in all.
Teach me to love Thy truth, For Thou art love.
And in Thy Book re-vealed I see the Lord.

WORDS: Mary Ann Lathbury
MUSIC: William F. Sherwin

BREAD OF LIFE

296 O Word of God Incarnate

I will delight myself in Thy statutes; I will not forget Thy word — Psalm 119:16 KJV

1. O Word of God incarnate, O Wisdom from on high,
2. The Church from her dear Master Received the gift divine,
3. It floateth like a banner Before God's host unfurled,
4. O make Thy Church, dear Savior, A lamp of purest gold,

O Truth unchanged, unchanging, O Light of our dark sky:
And still that light she lifteth O'er all the earth to shine,
It shineth like a beacon Above the darkling world.
To bear before the nations Thy true light, as of old.

We praise Thee for the radiance That from the hallowed page,
It is the golden casket Where gems of truth are stored;
It is the chart and compass That o'er life's surging sea,
O teach Thy wand'ring pilgrims By this their path to trace,

A lantern to our footsteps, Shines on from age to age.
It is the heav'n-drawn picture Of Christ, the living Word.
'Mid mists and rocks and quick-sands, Still guides, O Christ, to Thee.
Till, clouds and darkness ended, They see Thee face to face.

WORDS: William W. How
MUSIC: from *Meiningen Gesangbuch*, 1693; harm. by Felix Mendelssohn

MUNICH

The Church's One Foundation 297

Jesus Christ Himself being the chief corner stone — Ephesians 2:20 KJV

1. The Church-'s one foun - da - tion Is Je - sus Christ her Lord;
2. E - lect from ev - 'ry na - tion, Yet one o'er all the earth,
3. 'Mid toil and trib - u - la - tion, And tu - mult of her war,
4. Yet she on earth hath un - ion With God, the Three in One,

She is His new cre - a - tion By wa - ter and the Word:
Her char-ter of sal - va - tion, One Lord, one faith, one birth;
She waits the con - sum - ma - tion Of peace for - ev - er - more;
And mys-tic sweet com - mun - ion With those whose rest is won.

From heav'n He came and sought her To be His ho - ly bride;
One ho - ly name she bless - es, Par - takes one ho - ly food,
Till with the vi - sion glo - rious, Her long - ing eyes are blest,
O hap - py ones and ho - ly! Lord, give us grace that we

With His own blood He bought her, And for her life He died.
And to one hope she press - es, With ev - 'ry grace en - dued.
And the great Church vic - to - rious Shall be the Church at rest.
Like them, the meek and low - ly, On high may dwell with Thee.

WORDS: Samuel J. Stone
MUSIC: Samuel Sebastian Wesley

AURELIA

298 Blest Be the Tie That Binds

We have fellowship one with another — 1 John 1:7 KJV

1. Blest be the tie that binds Our hearts in Chris-tian love!
2. Be - fore our Fa - ther's throne We pour our ar - dent prayers;
3. We share our mu - tual woes, Our mu - tual bur - dens bear;
4. When we a - sun - der part It gives us in - ward pain;

The fel - low - ship of kin - dred minds Is like to that a - bove.
Our fears, our hopes, our aims are one, Our com - forts and our cares.
And oft - en for each oth - er flows The sym - pa - thiz - ing tear.
But we shall still be joined in heart, And hope to meet a - gain.

WORDS: John Fawcett
MUSIC: Johann G. Nägeli; arr. by Lowell Mason

DENNIS

299 In Christ There Is No East or West

We all come in the unity of the faith — Ephesians 4:13 KJV

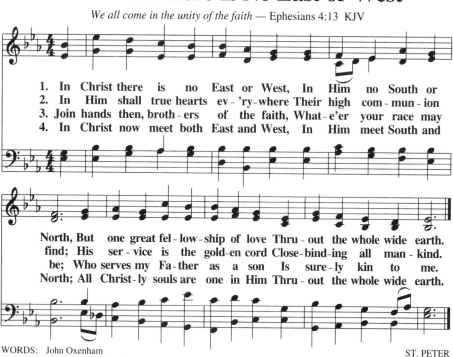

1. In Christ there is no East or West, In Him no South or
2. In Him shall true hearts ev - 'ry-where Their high com - mun - ion
3. Join hands then, broth - ers of the faith, What-e'er your race may
4. In Christ now meet both East and West, In Him meet South and

North, But one great fel - low - ship of love Thru - out the whole wide earth.
find; His ser - vice is the gold-en cord Close-bind-ing all man - kind.
be; Who serves my Fa-ther as a son Is sure-ly kin to me.
North; All Christ-ly souls are one in Him Thru - out the whole wide earth.

WORDS: John Oxenham
MUSIC: Alexander R. Reinagle

ST. PETER

Holy Ground

300

Put off thy shoes from off thy feet, for the place whereon thou standest
is holy ground — Exodus 3:5 KJV

We are stand - ing ___ on ho - ly ground, ___ And I

know that there are an-gels all a - round. ___ Let us

praise ___ Je - sus now. ___ We are

stand - ing in His pres-ence on ho - ly ground. ___

HOLY GROUND

WORDS: Geron Davis
MUSIC: Geron Davis

301   For All the Saints

Then shalt thou delight thyself in the Lord — Isaiah 58:14 KJV

Unison

1. For all the saints who from their la - bors rest,
2. Thou wast their Rock, their For - tress and their Might;
3. O blest com - mun - ion, fel - low - ship di - vine!
4. O may Thy sol - diers, faith - ful, true and bold,
5. And when the strife is fierce, the war - fare long,
6. From earth's wide bounds, from o - cean's far - thest coast,

Who Thee by faith be - fore the world con - fessed,
Thou, Lord, their Cap - tain in the well-fought fight;
We fee - bly strug - gle — they in glo - ry shine;
Fight as the saints who no - bly fought of old,
Steals on the ear the dis - tant tri - umph song,
Through gates of pearl streams in the count - less host,

Thy name, O Je - sus, be for - ev - er blest:
And Thou, in dark - ness drear, their one true light:
Yet all are one in Thee, for all are Thine:
And win with them the vic - tor's crown of gold:
And hearts are brave a - gain, and arms are strong:
Sing - ing to Fa - ther, Son, and Ho - ly Ghost:

WORDS: William W. How
MUSIC: Ralph Vaughan Williams, alt.

SINE NOMINE

For All the Saints

Al - le - lu - ia! Al - le - lu - ia!

I Love Thy Kingdom, Lord **302**

Lord, I have loved the habitation of Thy house — Psalm 26:8 KJV

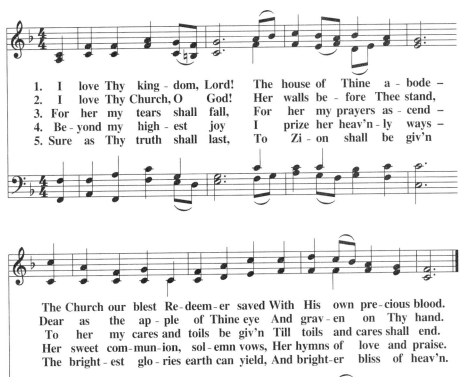

1. I love Thy king - dom, Lord! The house of Thine a - bode –
2. I love Thy Church, O God! Her walls be - fore Thee stand,
3. For her my tears shall fall, For her my prayers as - cend –
4. Be - yond my high - est joy I prize her heav'n - ly ways –
5. Sure as Thy truth shall last, To Zi - on shall be giv'n

The Church our blest Re-deem-er saved With His own pre-cious blood.
Dear as the ap - ple of Thine eye And grav - en on Thy hand.
To her my cares and toils be giv'n Till toils and cares shall end.
Her sweet com-mun-ion, sol-emn vows, Her hymns of love and praise.
The bright - est glo - ries earth can yield, And bright-er bliss of heav'n.

ST. THOMAS

WORDS: Timothy Dwight
MUSIC: Aaron Williams

303   I Need Thee Every Hour

Without Me ye can do nothing — John 15:5 KJV

1. I need Thee ev-'ry hour, Most gra - cious Lord,
2. I need Thee ev-'ry hour, Stay Thou near by;
3. I need Thee ev-'ry hour, In joy or pain;
4. I need Thee ev-'ry hour, Most Ho - ly One;

No ten - der voice like Thine Can peace af - ford.
Temp - ta - tions lose their pow'r When Thou art nigh.
Come quick - ly and a - bide, Or life is vain.
Oh, make me Thine in - deed, Thou bless - ed Son!

Refrain

I need Thee, O, I need Thee; Ev - 'ry hour I need Thee!

O bless me now, my Sav - ior, I come to Thee!

WORDS: Annie S. Hawks
MUSIC: Robert Lowry

NEED

Savior, More Than Life to Me   304

The Lord is the strength of my life — Psalm 27:1 KJV

1. Sav-ior, more than life to me, I am cling-ing, cling-ing close to
2. Thru this chang-ing world be-low, Lead me gen-tly, gen-tly as I
3. Let me love Thee more and more, Till this fleet-ing, fleet-ing life is

Thee; Let Thy pre-cious blood ap-plied, Keep me
go; Trust-ing Thee, I can-not stray, I can
o'er; Till my soul is lost in love, In a

ev-er, ev-er near Thy side.
nev-er, nev-er lose my way.
bright-er, bright-er world a-bove.

Refrain

Ev-'ry day, ev-'ry
Ev-'ry day and hour, ev-'ry

hour, Let me feel Thy cleans-ing pow'r; May Thy
day and hour,

ten-der love to me Bind me clos-er, clos-er, Lord, to Thee.

WORDS: Fanny J. Crosby
MUSIC: William H. Doane

EVERY DAY AND HOUR

305 Take My Hand, Precious Lord

I took them by the hand — Hebrews 8:9 KJV

Refrain

Pre-cious Lord, take my hand, Lead me on, let me stand, I am tired, I am weak, I am worn; _ Thru the storm, thru the night, Lead me on to the light, Take my hand, pre-cious Lord, Lead me home. _

1. When my way grows drear, pre-cious Lord, lin-ger near, When my
2. When the dark-ness ap-pears and the night draws near, And the

life is al-most gone, ____ Hear my cry, hear my call, Hold my
day is past and gone, ____ At the riv-er I stand, Guide my

8vb

WORDS: Thomas A. Dorsey
MUSIC: Thomas A. Dorsey

PRECIOUS LORD

Take My Hand, Precious Lord

hand lest I fall; Take my hand, pre-cious Lord, Lead me home. _
feet, hold my hand; Take my hand, pre-cious Lord, Lead me home. _

Take Time to Be Holy 306

Ye shall be holy; for I am holy — Leviticus 11:44 KJV

1. Take time to be ho - ly, Speak oft with the Lord; A - bide in Him
2. Take time to be ho - ly, The world rush-es on; Spend much time in
3. Take time to be ho - ly, Let Him be thy guide, And run not be -
4. Take time to be ho - ly, Be calm in thy soul – Each thought and each

al - ways And feed on His Word. Make friends of God's chil - dren,
se - cret With Je - sus a - lone. By look-ing to Je - sus,
fore Him, What - ev - er be - tide. In joy or in sor - row
mo - tive Be - neath His con - trol. Thus led by His Spir - it

Help those who are weak, For - get - ting in noth-ing His bless-ing to seek.
Like Him thou shalt be; Thy friends in thy con-duct His like-ness shall see.
Still fol - low the Lord, And, look-ing to Je - sus, Still trust in His Word.
To foun-tains of love, Thou soon shalt be fit - ted For ser-vice a - bove.

WORDS: William D. Longstaff
MUSIC: George C. Stebbins

HOLINESS

307 Nothing Between

Who shall separate us from the love of Christ? — Romans 8:35 KJV

1. Noth - ing be - tween my soul and the Sav - ior,
2. Noth - ing be - tween, like world - ly pleas - ure:
3. Noth - ing be - tween, like pride or sta - tion:
4. Noth - ing be - tween, e'en man - y hard tri - als,

Naught of this world's de - lu - sive dream: I have re-nounced all
Hab - its of life, tho' harm-less they seem, Must not my heart from
Self or friends shall not in - ter - vene; Tho' it may cost me
Tho' the whole world a - gainst me con - vene; Watch-ing with prayer and

sin - ful pleas-ure – Je - sus is mine! There's noth-ing be-tween.
Him ev - er sev - er – He is my all! There's noth-ing be-tween.
much trib - u - la - tion, I am re-solved! There's noth-ing be-tween.
much self-de - ni - al – Tri-umph at last, with noth-ing be-tween!

Refrain

Noth - ing be - tween my soul and the Sav - ior,

So that His bless - ed face may be seen; Noth-ing pre-vent-ing the

WORDS: Charles Albert Tindley
MUSIC: Charles Albert Tindley; arr. by Don Peterman

NOTHING BETWEEN

Nothing Between

least of His fa - vor: Keep the way clear! Let noth-ing be-tween.

O for a Closer Walk with God   308

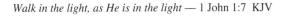

Walk in the light, as He is in the light — 1 John 1:7 KJV

1. O for a clos - er walk with God, A
2. Where is the bless - ed - ness I knew When
3. What peace - ful hours I then en - joyed! How
4. Re - turn, O Ho - ly Dove, re - turn, Sweet

calm and heav'n - ly frame, A light to shine up -
first I saw the Lord? Where is the soul - re -
sweet their mem - 'ry still! But they have left an
Mes - sen - ger of rest; I hate the sins that

on the road That leads me to the Lamb!
fresh - ing view Of Je - sus and His word?
ach - ing void The world can nev - er fill.
made Thee mourn, And drove Thee from my breast.

WORDS: William Cowper
MUSIC: Hugh Wilson

MARTYRDOM

309   Just a Closer Walk with Thee

Ye ought to walk and to please God — 1 Thessalonians 4:1 KJV

Refrain

Just a clos-er walk with Thee; Grant it, Je-sus, if you please,

Fine

Dai - ly walk-ing close to Thee, Let it be, dear Lord, let it be.

1. I am weak, but Thou art strong, Je - sus, keep me from all wrong,
2. Thru this world of toils and snares, If I fal - ter, Lord, who cares?
3. When my fee - ble life is o'er, Time for me won't be no more,

D.C.

I'll be sat - is - fied as long As I walk, let me walk close with Thee.
Who with me my bur-dens shares? None but Thee, dear Lord, none but Thee.
Guide me gent-ly, safe - ly o'er To Thy king - dom shore, to Thy shore.

WORDS: Anonymous
MUSIC: Anonymous

CLOSER WALK

Keep Me Every Day

310

Keep me as the apple of the eye — Psalm 17:8 KJV

1. Lord, I want to live for Thee, Ev - 'ry day and hour;
2. In my weak-ness be my strength; In my tri - als all,
3. Leave me not to walk a - lone, Lest I droop and die;

Let Thy Spir - it be with me In its sav - ing pow'r!
Be Thou near me all the day, Hear my ev - 'ry call!
Let Thy Spir - it go with me, And at - tend my cry!

Refrain

Keep my heart, and keep my hand, Keep my soul, I pray!

Keep my tongue to speak Thy praise, Keep me all the way!

WORDS: F. L. Eiland
MUSIC: Emmet S. Dean

311 Greater Is He That Is in Me

You are of God, little children, and have overcome them,
because He who is in you is greater than he who is in the world — 1 John 4:4 KJV

Refrain

Great-er is He that is in me, Great-er is He that is in me,

Fine

Great-er is He that is in me than he that is in the world! __

Stanzas

1. Sa-tan's like a roar-ing lion __ roam-ing to and fro; __
2. On the day of Pen-te-cost a rush-ing might-y wind, __

Seek-ing whom he may de-vour, the Bi-ble tells me so. __
Blew in-to the up-per room and bap-tized all of them. __

Man-y souls have been his prey to fall in some weak hour, __ But
With a pow-er great-er than __ an-y earth-ly foe, __ And

WORDS: Lanny Wolfe
MUSIC: Lanny Wolfe

Greater Is He That Is in Me

D.C.

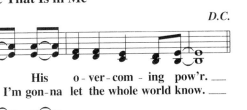

God has prom-ised us to-day His o - ver - com - ing pow'r. ___
I'm so glad I've got it, too, I'm gon-na let the whole world know. ___

How Sweet the Name of Jesus 312

*In the name of Jesus Christ ye shall receive
the gift of the Holy Ghost — Acts 2:38 KJV*

1. How sweet the name of Je - sus sounds In a be - liev - er's
2. It makes the wound-ed spir - it whole, And calms the trou - bled
3. Dear name! the rock on which I build, My shield and hid - ing
4. Je - sus, my shep-herd, broth - er, friend, My proph - et, priest, and

ear! It soothes his sor - rows, heals his wounds, And
breast; 'Tis man - na to the hun - gry soul, And
place; My nev - er - fail - ing trea - sure, filled With
king; My Lord, my life, my way, my end, Ac -

drives a - way his fear, And drives a - way his fear.
to the wea - ry, rest, And to the wea - ry, rest.
bound-less stores of grace! With bound-less stores of grace!
cept the praise I bring, Ac - cept the praise I bring.

WORDS: John Newton
MUSIC: Thomas Hastings

ORTONVILLE

313   Jesus, I Love You

Restore unto me the joy of Thy salvation,
and uphold me with Thy free Spirit — Psalm 51:12 KJV

Ref. Je - sus, I love You   — for   Your ten - der care;
1. Je - sus, I love You,   in You   I   will a - bide;
2. Je - sus, I love You,   be - cause Your name's so sweet,
3. Je - sus, I love You,   on You   I   can de - pend,
4. Je - sus, I love You,   I love Your pow'r di - vine,
5. Je - sus, I love You,   I need Thee ev - 'ry hour,

Je - sus, I love You,   I'll own You an - y - where;
Je - sus, I love You,   safe in Your arms I hide;
Je - sus, I love You,   You've made my life com - plete;
Je - sus, I love You,   my sor - rows You'll at - tend;
Je - sus, I love You,   I'll love You all the time;
Je - sus, I love You,   I need Thy sav - ing pow'r;

Je - sus, I love You   — 'cause You brought me
Je - sus, I love You,   Your love's so sweet and
Je - sus, I love You,   You're true tho' friends are
Je - sus, I love You,   be - cause You love me,
Je - sus, I love You,   in me Thy love im -
Je - sus, I love You,   You'll all my fears sub -

WORDS: Kenneth Morris
MUSIC: Kenneth Morris

Jesus, I Love You

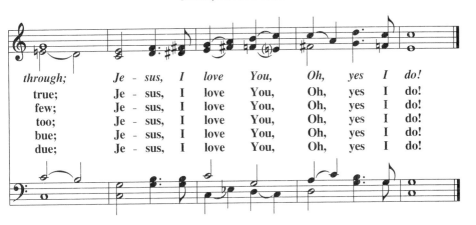

through; Je - sus, I love You, Oh, yes I do!
true; Je - sus, I love You, Oh, yes I do!
few; Je - sus, I love You, Oh, yes I do!
too; Je - sus, I love You, Oh, yes I do!
bue; Je - sus, I love You, Oh, yes I do!
due; Je - sus, I love You, Oh, yes I do!

Nearer, My God, to Thee   314

Let us draw near with a true heart — Hebrews 10:22 KJV

1. Near - er, my God, to Thee, Near - er to Thee! E'en tho' it
2. Tho' like the wan-der - er, The sun goes down, Dark - ness be
3. There let the way ap - pear, Steps un - to heav'n; All that Thou
4. Then with my wak-ing thoughts, Bright with Thy praise, Out of my
5. Or if on joy - ful wing, Cleav - ing the sky, Sun, moon, and

be a cross That rais - eth me; Still all my song shall be,
o - ver me, My rest a stone, Yet in my dreams I'd be
send - est me, In mer - cy giv'n – An - gels to beck - on me
ston - y griefs, Beth - el I raise; So by my woes to be
stars for-got, Up - ward I fly, Still all my song shall be,

Near - er, my God, to Thee, Near - er, my God, to Thee, Near - er to Thee!

WORDS: Sarah F. Adams
MUSIC: Lowell Mason

BETHANY

315 Stepping in the Light

That ye would walk worthy of God — 1 Thessalonians 2:12 KJV

1. Try - ing to walk in the steps of the Sav - ior,
2. Press - ing more close - ly to Him who is lead - ing –
3. Walk - ing in foot - steps of gen - tle for-bear - ance,
4. Try - ing to walk in the steps of the Sav - ior,

Try - ing to fol - low our Sav - ior and King,
When we are tempt - ed to turn from the way,
Foot - steps of faith - ful - ness, mer - cy and love,
Up - ward, still up - ward we'll fol - low our Guide;

Shap - ing our lives by His bless - ed ex - am - ple,
Trust - ing the arm that is strong to de - fend us,
Look - ing to Him for the grace free - ly prom - ised,
When we shall see Him, the King in His beau - ty,

Refrain

Hap-py, how hap-py, the songs that we bring.
Hap-py, how hap-py, our prais - es each day.
Hap-py, how hap-py, our jour - ney a - bove.
Hap-py, how hap-py, our place at His side.

How beau-ti-ful to walk in the

steps of the Sav - ior, Step-ping in the light, Step-ping in the light; How

WORDS: Eliza E. Hewitt
MUSIC: William J. Kirkpatrick

Stepping in the Light

beau-ti-ful to walk in the steps of the Sav-ior, Led in paths of light.

Near to the Heart of God   316

But it is good for me to draw near to God — Psalm 73:28 KJV

1. There is a place of qui-et rest, Near to the heart of God,
2. There is a place of com-fort sweet, Near to the heart of God,
3. There is a place of full re-lease, Near to the heart of God,

A place where sin can-not mo-lest, Near to the heart of God.
A place where we our Sav-ior meet, Near to the heart of God.
A place where all is joy and peace, Near to the heart of God.

Refrain

O Je-sus, blest Re-deem-er, Sent from the heart of God,

Hold us who wait be-fore Thee Near to the heart of God.

WORDS: Cleland B. McAfee
MUSIC: Cleland B. McAfee

McAFEE

317   Close to Thee

Draw nigh unto God, and He will draw nigh to you — James 4:8 KJV

1. Thou my ev - er - last - ing por - tion, More than friend or life to
2. Not for ease or world - ly pleas - ure, Nor for fame my prayer shall
3. Lead me thru the vale of shad - ows, Bear me o'er life's fit - ful

me, All a - long my pil-grim jour - ney, Sav - ior, let me walk with
be; Glad - ly will I toil and suf - fer, On - ly let me walk with
sea; Then the gate of life e - ter - nal May I en - ter, Lord, with

Thee. Close to Thee, Close to Thee, Close to Thee, Close to Thee; All a -
Thee. Close to Thee, Close to Thee, Close to Thee, Close to Thee; Glad - ly
Thee. Close to Thee, Close to Thee, Close to Thee, Close to Thee; Then the

long my pil-grim jour - ney, Sav - ior, let me walk with Thee.
will I toil and suf - fer, On - ly let me walk with Thee.
gate of life e - ter - nal May I en - ter, Lord, with Thee. A - men.

WORDS: Fanny J. Crosby
MUSIC: Silas J. Vail

CLOSE TO THEE

Stand By Me

318

And there is a friend that sticketh closer than a brother — Proverbs 18:24 KJV

1. When the storms of life are rag-ing, Stand by me;
2. In the midst of trib-u-la-tions, Stand by me; (Stand by me;)
3. In the midst of faults and fail-ures, Stand by me;
4. In the midst of per-se-cu-tion, Stand by me; (by me;)
5. When I'm grow-ing old and fee-ble, Stand by me;

When the storms of life are rag-ing, Stand by me;
In the midst of trib-u-la-tions, Stand by me;
In the midst of faults and fail-ures, Stand by me; (Stand by me;)
In the midst of per-se-cu-tion, Stand by me;
When I'm grow-ing old and fee-ble, Stand by me;

When the world is toss-ing me Like a ship up-on the sea,
When the hosts of hell as-sail, And my strength be-gins to fail,
When I do the best I can, And my friends mis-un-der-stand,
When my foes in war ar-ray Un-der-take to stop my way,
When my life be-comes a bur-den, And I'm near-ing chill-y Jor-dan,

Thou who rul-est wind and wa-ter, Stand by me.
Thou who nev-er lost a bat-tle, Stand by me. (Stand by me.)
Thou who know-est all a-bout me, Stand by me.
Thou who saved Paul and Si-las, Stand by me. (by me.)
O Thou "Lil-y of the Val-ley," Stand by me.

WORDS: Charles Albert Tindley
MUSIC: Charles Albert Tindley; arr. by F. A. Clark

STAND BY ME

319 Walking in the Light of Jesus' Love

The true Light, which lighteth every man that cometh into the world — John 1:9 KJV

1. Walk-ing with Je - sus in His love - light, With Him as my dai - ly guide, Sat - is - fied ful - ly I jour - ney on - ward In the foot-steps of the cru - ci - fied. (the cru - ci - fied.)
2. Be - side still wa - ters Je - sus leads me, And my strength He does re - store, He bids me lie down in green pas-tures, When I rest we jour-ney on once more. (yes, on once more.)
3. I know His good - ness and His mer - cy Shall my ev - 'ry step at-tend, Up - on the moun-tain or in the val - ley, I'll keep walk - ing with my dear-est Friend. (my dear-est Friend.)

Refrain

I'm walk-ing in the light of Je - sus' love, I'm walk-ing in the light of Je-sus' love. I've peace and joy di-vine,

WORDS: Virgie C. DeWitty
MUSIC: Virgie C. DeWitty
© 1958 by Virgie Carrington DeWitty. Used by permission.

Walking in the Light of Jesus' Love

for Je - sus' love is mine, I'm walk-ing in the light of His

love. (The light of His love.) Walk-ing, walk - ing,

walk-ing in the light of Je-sus' love. I've peace and joy di-vine

for Je - sus' love is mine; Oh, I'm walk-ing in the light of His

1 love. (The light of His love.)

2 love. (The light of His love.)

320   Grow Closer

And there is a friend that sticketh closer than a brother — Proverbs 18:24 KJV

Unison

1. There's a still, small voice say-ing to me: Clos-er,
2. Yes, I hear a voice plead-ing with me: Quiet-ly,

clos-er, grow clos-er to me; In a whis-pered tone nev-er
quiet-ly com-mune with me; Just steal a-way in

leaves me a-lone, Clos-er, clos-er, grow clos-er to Him.
se-cret and pray Quiet-ly, quiet-ly, come break bread with me.

Refrain

Oh, I want to hear ev-'ry mes-sage clear, Yes, I want ev-'ry
So I med-i-tate, then in si-lence wait, For the joy that

word to come through. ___ For if I make it in, I must
show-ers o'er me. ___ Yes, the Spir-it dwells there, when I

WORDS: Doris Akers
MUSIC: Doris Akers

Grow Closer

walk close to Him, Clos-er, clos-er, grow clos-er to Him.
meet God in prayer, Quiet-ly, quiet-ly, quiet mo-ments with Him.

Children of God 321

And they shall march every one on his ways — Joel 2:7 KJV

Ref. Chil-dren of God, we are march-ing to Zi - on. Chil-dren of
1. In my walk you can see me try - ing. In my
2. In my talk you can hear me try - ing. In my
3. In my prayer you can hear me try - ing. In my
4. Chris - tians, pray that we keep on march-ing. Chris - tians,

God, we are march-ing to Zi - on. Chil-dren of God, we are
walk you can see me try - ing. In my walk you can
talk you can hear me try - ing. In my talk you can
prayer you can hear me try - ing. In my prayer you can
pray that we keep on march-ing. Chris - tians, pray that we

march - ing to Zi - on, step by step all the way.
see me try - ing, step by step all the way.
hear me try - ing, step by step all the way.
hear me try - ing, step by step all the way.
keep on march - ing, step by step all the way.

WORDS: Anderson T. Dailey
MUSIC: Anderson T. Dailey

322 Trust and Obey

I waited patiently for the Lord...Thou art my help and my deliverer; make no tarrying, O my God — Psalm 40:1, 17 KJV

1. When we walk with the Lord In the light of His Word,
2. Not a shad-ow can rise, Not a cloud in the skies,
3. Not a bur-den we bear, Not a sor-row we share,
4. But we nev-er can prove The de-lights of His love
5. Then in fel-low-ship sweet We will sit at His feet,

What a glo-ry He sheds on our way! While we do His good
But His smile quick-ly drives it a-way; Not a doubt nor a
But our toil He doth rich-ly re-pay; Not a grief nor a
Un-til all on the al-tar we lay, For the fa-vor He
Or we'll walk by His side in the way; What He says we will

will He a-bides with us still, And with all who will
fear, Not a sigh nor a tear, Can a-bide while we
loss, Not a frown nor a cross, But is blest if we
shows And the joy He be-stows Are for them who will
do, Where He sends we will go — Nev-er fear, on-ly

Refrain

trust and o-bey. Trust and o-bey — For there's no oth-er
way To be hap-py in Je-sus But to trust and o-bey.

WORDS: John H. Sammis
MUSIC: Daniel B. Towner

TRUST AND OBEY

Thank You, Lord

323

Therefore will I give thanks unto Thee, O Lord — Psalm 18:49 KJV

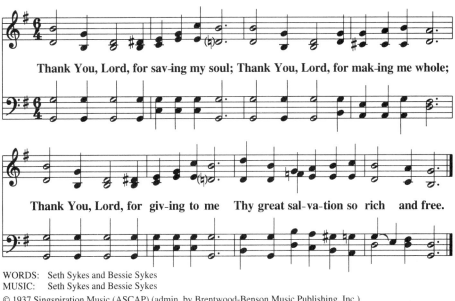

Thank You, Lord, for sav-ing my soul; Thank You, Lord, for mak-ing me whole;

Thank You, Lord, for giv-ing to me   Thy great sal-va-tion so rich   and free.

WORDS: Seth Sykes and Bessie Sykes
MUSIC: Seth Sykes and Bessie Sykes

Thank You, Lord

324

*And whatever ye shall ask in My name, that will I do,
that the Father may be glorifed in the Son — John 14:13 KJV*

Unison

1. Thank You,   Lord,   Thank You,   Lord,   Thank You,
2. Been so   good,   Been   so   good,   Been   so
3. Love You,   Lord,   Love You,   Lord,   Love You,

Lord.
good.
Lord.

I just want to thank   You,   Lord.

WORDS: Traditional
MUSIC: Traditional; arr. by J. Jefferson Cleveland and Verolga Nix

325 Count Your Blessings

Blessing I will bless thee, and multiplying I will multiply thee — Hebrews 6:14 KJV

1. When up-on life's bil-lows you are tem-pest tossed,
2. Are you ev-er bur-dened with a load of care?
3. When you look at oth-ers with their lands and gold,
4. So a-mid the con-flict, wheth-er great or small,

When you are dis-cour-aged, think-ing all is lost,
Does the cross seem heav-y you are called to bear?
Think that Christ has prom-ised you His wealth un-told;
Do not be dis-cour-aged – God is o-ver all;

Count your man-y bless-ings – name them one by one,
Count your man-y bless-ings – ev-ery doubt will fly,
Count your man-y bless-ings – mon-ey can-not buy,
Count your man-y bless-ings – an-gels will at-tend,

And it will sur-prise you what the Lord hath done.
And you will be sing-ing as the days go by.
Your re-ward in heav-en nor your home on high.
Help and com-fort give you to your jour-ney's end.

WORDS: Johnson Oatman, Jr.
MUSIC: Edwin O. Excell

BLESSINGS

Count Your Blessings

326   We Gather Together

Rejoice and praise God with a loud voice — Luke 19:37 KJV

1. We gath - er to - geth - er to ask the Lord's bless - ing, He
2. Be - side us to guide us, our God with us join - ing, Or -
3. We all do ex - tol Thee, Thou lead - er in bat - tle, And

chas - tens and has - tens His will to make known. The
dain - ing, main - tain - ing His king - dom di - vine; So
pray that Thou still our de - fend - er wilt be. Let

wick - ed op - press - ing now cease from dis - tress - ing, Sing
from the be - gin - ning the fight we were win - ning, Thou
Thy con - gre - ga - tion es - cape trib - u - la - tion; Thy

prais - es to His name, He for - gets not His own.
Lord, wast at our side: the glo - ry be Thine!
name be ev - er praised: O Lord, make us free! A - men.

WORDS: Netherlands folk song; trans. by Theodore Baker
MUSIC: Netherlands melody; arr. by Edward Kremser

KREMSER

Come, Ye Thankful People, Come 327

Enter into His gates with thanksgiving, and into His courts with praise:
be thankful unto Him, and bless His name — Psalm 100:4 KJV

1. Come, ye thank-ful   peo - ple, come – Raise the song of   har-vest home:
2. All   the world is   God's own field,   Fruit un - to His praise to yield:
3. For   the Lord our   God shall come   And shall take His   har-vest home:
4. E - ven so, Lord, quick-ly come   To Thy fi - nal har-vest home:

All   is safe-ly gath - ered in   Ere the win-ter storms be - gin.
Wheat and tares to - geth - er sewn, Un - to joy or   sor - row grown.
From His field shall in   that day All of - fens-es   purge a - way –
Gath - er Thou Thy peo - ple in,   Free from sor-row, free from sin;

God, our Mak - er, doth pro - vide For our wants to   be sup - plied:
First the blade and then the ear, Then the full corn shall ap - pear:
Give His an - gels charge at   last In   the fire the tares to   cast,
There, for - ev - er   pu - ri - fied, In   Thy pres-ence to a - bide:

Come to God's own tem - ple, come – Raise the song of har-vest home.
Lord of har-vest, grant that we Whole-some grain and pure may be.
But the fruit - ful ears to store In His gar - ner ev - er - more.
Come, with all Thine an - gels, come – Raise the glo-rious har-vest home.

WORDS: Henry Alford
MUSIC: George J. Elvey

ST. GEORGE'S WINDSOR

328 Every Day Is Thanksgiving

Let us come before His presence with thanksgiving – Psalm 95:2 KJV

Ev - 'ry day   is   a   day   of   thanks-giv-ing.

God's been so   good   to me;   Ev-'ry day He's bless-ing me.

Ev - 'ry day   is   a   day   of   thanks-giv-ing; Take the time to

glo - ri - fy   the Lord   to-day.

Fine   *Solo*

I

WORDS: Leonard Gregory Burks
MUSIC: Leonard Gregory Burks; transcribed by Michael L. Pickett
© 1988 Legre' Publications Company

Every Day Is Thanksgiving

329 My Tribute

Not unto us, O Lord, not unto us — Psalm 115:1 KJV

How can I say thanks for the things You have done for me —
Things so un-de-served, yet You give to prove Your love for me? The
voic-es of a mil-lion an-gels could not ex - press my grat-i -
tude — All that I am and ev-er hope to be, I owe it all to Thee.
To God be the glo - ry, To God be the glo - ry! To

My Tribute

God be the glo - ry for the things He has done. With His

blood He has saved me; With His pow'r He has raised me; To

Fine

God be the glo - ry For the things He has done. Just let me

live my life; Let it be pleas-ing, Lord, to Thee. And should I

D.S. al Fine

gain an-y praise, Let it go to Cal - va - ry. With His

330 Now Thank We All Our God

Praise ye the Lord. Praise God in His sanctuary:
praise Him in the firmament of His power – Psalm 150:1 KJV

1. Now thank we all our God, With heart and hands and voic - es,
2. O may this boun-teous God, Thru all our life be near us,
3. All praise and thanks to God The Fa - ther now be giv - en,

Who won-drous things hath done, In whom this world re - joic es;
With ev - er joy - ful hearts, And bless - ed peace to cheer us;
The Son and Him who reigns With Them in high-est heav - en;

Who from our moth-er's arms Hath blessed us on our way
And keep us in His grace, And guide us when per - plexed,
The one e - ter - nal God, Whom earth and heav'n a - dore;

With count-less gifts of love, And still is ours to - day.
And free us from all ills, In this world and the next.
For thus it was, is now, And shall be ev - er - more.

WORDS: Martin Rinkart; trans. by Catherine Winkworth
MUSIC: Johann Crüger

NUN DANKET

An Evening Prayer

331

And forgive us our sins;
for we also forgive every one that is indebted to us — Luke 11:4 KJV

1. If   I   have wound-ed an - y soul   to - day,   If
2. If   I   have ut - tered i - dle words or vain,   If
3. If   I   have been per-verse, or hard,   or cold,   If
4. For - give   the sins   I have con-fessed to Thee; For -

I   have caused one foot to   go   a - stray,   If
I   have turned a - side from want   or   pain,   Lest
I   have longed for shel - ter in   the fold,   When
give   the se - cret sins I   do   not see;   O

I   have walked in my own   will - ful way,
I   of - fend some oth - er thru   the strain,   Dear
Thou hast giv - en me some fort   to hold,
guide   me, love me, and my keep - er be.

Lord,   for - give! (for-give!) *(Inst. only)*   A - men. (A - men.)

WORDS: C. M. Battersby
MUSIC: Charles H. Gabriel

332   Sweet Hour of Prayer

When thou prayest, enter into thy closet — Matthew 6:6 KJV

1. Sweet hour of prayer, sweet hour of prayer, That calls me from a world of care And bids me at my Fa - ther's throne Make all my wants and wish - es known! In sea - sons of dis - tress and grief My soul has oft - en found re - lief, And

2. Sweet hour of prayer, sweet hour of prayer, Thy wings shall my pe - ti - tion bear To Him whose truth and faith - ful - ness En - gage the wait - ing soul to bless; And since He bids me seek His face, Be - lieve His Word and trust His grace, I'll

3. Sweet hour of prayer, sweet hour of prayer, May I thy con - so - la - tion share, Till from Mount Pis - gah's loft - y height I view my home and take my flight: This robe of flesh I'll drop, and rise To seize the ev - er - last - ing prize, And

WORDS: William W. Walford
MUSIC: William B. Bradbury

SWEET HOUR

Sweet Hour of Prayer

oft es-caped the tempt-er's snare By thy re-turn, sweet hour of prayer.
cast on Him my ev-'ry care, And wait for thee, sweet hour of prayer.
shout, while pass-ing thru the air, "Fare-well, fare-well, sweet hour of prayer!"

Thy Peace for Us   333

If so be that the Spirit of God dwell in you — Romans 8:9 KJV

Let Thy Ho - ly Spir - it dwell in us, Thy
Take our lives, our sins and our bur - dens; Thy

1 will for us each day.   2 peace for

us, we pray. ___   A - men.   A - men.

WORDS: E. D. Thompson
MUSIC: E. D. Thompson

334 The Beautiful Garden of Prayer

I give myself unto prayer — Psalm 109:4 KJV

1. There's a gar-den where Je-sus is wait-ing, There's a
2. There's a gar-den where Je-sus is wait-ing, And I
3. There's a gar-den where Je-sus is wait-ing, And He

place that is won-drous-ly fair, For it glows with the light of His
go, with my bur-den and care, Just to learn from His lips words of
bids you to come meet Him there, Just to bow and re-ceive a new

pres-ence – 'Tis the beau-ti-ful gar-den of prayer.
com-fort – In the beau-ti-ful gar-den of prayer.
bless-ing – In the beau-ti-ful gar-den of prayer.

Refrain

O the beau-ti-ful gar-den, the gar-den of prayer, O the

beau-ti-ful gar-den of prayer! There my Sav-ior a-waits, and He

WORDS: Eleanor Allen Schroll
MUSIC: James H. Fillmore

The Beautiful Garden of Prayer

o-pens the gates To the beau-ti-ful gar-den of prayer.

Lord, I'm Coming Home   335

I will set out and go back to my father — Luke 15:18 NIV

1. I've wan-dered far a-way from God – Now I'm com-ing home;
2. I've wast-ed man-y pre-cious years – Now I'm com-ing home;
3. I've tired of sin and stray-ing, Lord – Now I'm com-ing home;
4. My soul is sick, my heart is sore – Now I'm com-ing home;

The paths of sin too long I've trod – Lord, I'm com-ing home.
I now re-pent with bit-ter tears – Lord, I'm com-ing home.
I'll trust Thy love, be-lieve Thy word – Lord, I'm com-ing home.
My strength re-new, my hope re-store – Lord, I'm com-ing home.

Refrain

Com-ing home, com-ing home, Nev-er-more to roam;

O-pen now Thine arms of love – Lord, I'm com-ing home.

WORDS: William J. Kirkpatrick   COMING HOME
MUSIC: William J. Kirkpatrick

336 I Am Praying for You

We give thanks to God and the Father of our Lord Jesus Christ,
praying always for you — Colossians 1:3 KJV

1. __ I have a Sav - ior, He's plead - ing in glo - ry,
2. __ I have a Fa - ther; to me He has giv - en
3. __ I have a robe: 'tis re - splen - dent in white - ness,
4. When Je - sus has found you, tell oth - ers the sto - ry,

A dear, lov - ing Sav - ior, though earth - friends be few;
A hope for e - ter - ni - ty, bless - ed and true;
A - wait - ing in glo - ry my won - der - ing view;
That my lov - ing Sav - ior is your Sav - ior, too;

And now He is watch - ing in ten - der - ness o'er me,
And soon will He call me to meet Him in heav - en,
Oh, when I re - ceive it all shin - ing in bright - ness,
Then pray that your Sav - ior may bring them to glo - ry,

And, oh, that my Sav - ior were your Sav - ior, too.
But, oh, that He'd let me bring you with me, too!
Dear friend, could I see you re - ceiv - ing one, too!
And prayer will be an - swered – 'twas an - swered for you!

WORDS: S. O'Malley Cluff
MUSIC: Ira D. Sankey

INTERCESSION

I Am Praying for You

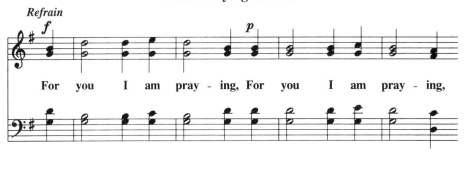

For you I am pray - ing, For you I am pray - ing,

For you I am pray - ing, I'm pray - ing for you.

For this reason I kneel before the Father, from whom his whole family in heaven and on earth derives its name. I pray that out of his glorious riches he may strengthen you with power through his Spirit in your inner being, so that Christ may dwell in your hearts through faith. And I pray that you, being rooted and established in love, may have power, together with all the saints, to grasp how wide and long and high and deep is the love of Christ, and to know this love that surpasses knowledge — that you may be filled to the measure of all the fullness of God. Now to him who is able to do immeasurably more than all we ask or imagine, according to his power that is at work within us, to him be glory in the church and in Christ Jesus throughout all generations, for ever and ever! Amen. (Adapted from Ephesians 3:14-21 KJV)

337 When I Kneel Down to Pray

Lord, teach us to pray — Luke 11:1 KJV

Unison or 2-part

1. Some-how the Sav - ior seems a lit - tle
2. A se - cret place of qui - et med - i -
3. I tar - ry there with Christ a lit - tle

near - er, When I kneel down to
ta - tion, When I kneel down to
long - er, When I kneel down to

pray, And fel - low - ship with Him a lit - tle
pray, In - creas - es all the joy of that re -
pray, And rise to face the world a lit - tle

dear - er, When I kneel down to
la - tion, When I kneel down to
strong - er, When I kneel down to

MUSIC: A. H. Ackley
MUSIC: B. D. Ackley

When I Kneel Down to Pray

338 My Mother's Prayer

For this child I prayed ... as long as he liveth
he shall be lent to the Lord — 1 Samuel 1:27-28 KJV

1. I nev - er can for - get the day I
2. I nev - er can for - get the voice That
3. Tho' years have gone, I can't for - get Those
4. I nev - er can for - get the hour I

heard my moth - er kind - ly say, "You're leav - ing now my
al - ways made my heart re - joice; Tho' I have wan - dered
words of love – I hear them yet; I see her by the
felt the Sav - ior's cleans-ing pow'r; My sin and guilt He

ten - der care; Re - mem-ber, child, your moth-er's prayer."
God knows where, Still I re - mem - ber moth-er's prayer.
old arm chair, My moth-er dear, in hum - ble prayer.
can-celled there, 'Twas there He an - swered moth-er's prayer.

Refrain

1.-3. When - e'er I think of her so dear, I
4. Oh, praise the Lord for sav - ing grace! We'll

WORDS: J. W. Van DeVenter
MUSIC: W. S. Weeden

My Mother's Prayer

feel her an - gel spir - it near; A voice comes float - ing
meet up yon - der face to face, The home a - bove to -

on the air, Re - mind-ing me of moth-er's prayer.
geth-er share, In an - swer to my moth-er's prayer. A - men.

And she was in bitterness of soul, and prayed unto the Lord, and wept sore. And she vowed a vow, and said, "O Lord of hosts, if thou wilt indeed look on the affliction of thine handmaid, and remember me, and not forget thine handmaid, but wilt give unto thine handmaid a man child, then I will give him unto the Lord all the days of his life, and there shall no razor come upon his head." And it came to pass, as she continued praying before the Lord, that Eli marked her mouth. Now Hannah, she spake in her heart; only her lips moved, but her voice was not heard; therefore Eli thought she had been drunken. And Eli said unto her, "How long wilt thou be drunken? Put away thy wine from thee." And Hannah answered and said, "No, my lord, I am a woman of a sorrowful spirit: I have drunk neither wine nor strong drink, but have poured out my soul before the Lord. Count not thine handmaid for a daughter of Belial: for out of the abundance of my complaint and grief have I spoken hitherto." Then Eli answered and said, "Go in peace: and the God of Israel grant thee thy petition that thou hast asked of him." And she said, "Let thine handmaid find grace in thy sight." So the woman went her way, and did eat, and her countenance was no more sad. And they rose up in the morning early, and worshipped before the Lord, and returned, and came to their house to Ramah: and Elkanah knew Hannah his wife; and the Lord remembered her. Wherefore it came to pass, when the time was come about after Hannah had conceived, that she bare a son, and called his name Samuel, saying, "Because I have asked him of the Lord." (1 Samuel 1:10-20 KJV)

339 Just a Little Talk with Jesus

Hear my prayer, O Lord; give ear to my supplications — Psalm 143:1 KJV

1. I once was lost in sin but Je-sus took me in, And
2. Some-times my path seems drear, with-out a ray of cheer, And
3. I may have doubts and fears, my eyes be filled with tears, But

then a lit-tle light from heav-en filled my soul; It
then a cloud of doubt may hide the light of day; The
Je-sus is a friend who watch-es day and night; I

bathed my heart in love and wrote my name a-bove, And
mists of sin may rise and hide the star-ry skies, But
go to Him in prayer, He knows my ev-'ry care, And

Refrain

just a lit-tle talk with Je-sus made me whole.
just a lit-tle talk with Je-sus clears the way. Now let us
just a lit-tle talk with Je-sus makes it right.

WORDS: Cleavant Derricks
MUSIC: Cleavant Derricks

Just a Little Talk with Jesus

340 I Must Tell Jesus

Ask and it shall be given you — Matthew 7:7 KJV

1. I must tell Je - sus all of my tri - als, I can-not
2. I must tell Je - sus all of my trou - bles, He is a
3. Tempt-ed and tried, I need a great Sav - ior, One who can
4. O how the world to e - vil al - lures me! O how my

bear these bur-dens a - lone; In my dis-tress He kind-ly will
kind, com - pas-sion-ate Friend; If I but ask Him, He will de -
help my bur-dens to bear; I must tell Je - sus, I must tell
heart is tempt-ed to sin! I must tell Je - sus, and He will

help me, He ev - er loves and cares for His own.
liv - er, Make of my trou - bles quick-ly an end.
Je - sus, He all my cares and sor-rows will share.
help me O - ver the world the vic - t'ry to win.

Refrain

I must tell Je - sus! I must tell Je - sus! I can-not

WORDS: Elisha A. Hoffman
MUSIC: Elisha A. Hoffman

ORWIGSBURG

I Must Tell Jesus

bear my bur-dens a - lone; I must tell Je - sus! I must tell

Je - sus! Je - sus can help me, Je - sus a - lone.

Lead Me, Lord

341

Make Thy way straight before my face — Psalm 5:8 KJV

Lead me, Lord, lead me in Thy right-eous-ness,

Make Thy way plain be - fore my face. A - men.

WORDS: Psalm 5:8
MUSIC: Samuel Sebastian Wesley

LEAD ME, LORD

342 I Found the Answer

I will call upon Thee: for Thou wilt answer me — Psalm 86:7 KJV

1. I was weak and wea - ry, I had gone a - stray,
2. I was sad and lone - ly, all my hopes were gone,
3. Keep your Bi - ble with you, read it ev - 'ry day,

Walk - ing in the dark - ness, I could - n't find my way.
Days were long and drea - ry, I could - n't car - ry on.
Al - ways count your bless - ings and al - ways stop to pray.

Then a light came shin - ing to lead me from des - pair,
Then I found the cour - age to keep my head up high,
Learn to keep be - liev - ing and faith will see you thru,

All my sins for - giv - en, and I was free from care.
Once a - gain I'm hap - py, and here's the rea - son why:
Seek to know con - tent - ment, and it will come to you.

WORDS: Johnny Lange
MUSIC: Johnny Lange

I Found the Answer

343 I Asked the Lord

Ask anything in My name, I will do it — John 14:14 KJV

I asked the Lord to com-fort me when things were-n't go - ing my way, He said to me, "I will com - fort you, and lift your cares a - way." I asked the Lord to walk with me, when dark - ness was all that I knew, He said to me, "Nev-er be a-fraid, for I will see you through." I

WORDS: Johnny Lange and Jimmy Duncan
MUSIC: Johnny Lange and Jimmy Duncan

I Asked the Lord

344 The Lord's Prayer

Hallowed be Thy name — Matthew 6:9 KJV

Our Fa-ther, who art in heav'n, hal-low-ed be Thy name. Thy king-dom come, Thy will be done on earth, as it is in heav'n. Give us this day our dai-ly bread. And for-give us our tres-pass-es, as we for-give those who tres-pass a-gainst us. And lead us not in-to temp-ta-tion,

WORDS: Matthew 6:9-13; 1 Chronicles 29:11
MUSIC: Lowell Mason

The Lord's Prayer

but de - liv - er us from e - vil; for Thine is the king-dom, and the

pow-er, and the glo-ry, for - ev - er and ev - er. A - men.

"Be careful not to do your 'acts of righteousness' before men, to be seen by them. If you do, you will have no reward from your Father in heaven. "So when you give to the needy, do not announce it with trumpets, as the hypocrites do in the synagogues and on the streets, to be honored by men. I tell you the truth, they have received their reward in full. But when you give to the needy, do not let your left hand know what your right hand is doing, so that your giving may be in secret. Then your Father, who sees what is done in secret, will reward you. "And when you pray, do not be like the hypocrites, for they love to pray standing in the synagogues and on the street corners to be seen by men. I tell you the truth, they have received their reward in full. But when you pray, go into your room, close the door and pray to your Father, who is unseen. Then your Father, who sees what is done in secret, will reward you. And when you pray, do not keep on babbling like pagans, for they think they will be heard because of their many words. Do not be like them, for your Father knows what you need before you ask him. "This, then, is how you should pray." (Adapted from Matthew 6:1-9 KJV)

345 How Long Has It Been?

Give ear to my words, O Lord — Psalm 5:1 KJV

1. How long has it been since you talked with the Lord And told Him your heart's hidden secrets? ___ How long since you prayed? How long since you stayed On your knees till the light shone through? ___ How long has it been since your mind felt at ease? How long since your heart knew no

2. How long has it been since you knelt by your bed And prayed to the Lord up in heaven? ___ How long since you knew that He'd answer you, And would keep you the long night through? ___ How long has it been since you woke with the dawn, And felt that the day's worth the

How Long Has It Been?

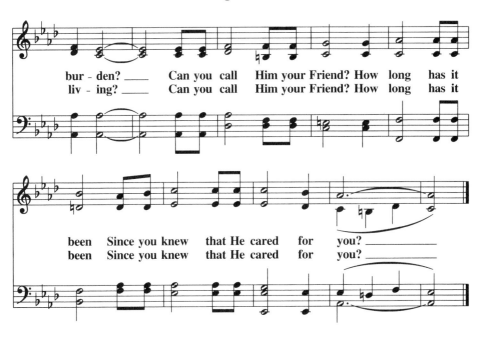

bur - den? ____ Can you call Him your Friend? How long has it
liv - ing? ____ Can you call Him your Friend? How long has it

been Since you knew that He cared for you? ____
been Since you knew that He cared for you? ____

Kum Ba Yah   346

And the Lord, whom ye seek, shall suddenly come — Malachi 3:1 KJV

Unison

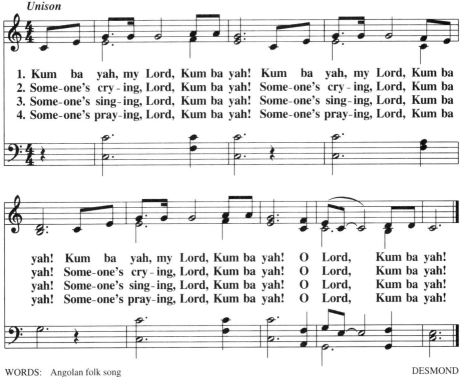

1. Kum ba yah, my Lord, Kum ba yah! Kum ba yah, my Lord, Kum ba
2. Some-one's cry-ing, Lord, Kum ba yah! Some-one's cry-ing, Lord, Kum ba
3. Some-one's sing-ing, Lord, Kum ba yah! Some-one's sing-ing, Lord, Kum ba
4. Some-one's pray-ing, Lord, Kum ba yah! Some-one's pray-ing, Lord, Kum ba

yah! Kum ba yah, my Lord, Kum ba yah! O Lord, Kum ba yah!
yah! Some-one's cry-ing, Lord, Kum ba yah! O Lord, Kum ba yah!
yah! Some-one's sing-ing, Lord, Kum ba yah! O Lord, Kum ba yah!
yah! Some-one's pray-ing, Lord, Kum ba yah! O Lord, Kum ba yah!

WORDS: Angolan folk song
MUSIC: Angolan folk song

DESMOND

347   Let the Words of My Mouth

Let the words of my mouth...be acceptable in Thy sight — Psalm 19:14 KJV

Let the words of my mouth, Let the words of my mouth And the med-i-ta-tions of my heart be ac-cept-a-ble in Thy sight; Wilt Thou teach me how to serve Thee? Wilt Thou teach me how to pray?

Our Father who art in heaven, hallowed be   Thy   name.
Give us this day our   dai - ly   bread:
Lead us not into temptation, but deliver us   from   e - vil:

Thy kingdom come: Thy will be done on earth as it is in heav-en.
Forgive us our tresspasses, as we forgive those who tres-pass a-gainst us.
For Thine is the Kingdom, and the
     power, and the glory, for-ev - er and ev - er. A - men.

WORDS: Psalm 19:14; C. E. Leslie; and Matthew 6:9-13
MUSIC: C. E. Leslie

Revive Us Again

348

Renew them again unto repentance — Hebrews 6:6 KJV

1. We praise Thee, O God, for the Son of Thy love,
2. We praise Thee, O God, for Thy Spir - it of light,
3. All glo - ry and praise to the Lamb that was slain,
4. Re - vive us a - gain, fill each heart with Thy love;

For Je - sus who died and is now gone a - bove.
Who has shown us our Sav - ior and scat - tered our night.
Who has borne all our sins and has cleansed ev - 'ry stain.
May each soul be re - kin - dled with fire from a - bove.

Refrain

Hal - le - lu - jah, Thine the glo - ry! Hal - le - lu - jah, A - men!

Hal - le - lu - jah, Thine the glo - ry! Re - vive us a - gain.

WORDS: William P. Mackay
MUSIC: John J. Husband

REVIVE US AGAIN

349 Send a Great Revival in My Soul

Though I walk in the midst of trouble, thou wilt revive me — Psalm 138:7 KJV

Send a great re-viv-al in my soul,
soul, in my soul,

Send a great re-viv-al in my soul,
soul, in my soul,

Let the Ho-ly Spir-it come and take con-trol, And

send a great re-viv-al in my soul.
soul, in my soul.

WORDS: B. B. McKinney
MUSIC: B. B. McKinney

TRAVIS AVENUE

There Shall Be Showers of Blessing 350

I will make them and the places all around My hill a blessing; and I will cause showers to come down in their season; there shall be showers of blessing — Ezekiel 34:26 KJV

1. "There shall be show-ers of bless-ing" – This is the prom-ise of love;
2. "There shall be show-ers of bless-ing" – Pre-cious re - viv - ing a - gain;
3. "There shall be show-ers of bless-ing" – Send them up - on us, O Lord;
4. "There shall be show-ers of bless-ing" – O that to - day they might fall,

There shall be sea - sons re - fresh - ing, Sent from the Sav - ior a - bove.
O - ver the hills and the val - leys Sound of a - bun-dance of rain.
Grant to us now a re - fresh - ing, Come and now hon - or Thy Word.
Now as to God we're con - fess - ing, Now as on Je - sus we call!

Refrain

Show - ers of bless - ing, Show-ers of bless-ing we need;
Show - ers, show-ers of bless - ing,

Mer - cy-drops 'round us are fall - ing, But for the show-ers we plead.

WORDS: Daniel W. Whittle
MUSIC: James McGranahan

SHOWERS OF BLESSING

351   Cheerful Giving

Not grudgingly, or of necessity: for God loveth a cheerful giver — 2 Corinthians 9:7   KJV

1. Give as the Lord hath pros-pered thee, Give, give to the Lord;
2. Give to the poor a - long the way, Give, give to the Lord;
3. Give tho' so poor thy gift may seem, Give, give to the Lord;

Give with a will - ing mind and free, Give, give to the Lord;
Give to the heath-en far a - way, Give, give to the Lord;
Give but the cup in Je - sus' name, Give, give to the Lord;

He hath sup-plied thee o'er and o'er, Blessed thee in bas - ket and in store,
Give to His need - y as they cry, Give to His peo - ple ere they die,
Cheer-ful then give the good thou hast, Fear - less thy bread on wa-ters cast,

Prom-ised to fill thee more and more, Thy gra - cious Lord.
Give to His gos - pel that it fly, O give, give, give.
It will re-turn to thee at last In har - vests great.

WORDS: P. H.
MUSIC: J. H. F.

Cheerful Giving

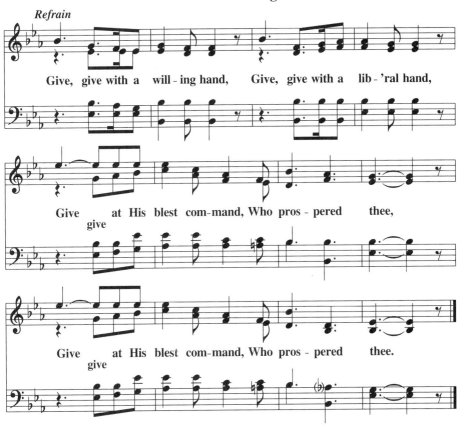

Give, give with a will-ing hand, Give, give with a lib-'ral hand,

Give at His blest com-mand, Who pros-pered thee,
give

Give at His blest com-mand, Who pros-pered thee.
give

We Give Thee But Thine Own   352

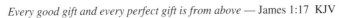

Every good gift and every perfect gift is from above — James 1:17 KJV

We give Thee but Thine own, What-e'er the gift may be; All

that we have is Thine a-lone, A trust, O Lord, from Thee. A-men.

WORDS: William W. How
MUSIC: Joseph Barnby

ST. ANDREW

353 Trust, Try, and Prove Me

"Prove Me now" … saith the Lord — Malachi 3:10 KJV

1. Bring ye all the tithes in-to the store-house,
2. When my wa-v'ring faith in tri-al fal-ters,
3. I have yield-ed Him my life for-ev-er,

All your mon-ey, tal-ents, time and love;
When His guid-ing hand I can-not see,
All I am, or have, or hope to be;

Con-se-crate them all up-on the al-tar,
Then in won-drous love and ten-der mer-cy,
Naught on earth my hold on Him can sev-er,

While your Sav-ior from a-bove speaks sweet-ly,
Thru His Word He says to me, My child, just
While I hear Him say to me, My child, just

Refrain

Trust Me,
Trust Me, yes, then

try Me, Prove Me, saith the Lord of hosts, And see if a
try Me, prove Me,

WORDS: Lida S. Leech
MUSIC: Lida S. Leech
GIVING

Trust, Try and Prove Me

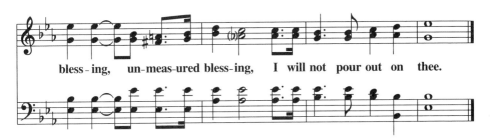

bless-ing, un-meas-ured bless-ing, I will not pour out on thee.

That All May Know Him 354

Show me Thy ways, O Lord; teach me Thy paths — Psalm 25:4 KJV

1. That all may know Him, that all may know Him, I'll
2. That all may love Him, that all may love Him, I'll
3. That all may serve Him, that all may serve Him, I'll

give my tithes and gifts to make it so; That all may know Him, that all may
give my time and work to make it so; That all may love Him, that all may
give my life, my all to make it so; That all may serve Him, that all may

know Him, (know Him,) Wher - ev - er Je - sus leads me I will go.
love Him, (love Him,) Wher - ev - er Je - sus leads me I will go.
serve Him, (serve Him,) Wher - ev - er Je - sus leads me I will go.

WORDS: Bob Entrekin
MUSIC: Bob Entrekin
© 1961 by Bob Entrekin. All rights reserved. Used by permission.

355   Bless Thou the Gifts

Be glad and rejoice for the Lord will do great things — Joel 2:21 KJV

Bless Thou the gifts our hands have brought; Bless
Thou the work our hearts have planned; Ours is the faith, the
will, the thought; The rest, O God, is in Thy hand. A - men.

WORDS: Samuel Longfellow
MUSIC: Robert Schumann

CANONBURY

356   All Things Come of Thee

All things come of Thee and of Thine own have we given Thee — 1 Chronicles 29:14 KJV

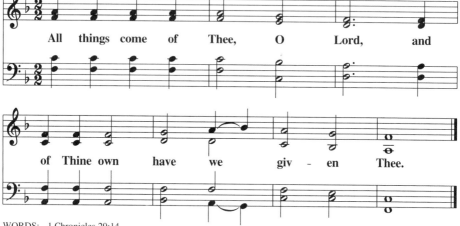

All things come of Thee, O Lord, and
of Thine own have we giv - en Thee.

WORDS: 1 Chronicles 29:14
MUSIC: Attr. to Ludwig van Beethoven

Something for Thee

357

I will bless the Lord at all times:
His praise shall continually be in my mouth — Psalm 34:1 KJV

1. Sav - ior, Thy dy - ing love Thou gav - est me,
2. At the blest mer - cy seat, Plead - ing for me,
3. Give me a faith - ful heart, Like - ness to Thee,
4. All that I am and have – Thy gifts so free –

Nor should I aught with-hold, Dear Lord, from Thee:
My fee - ble faith looks up, Je - sus, to Thee:
That each de - part - ing day Hence - forth may see
In joy, in grief, thru life, Dear Lord, for Thee!

In love my soul would bow, My heart ful - fill its vow,
Help me the cross to bear, Thy won-drous love de - clare,
Some work of love be - gun, Some deed of kind - ness done,
And when Thy face I see, My ran-somed soul shall be,

Some of - f'ring bring Thee now, Some - thing for Thee.
Some song to raise, or prayer, Some - thing for Thee.
Some wan-d'rer sought and won, Some - thing for Thee.
Thru all e - ter - ni - ty, Some - thing for Thee.

WORDS: Sylvanus D. Phelps
MUSIC: Robert Lowry

SOMETHING FOR JESUS

358 Let Us Break Bread Together

Ye do show the Lord's death till He come — 1 Corinthians 11:26 KJV

Unison

1. Let us break bread to-geth-er on our knees. _____
2. Let us drink the cup to-geth-er on our knees. _____
3. Let us praise God to-geth-er on our knees. _____

Let us break bread to-geth-er on our knees. _____
Let us drink the cup to-geth-er on our knees. _____
Let us praise God to-geth-er on our knees. _____

When I fall on my knees, with my face to the ris-ing
When I fall on my knees, with my face to the ris-ing
When I fall on my knees, with my face to the ris-ing

sun, O Lord, have mer-cy on me. _____
sun, O Lord, have mer-cy on me. _____
sun, O Lord, have mer-cy on me. _____

WORDS: Traditional
MUSIC: Traditional

BREAK BREAD

Bread of Life

359

He shall feed His flock like a shepherd — Isaiah 40:11 KJV

1. Here at Thy ta - ble, Lord, This sa - cred hour,
2. Sit at the feast, dear Lord, Break Thou the bread;
3. So shall our life of faith Be full, be sweet;
4. Come then, O ho - ly Christ, Feed us, we pray;

O let us feel Thee near, In lov - ing pow'r;
Fill Thou the cup that brings Life to the dead:
And we shall find our strength For each day meet:
Touch with Thy pierc - ed hand Each com - mon day;

Call - ing our thoughts a - way From self and sin,
That we may find in Thee, Com - fort and peace;
Fed by Thy liv - ing bread, All hun - ger past,
Mak - ing this earth - ly life Full of Thy grace,

As to Thy ban - quet hall We en - ter in.
And from all sor - row win A full re - lease.
We shall be sat - is - fied, And saved at last.
Till in the home of heav'n We find our place. A - men.

WORDS: May P. Hoyt
MUSIC: William F. Sherwin

BREAD OF LIFE

360   A Christian Home

Teach me, O Lord, the way of Thy statutes — Psalm 119:33 KJV

1. O give us homes built firm up-on the Sav-ior, _____
2. O give us homes with god-ly fa-thers, moth-ers, _____
3. O give us homes where Christ is Lord and Mas-ter, _____
4. O Lord, our God, our homes are Thine for-ev-er! _____

Where Christ is Head and Coun-sel-lor and Guide; _____
Who al-ways place their hope and trust in Him; _____
The Bi-ble read, the pre-cious hymns still sung; _____
We trust to Thee their prob-lems, toil, and care; _____

Where ev-'ry child is taught His love and fa-vor _____
Whose ten-der pa-tience tur-moil nev-er both-ers, _____
Where prayer comes first in peace or in dis-as-ter, _____
Their bonds of love no en-e-my can sev-er _____

And gives His heart to Christ, the cru-ci-fied: _____
Whose calm and cour-age trou-ble can-not dim; _____
And praise is nat-ural speech to ev-'ry tongue; _____
If Thou art al-ways Lord and Mas-ter there: _____

WORDS: Barbara B. Hart   FINLANDIA
MUSIC: Jean Sibelius; arr. from *The Hymnal*, 1933

A Christian Home

How sweet to know that tho' his foot-steps wa-ver
A home where each finds joy in serv-ing oth-ers,
Where moun-tains move be-fore a faith that's vast-er,
Be Thou the cen - ter of our least en-deav-or;

His faith-ful Lord is walk-ing by his side!
And love still shines, tho' days be dark and grim.
And Christ suf - fi - cient is for old and young.
Be Thou our Guest, our hearts and homes to share.

But Samuel ministered before the Lord, being a child, girded with a linen ephod. Moreover his mother made him a little coat, and brought it to him from year to year, when she came up with her husband to offer the yearly sacrifice. And Eli blessed Elkanah and his wife, and said, "The Lord give thee seed of this woman for the loan which is lent to the Lord." And they went unto their own home. And the Lord visited Hannah, so that she conceived, and bare three sons and two daughters. And the child Samuel grew before the Lord. (1 Samuel 2:18-21 KJV)

361 O Perfect Love, All Human Thought Transcending

But I speak concerning Christ and the church — Ephesians 5:32 KJV

1. O per-fect Love, all hu-man thought tran-scend-ing,
2. O per-fect Life, be Thou their full as-sur-ance
3. Grant them the joy which bright-ens earth-ly sor-row;

Low-ly we kneel in prayer be-fore Thy throne,
Of ten-der char-i-ty and stead-fast faith,
Grant them the peace which calms all earth-ly strife,

That theirs may be the love which knows no end-ing,
Of pa-tient hope and qui-et, brave en-dur-ance,
And to life's day the glo-rious un-known mor-row

Whom Thou for-ev-er-more dost join in one.
With child-like trust that fears no pain nor death.
That dawns up-on e-ter-nal love and life. A-men.

WORDS: Dorothy B. Gurney
MUSIC: Joseph Barnby

O PERFECT LOVE

O How I Love Jesus

362

As the Father hath loved Me, so have I loved you: continue ye in My love — John 15:9 KJV

1. There is a name I love to hear, I love to sing its worth;
2. It tell me of a Sav-ior's love Who died to set me free;
3. It tells me what my Fa-ther hath In store for ev-'ry day,
4. It tells of One whose lov-ing heart Can feel my deep-est woe,

It sounds like mu-sic in mine ear, The sweet-est name on earth.
It tells me of His pre-cious blood, The sin-ner's per-fect plea.
And tho' I tread a dark-some path, Yields sun-shine all the way.
Who in each sor-row bears a part, that none can bear be-low.

Refrain

O, how I love Je-sus, O, how I love Je-sus,

O, how I love Je-sus, Be-cause He first loved me!

WORDS: Frederick Whitfield
MUSIC: American Melody

O HOW I LOVE JESUS

363 It's Wonderful to Live for Jesus

For to me to live is Christ — Philippians 1:21 KJV

1. It's won-der-ful to walk with Je-sus each and ev-'ry day. It's won-der-ful to talk with Je-sus all a-long the way. It's won-der-ful to trust in Je-sus. He'll make your joys com-

2. It's won-der-ful to real-ly serve Him each and ev-'ry day. It's won-der-ful to sing His prais-es all a-long the way. It's won-der-ful to trust in Je-sus. Your ev-'ry need He'll

WORDS: Rev. Charles A. Craig, Jr.
MUSIC: Rev. Charles A. Craig, Jr.; arr. by R. H. GoodPasteur

It's Wonderful to Live for Jesus

364 Since Jesus Came Into My Heart

If any man be in Christ, he is a new creature — 2 Corinthians 5:17 KJV

1. What a won-der-ful change in my life has been wrought Since
2. I have ceased from my wan-d'ring and go-ing a-stray, Since
3. I'm pos-sessed of a hope that is stead-fast and sure, Since
4. There's a light in the val-ley of death now for me, Since
5. I shall go there to dwell in that Cit-y I know, Since

Je-sus came in-to my heart; I have light in my soul for which
Je-sus came in-to my heart; And my sins which were man-y are
Je-sus came in-to my heart; And no dark clouds of doubt now my
Je-sus came in-to my heart; And the gates of the Cit-y be-
Je-sus came in-to my heart; And I'm hap-py, so hap-py as

long I have sought, Since Je-sus came in-to my heart.
all washed a-way, Since Je-sus came in-to my heart.
path-way ob-scure, Since Je-sus came in-to my heart.
yond I can see, Since Je-sus came in-to my heart.
on-ward I go, Since Je-sus came in-to my heart.

Refrain

Since Je-sus came in-to my heart, Since
Since Je-sus came in, came in-to my heart, Since

WORDS: R. H. McDaniel
MUSIC: Charles H. Gabriel

McDANIEL

Since Jesus Came Into My Heart

Je-sus came in-to my heart; Floods of joy o'er my soul like the
Je-sus came in, came in-to my heart;

sea bil-lows roll, Since Je - sus came in - to my heart.

I've Got Peace Like a River 365

Now the Lord of peace Himself give you peace always — 2 Thessalonians 3:16 KJV

1. I've got peace like a riv-er, I've got peace like a riv-er, I've got
2. I've got love like a riv-er, I've got love like a riv-er, I've got
3. I've got joy like a riv-er, I've got joy like a riv-er, I've got

peace like a riv-er in my soul. ___ I've got riv-er in my soul. ___
love like a riv-er in my soul. ___ I've got riv-er in my soul. ___
joy like a riv-er in my soul. ___ I've got riv-er in my soul. ___

WORDS: African-American spiritual
MUSIC: African-American spiritual

PEACE LIKE A RIVER

366   We're Marching to Zion

And the ransomed of the Lord shall return, and come to Zion with songs — Isaiah 35:10 KJV

1. Come, we that love the Lord, And let our joys be
2. Let those re - fuse to sing Who nev - er knew our
3. The hill of Zi - on yields A thou - sand sa - cred
4. Then let our songs a - bound, And ev - 'ry tear be

known, Join in a song with sweet ac - cord, Join
God; But chil - dren of the heav'n - ly King, But
sweets Be - fore we reach the heav'n - ly fields, Be -
dry; We're march - ing thru Im - man - uel's ground, We're

in a song with sweet ac - cord, And thus sur -
chil - dren of the heav'n - ly King, May speak their
fore we reach the heav'n - ly fields, Or walk the
march - ing thru Im - man - uel's ground, To fair - er

1. And thus sur-round the

round the throne, And thus sur-round the throne.
joys a - broad, May speak their joys a - broad.
gold - en streets, Or walk the gold - en streets.
worlds on high, To fair - er worlds on high.

throne, And thus sur - round the throne.

WORDS: Isaac Watts; refrain by Robert Lowry
MUSIC: Robert Lowry

MARCHING TO ZION

We're Marching to Zion

Refrain

We're march - ing to Zi - on,   Beau - ti-ful, beau - ti-ful Zi - on;
We're march-ing on   to   Zi - on,

We're march-ing up-ward to Zi - on, The beau-ti-ful cit-y of God.
Zi - on, Zi - on,

Come, We That Love the Lord   367

I will sing of the mercies of the Lord forever — Psalm 89:1 KJV

1. Come, we that love the Lord,   And let our joys be known; Join
2. Let those re - fuse to sing   Who nev - er knew our God; But
3. The hill of Zi - on yields   A thou - sand sa - cred sweets Be -
4. Then let our songs a - bound   And ev - 'ry tear be dry; We're

in a song with sweet ac - cord, And thus sur - round the throne.
chil - dren of the heav'n - ly King May speak their joys a - broad.
fore we reach the heav'n - ly fields Or walk the gold - en streets.
march-ing thru Em - man-uel's ground To fair - er worlds on high.

WORDS: Isaac Watts   ST. THOMAS
MUSIC: Aaron Williams

368 Sunshine in My Soul

For God, who commanded the light to shine out of darkness,
hath shined in our hearts — 2 Corinthinas 4:6 KJV

1. There is sun - shine in my soul to - day, More glo - ri - ous and bright Than glows in an - y earth - ly sky, For Je - sus is my light.
2. There is mu - sic in my soul to - day, A car - ol to my King, And Je - sus, lis - ten - ing, can hear The songs I can - not sing.
3. There is mu - sic in my soul to - day, For when the Lord is near, The dove of peace sings in my heart, The flow'rs of grace ap - pear.
4. There is glad - ness in my soul to - day, And hope and praise and love For bless - ings which He gives me now, For joys "laid up" a - bove.

Refrain

O there's sun - shine, bless - ed sun - shine,
O there's sun - shine in my soul, bless - ed sun - shine in my soul,

WORDS: Eliza E. Hewitt
MUSIC: John R. Sweney

SUNSHINE

Sunshine in My Soul

When the peace - ful, hap - py mo-ments roll; When
hap - py mo-ments roll;
Je - sus shows His smil - ing face, There is sun-shine in my soul.

The Lord is my light and my salvation; whom shall I fear? The Lord is the strength of my life; of whom shall I be afraid? When the wicked, even mine enemies and my foes, came upon me to eat up my flesh, they stumbled and fell. Though an host should encamp against me, my heart shall not fear: though war should rise against me, in this will I be confident. One thing have I desired of the Lord, that will I seek after; that I may dwell in the house of the Lord all the days of my life, to behold the beauty of the Lord, and to inquire in his temple. For in the time of trouble he shall hide me in his pavilion: in the secret of his tabernacle shall he hide me; he shall set me up upon a rock. And now shall mine head be lifted up above mine enemies round about me: therefore will I offer in his tabernacle sacrifices of joy; I will sing, yea, I will sing praises unto the Lord. (Psalm 27:1-6 KJV)

369 Heavenly Sunlight

In Him was life; and the life was the light of men — John 1:4 KJV

1. Walk-ing in sun-light all of my jour-ney, O-ver the moun-tains,
2. Shad-ows a-round me, shad-ows a-bove me, Nev-er con-ceal my
3. In the bright sun-light, ev-er re-joic-ing, Press-ing my way to

thru the deep vale: Je-sus has said, "I'll nev-er for-sake thee" —
Sav-ior and Guide; He is the Light, in Him is no dark-ness —
man-sions a-bove; Sing-ing His prais-es, glad-ly I'm walk-ing —

Refrain

Prom-ise di-vine that nev-er can fail.
Ev-er I'm walk-ing close to His side. Heav-en-ly sun-light,
Walk-ing in sun-light, sun-light of love.

heav-en-ly sun-light — Flood-ing my soul with glo-ry di-vine;

Hal-le-lu-jah! I am re-joic-ing, Sing-ing His prais-es — Je-sus is mine.

WORDS: Henry J. Zelley
MUSIC: George H. Cook

SUNLIGHT

In My Heart There Rings a Melody 370

Admonishing one another in psalms and hymns and spiritual songs — Colossians 3:16 KJV

1. I have a song that Je-sus gave me, It was sent from heav'n a-
2. I love the Christ who died on Cal-v'ry, For He washed my sins a-
3. 'Twill be my end-less theme in glo-ry, With the an-gels I will

bove; There nev-er was a sweet-er mel-o-dy, 'Tis a
way; He put with-in my heart a mel-o-dy, And I
sing; 'Twill be a song with glo-rious har-mo-ny, When the

Refrain

mel-o-dy of love.
know it's there to stay.
courts of heav-en ring.

In my heart there rings a mel-o-dy, There

rings a mel-o-dy with heav-en's har-mo-ny; In my heart there

rings a mel-o-dy; There rings a mel-o-dy of love.

WORDS: Elton M. Roth
MUSIC: Elton M. Roth

HEART MELODY

371 It's in My Heart

My heart rejoiceth in the Lord — 1 Samuel 2:1 KJV

1. Tho' some may sing to pass the wea-ry night a-long, Tho' some may sing to en-ter-tain a world-ly throng, (a world-ly throng,) I sing be-cause I wor-ship God in song, It's in my heart, It's in my heart.

2. You ask me why I know His blood can cleanse a-lone, You ask me why I know He sits up-on the throne, (up-on the throne,) And why I know He chose me for His own, It's in my heart, It's in my heart.

3. You ask me how I find the time to read and pray, You ask me how I smile when things are far from gay, (are far from gay,) And how I sing His prais-es, come what may, It's in my heart, It's in my heart.

4. I may not know the skill-ful use of tongue or pen, To prove my Lord's re-turn to un-be-liev-ing men, (un-b'liev-ing men,) But this I know, He's com-ing back a-gain, It's in my heart, It's in my heart.

WORDS: Arthur Slater
MUSIC: Arthur Slater; arr. by J. G. Boersma

It's In My Heart

372 Ring the Bells of Heaven!

His father saw him...and ran and fell on his neck — Luke 15:20 KJV

1. Ring the bells of heav - en! there is joy to - day
2. Ring the bells of heav - en! there is joy to - day
3. Ring the bells of heav - en! spread the feast to - day!

For a soul re - turn - ing from the wild!
For the wan - d'rer now is rec - on - ciled;
An - gels, swell the glad tri - um - phant strain!

See! the Fa - ther meets him out up - on the way,
Yes, a soul is res - cued from his sin - ful way,
Tell the joy - ful tid - ings, bear it far a - way!

Wel - com-ing His wea - ry, wan - d'ring child.
And is born a - new a ran - somed child.
For a pre - cious soul is born a - gain.

WORDS: William O Cushing
MUSIC: George F. Root

RING THE BELLS

Ring the Bells of Heaven!

373   O Happy Day!

This day is holy unto our Lord — Nehemiah 8:10 KJV

1. O hap - py day that fixed my choice On Thee, my Sav - ior and my God!
2. O hap - py bond that seals my vows To Him who mer - its all my love!
3. 'Tis done, the great trans - ac-tion's done – I am my Lord's and He is mine;
4. Now rest, my long - di - vid - ed heart, Fixed on this bliss - ful cen-ter, rest;

Well may this glow-ing heart re - joice And tell its rap-tures all a - broad.
Let cheer-ful an-thems fill His house, While to that sa - cred shrine I move.
He drew me, and Ï fol-lowed on, Charmed to con-fess the voice di - vine.
Nor ev - er from my Lord de - part, With Him of ev - 'ry good pos-sessed.

Refrain

Hap - py day, hap - py day, When Je - sus washed my sins a - way!

He taught me how to watch and pray And live re - joic - ing ev-'ry day;

Hap - py day, hap - py day, When Je - sus washed my sins a - way!

WORDS: Philip Doddridge

MUSIC: Edward F. Rimbault

HAPPY DAY

Can't Nobody Do Me Like Jesus   374

I will lift up my eyes unto the hills, from whence comes my help — Psalm 121:1 KJV

1. Can't no - bod - y   do me like   Je - sus,
2. Healed my bod - y,   told me to   live   on,
3. Saved my soul,   told me to   run   on,

Can't no - bod - y   do me like the Lord.
Healed my bod - y,   told me to live on.
Saved my soul,   told me to run on.

Can't no - bod - y   do me like   Je - sus,
Healed my bod - y,   told me to   live   on,
Saved my soul,   told me to   run   on,

Can't no - bod - y   do   me   like   the   Lord.
Can't no - bod - y   do   me   like   the   Lord.
Can't no - bod - y   do   me   like   the   Lord.

WORDS: Traditional
MUSIC: Traditional

375 He's My Everything

For Thou art my lamp, O Lord:
and the Lord will lighten my darkness — 2 Samuel 22:29 KJV

1. Some folk wor-ship mon-ey and the lux-ury that it
2. When my load is heav-y and it's more than I can
3. If I'm bound by trou-ble _____ He is my re -

brings, Some folk live for glo-ry to
bear, I de-pend on Je-sus; __
lease, He shines on my path-way __

hear their prais-es ring. But I live for Je - sus
He will al-ways share. He's my strength in weak-ness,
and my joys in - crease. He's the King Al - might-y

and to Him I cling, Je - sus
He is al - ways there, Je - sus
and the Prince of Peace, Je - sus

WORDS: Rev. Thomas Phillips and Camille Harrison
MUSIC: Rev. Thomas Phillips and Camille Harrison

He's My Everything

Refrain

is my ev-'ry - thing.   Oh,   He's my ev-'ry -

thing,   He's   my   ev-'ry - thing,

Je - sus   is   my ev-'ry -   thing; _____ He's the

light   in my dark-ness,   keeps me sing-ing tho' I cry;

Je - sus   is   my   ev-'ry - thing. _____

376   He's Sweet, I Know

O taste and see that the Lord is good — Psalm 34:8 KJV

Unison

1. I can't for-get when I was sad, Head hang-ing
2. Some-time I'm tried by Sa-tan's snare, My bur-den
3. I have my tick-et here in my hand, I'm go-ing

down and soul feel-ing bad, All I could say was, "Lord, take my
seem(s) so hard to bear, I'm talked a-bout what-e'er I
to that beau-ti-ful land, Some-time I weep and some-time I

heart." Je-sus heard and saved me and gave me a start.
do, But I know a Sav-ior and He'll take me thru.
moan, But I'm bound for Glo-ry and I'm go-ing on.

Refrain (parts)

He's sweet, I know, He's sweet, I
My Sav-ior,

WORDS: A. Jackson
MUSIC: A. Jackson
© owned by A. Jackson. Used by permission.

He's Sweet, I Know

know; Dark clouds may rise and strong wind may

know, My Sav - ior; clouds may rise wind may,

rise and

blow. I'll tell the world wher - e'er I

wind may blow, but

world, I'll tell it

go, I have found a Sav - ior; He's sweet, I know.

I will extol the Lord at all times; his praise will always be on my lips. My soul will boast in the Lord; let the afflicted hear and rejoice. Glorify the Lord with me; let us exalt his name together. I sought the Lord, and he answered me; he delivered me from all my fears. Those who look to him are radiant; their faces are never covered with shame. This poor man called, and the Lord heard him; he saved him out of all his troubles. The angel of the Lord encamps around those who fear him, and he delivers them. Taste and see that the Lord is good.
(Adapted from Psalm 34:1-8 KJV)

377 Fill My Cup, Lord

Give me this water, that I thirst not — John 4:15 KJV

1. Like the wom-an at the well I was seek-ing   For
2. There are mil-lions in this world who are crav-ing   The
3. So, my broth-er, if the things this world gave you   Leave

things that could not sat-is-fy;   And then   I heard my Sav-ior
pleas-ure earth-ly things af-ford;   But none   can match the won-drous
hun-gers that won't pass a-way,   My bless-ed   Lord will come and

speak-ing: "Draw from My well that nev-er shall run dry."
treas-ure   That I find in Je-sus Christ my Lord.
save you,   If you kneel to Him and hum-bly pray:

Refrain

Fill my cup, Lord,   I lift it up, Lord!   Come and

WORDS: Richard Blanchard
MUSIC: Richard Blanchard
FILL MY CUP

Fill My Cup, Lord

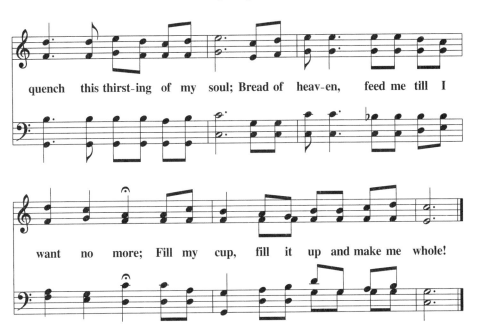

quench this thirst-ing of my soul; Bread of heav-en, feed me till I want no more; Fill my cup, fill it up and make me whole!

Now Jacob's well was there. Jesus therefore, being wearied with his journey, sat thus on the well: and it was about the sixth hour. There cometh a woman of Samaria to draw water: Jesus saith unto her, Give me to drink. (For his disciples were gone away unto the city to buy meat.) Then saith the woman of Samaria unto him, How is it that thou, being a Jew, askest drink of me, which am a woman of Samaria? for the Jews have no dealings with the Samaritans. Jesus answered and said unto her, If thou knewest the gift of God, and who it is that saith to thee, Give me to drink; thou wouldest have asked of him, and he would have given thee living water. The woman saith unto him, Sir, thou hast nothing to draw with, and the well is deep: from whence then hast thou that living water? Art thou greater than our father Jacob, which gave us the well, and drank thereof himself, and his children, and his cattle? Jesus answered and said unto her, Whosoever drinketh of this water shall thirst again: But whosoever drinketh of the water that I shall give him shall never thirst; but the water that I shall give him shall be in him a well of water springing up into everlasting life. The woman saith unto him, "Sir, give me this water, that I thirst not, neither come hither to draw." (John 4:6-15 KJV)

378 No One Ever Cared for Me Like Jesus

Greater love hath no man than this:
that a man lay down his life for his friends — John 15:13 KJV

1. I would love to tell you what I think of Je - sus
2. All my life was full of sin when Je - sus found me,
3. Ev - 'ry day He comes to me with new as - sur - ance,

Since I found in Him a friend so strong and true;
All my heart was full of mis - er - y and woe;
More and more I un - der - stand His words of love;

I would tell you how He changed my life com - plete - ly,
Je - sus placed His strong and lov - ing arms a - bout me,
But I'll nev - er know just why He came to save me,

He did some-thing that no oth - er friend could do.
And He led me in the way I ought to go.
Till some day I see His bless - ed face a - bove.

WORDS: C. F. Weigle
MUSIC: C. F. Weigle

No One Ever Cared for Me Like Jesus

Refrain

No one ev-er cared for me like Je-sus, There's no oth-er friend so kind as He; No one else could take the sin and dark-ness from me, O how much He cared for me.

And Jesus went about all the cities and villages, teaching in their synagogues, and preaching the gospel of the kingdom, and healing every sickness and every disease among the people. But when he saw the multitudes, he was moved with compassion on them, because they fainted, and were scattered abroad, as sheep having no shepherd. Then saith he unto his disciples, "The harvest truly is plenteous, but the labourers are few; Pray ye therefore the Lord of the harvest, that He will send forth labourers into His harvest." (Matthew 9:35-38 KJV)

379   Is He Yours?

The Lord is my strength and my song — Psalm 118:14 KJV

1. I am not blessed with rich - es, Am help - less as can be;
2. He's my wa - ter when I'm thirst - y, When hun - gry, He's my bread;
3. You may be poor and help-less, You may be old and gray;
4. He sat - is - fied my moth-er When death came steal-ing on.

I'm some-times void of shel - ter and of clothes; ____
My pro - tec - tion from the storm - y wind that blows; ____
Like Job, from head to foot be full of sores; ____
She used to say when - e'er my eye - lids close, ____

I have this sat - is - fac-tion As I sail this storm - y sea,
My com-fort when I'm lone-ly, When oth - er friends have fled;
Just take your case to Je - sus, And your night will turn to day;
"My Je - sus will be with me, And take me safe - ly home;

King Je - sus is my Pi - lot, Is He yours? ____
This Friend will nev - er leave you, Is He yours? ____
He's my joy, my hope, my com-fort, Is He yours? ____
For years He's been my Doc-tor, Is He yours?" ____

WORDS: Lucie E. Campbell
MUSIC: Lucie E. Campbell

Is He Yours?

380 Saved, Saved!

Even when we were dead in sins, [God] hath quickened us together with Christ, (by grace ye are saved) — Ephesians 2:5 KJV

1. I've found a friend who is all to me, His
2. He saves me from ev-'ry sin and harm, Se -
3. When poor and need - y and all a - lone, In

love is ev - er true; I love to tell how He
cures my soul each day; I'm lean - ing strong on His
love He said to me, "Come un - to me and I'll

lift - ed me, And what His grace can do for you.
might - y arm – I know He'll guide me all the way.
lead you home To live with Me e - ter - nal - ly."

Refrain (parts)

Saved by His pow'r di-vine, Saved to new life sub-lime!
Saved by His pow'r, Saved to new life,

Life now is sweet and my joy is com-plete, for I'm saved, saved, saved.

WORDS: Jack P. Scholfield
MUSIC: Jack P. Scholfield

RAPTURE

He's So Real

381

Jesus Christ is the same yesterday, and today and forever — Hebrews 13:8 KJV

WORDS: Charles H. Nicks, Jr.
MUSIC: Charles H. Nicks, Jr.; arr. by Ruth L. Davis

382 Something Within

Greater is He that is in you, than he that is in the world — 1 John 4:4 KJV

Slowly, with expression

1. Preach-ers and teach - ers would make their ap - peal,
2. Have you that some - thing, that burn - ing de - sire?
3. I met God one morn, my soul feel-ing bad,

Fight - ing as sol - diers on great bat - tle - fields;
Have you that some - thing, that nev - er doth tire?
Heart heav - y la - den with a bowed down head.

When to their plead - ings my poor heart did yield,
Oh, if you have it — that Heav - en - ly Fire!
He lift'd my bur - den and made me so glad,

All I could say, there is some-thing with - in.
Then let the world know there is some-thing with - in.
All that I know there is some-thing with - in.

WORDS: L. E. Campbell
MUSIC: L. E. Campbell

Something Within

383   I'm Happy with Jesus Alone

I count all things but loss for the excellency
of the knowledge of Christ Jesus my Lord — Philippians 3:8 KJV

1. There's noth - ing so pre - cious as Je - sus to me;
2. When sin - ful and doomed to a life of de - spair,
3. When noth - ing but death for my ran - som could pay,
4. 'Twas Je - sus who called me and showed me the way
5. Should fa - ther and moth - er for - sake me be - low,

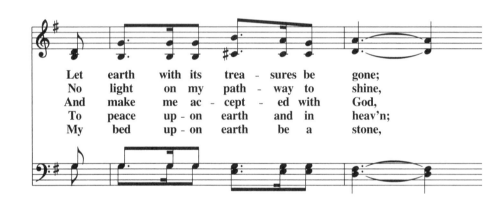

Let earth with its trea - sures be gone;
No light on my path - way to shine,
And make me ac - cept - ed with God,
To peace up - on earth and in heav'n;
My bed up - on earth be a stone,

I'm rich as can be when my Sav - ior I see;
'Twas Je - sus who found me and made me an heir
'Twas Je - sus who free - ly Him - self made a prey
'Tis Je - sus who teach - es me dai - ly to pray
I'll cling to my Sav - ior who loves me, I know,

WORDS: Charles P. Jones
MUSIC: Charles P. Jones

I'm Happy with Jesus Alone

384 Redeemed

Let the redeemed of the Lord say so — Psalm 107:2 KJV

1. Re - deemed, how I love to pro - claim it! Re -
2. Re - deemed, and so hap - py in Je - sus, No
3. I think of my bless - ed Re - deem - er, I
4. I know I shall see in His beau - ty The

deemed by the blood of the Lamb; Re -
lan - guage my rap - ture can tell; I
think of Him all the day long; I
King in whose law I de - light; Who

deemed thru His in - fi - nite mer - cy, His
know that the light of His pres - ence With
sing, for I can - not be si - lent, His
lov - ing - ly guard - eth my foot - steps And

child, and for - ev - er, I am.
me doth con - tin - ual - ly dwell.
love is the theme of my song.
giv - eth me songs in the night.

WORDS: Fanny J. Crosby
MUSIC: William J. Kirkpatrick

REDEEMED

Redeemed

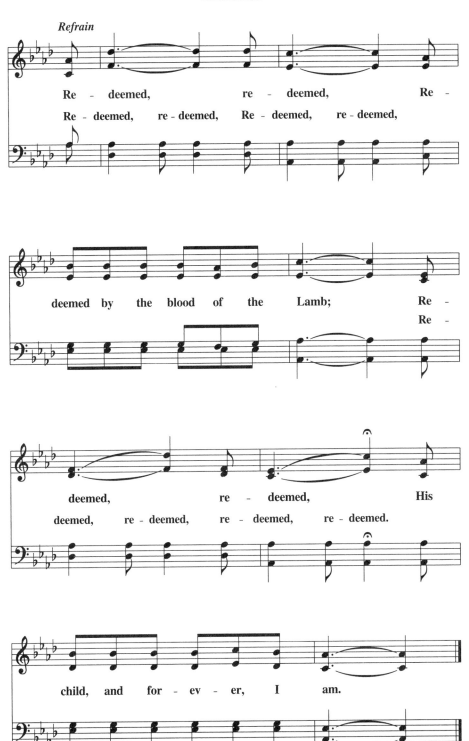

385 Love Lifted Me

I will extol Thee, O Lord; for Thou hast lifted me up,
and hast not made my foes to rejoice over me — Psalm 30:1 KJV

1. I was sink - ing deep in sin, Far from the peace - ful shore,
2. All my heart to Him I give, Ev - er to Him I'll cling,
3. Souls in dan - ger, look a - bove, Je - sus com - plete - ly saves;

Ver - y deep - ly stained with - in, Sink-ing to rise no more;
In His bless - ed pres - ence live, Ev - er His prais - es sing.
He will lift you by His love Out of the an - gry waves.

But the Mas - ter of the sea Heard my de - spair - ing cry,
Love so might - y and so true Mer - its my soul's best songs;
He's the Mas - ter of the sea, Bil - lows His will o - bey;

From the wa - ters lift - ed me – Now safe am I.
Faith - ful, lov - ing serv - ice, too, To Him be - longs.
He your Sav - ior wants to be – Be saved to - day.

WORDS: James Rowe
MUSIC: Howard E. Smith

SAFETY

Love Lifted Me

386 It's Real

Jesus Christ...washed us from our sins in His own blood — Revelation 1:5 KJV

1. O how well do I re-mem-ber how I doubt-ed day by
2. When the truth came close and search-ing, all my joy would dis - ap -
3. But at last I tired of liv - ing such a life of fear and
4. So I prayed to God in ear - nest, and not car - ing what folks

day. For I did not know for cer - tain that my
pear. For I did not have the wit - ness of the
doubt. For I want - ed God to give me some - thing
said. I was hun - gry for the bless - ing; my poor

sins were washed a - way; When the Spir - it tried to
Spir - it bright and clear; If at times the com - ing
I would know a - bout; So the truth would make me
soul it must be fed; When at last by faith I

tell me, I would not the truth re - ceive. I en -
judg - ment would ap - pear be - fore my mind, O it
hap - py, and the light would clear - ly shine, And the
touched Him, and, like sparks from smit - ten steel, Just so

WORDS: H. L. Cox
MUSIC: H. L. Cox

It's Real

387   He Delivered Me

But out of them all the Lord delivered me — 2 Timothy 3:11 KJV

Refrain, in Unison

He de - liv - ered me, _____ He de -

liv - ered me _____ He de - liv - ered

me, _____ yes, He de - liv - ered me. _____

1. I was lost, could-n't find my way,
2. There was a time when I was ill,

WORDS: Doris Akers
MUSIC: Doris Akers; arr. by Charles J. Levy

He Delivered Me

388 The Old Account Settled Long Ago

For whosoever shall call upon the name of the Lord shall be saved — Romans 10:13 KJV

1. There was   a time I know   When in   the book of heav'n
2. The old ac-count was large,   And grow - ing ev - 'ry day,
3. When at   the judg-ment bar   I   stand be - fore my King,
4. O   sin - ner, seek the Lord,   Re - pent of all your sin,

An   old   ac-count was stand-ing   For   sins yet un - for-giv'n;
For   I   was al - ways sin-ning,   And   nev - er tried to pay;
And   He   the book will   o - pen,   He   can - not find a thing;
For thus He has com-mand-ed,   If   you would en - ter in;

My   name was at   the   top   And man - y things be - low,
But   when I looked a - head   And saw such pain and woe,
Then will my heart be glad,   While tears of   joy will flow
And then if you should live   A   hun-dred years be - low,

I   went un - to   the Keep - er,   And   set-tled long   a - go.
I   said that I   would set - tle,   And   set-tled long   a - go.
Be - cause I had it set - tled,   And   set-tled long   a - go.
E'en here you'll not re - gret it,   You   set-tled long   a - go.

WORDS: F. M. Graham
MUSIC: F. M. Graham

The Old Account Settled Long Ago

389   How I Got Over

And we know that all things work together for good — Romans 8:28 KJV

How I got o - ver, (How I got) o - ver, my

Lord, And my soul looked back and won-dered, (won-dered,

won-dered,) How I got o - ver, my Lord.

1. The tall - est tree (in)
2. Lord, I've been 'buked (and)
3. Oh, Jor - dan's riv - er (is so)

WORDS: Rev. C. H. Cobbs
MUSIC: Rev. C. H. Cobbs; arr. by Kenneth Morris

How I Got Over

390   Just When I Need Him Most

I am with you always, even unto the end of the world — Matthew 28:20 KJV

1. Just when I need Him, Je - sus is near,
2. Just when I need Him, Je - sus is true,
3. Just when I need Him, Je - sus is strong,
4. Just when I need Him, He is my all,

Just when I fal - ter, just when I fear; Read - y to help me,
Nev - er for - sak - ing all the way thru; Giv - ing for bur - dens
Bear - ing my bur - dens all the day long; For all my sor - row
An - swer - ing when up - on Him I call; Ten - der - ly watch - ing

read - y to cheer, Just when I need Him most.
pleas - ures a - new, Just when I need Him most.
giv - ing a song, Just when I need Him most.
lest I should fall, Just when I need Him most.

Refrain

Just when I need Him most, Just when I need Him most;

Je - sus is near to com - fort and cheer, Just when I need Him most.

WORDS: William C. Poole
MUSIC: Charles H. Gabriel

GABRIEL

A Child of the King

391

If children, then heirs; heirs of God, and joint-heirs with Christ — Romans 8:17 KJV

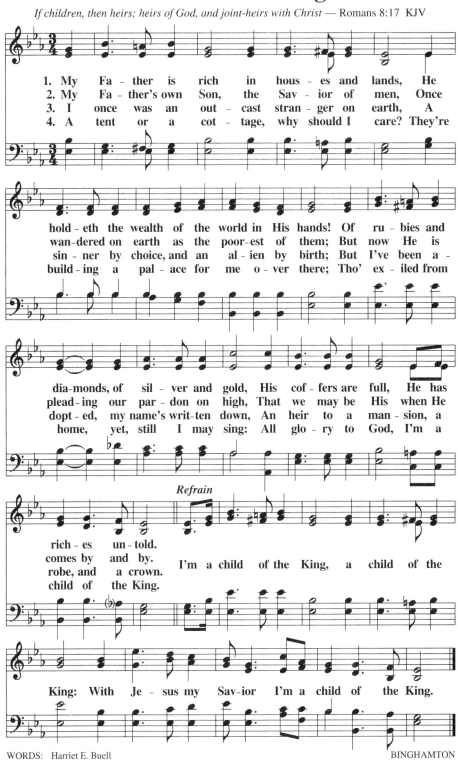

1. My Fa-ther is rich in hous-es and lands, He
2. My Fa-ther's own Son, the Sav-ior of men, Once
3. I once was an out-cast stran-ger on earth, A
4. A tent or a cot-tage, why should I care? They're

hold-eth the wealth of the world in His hands! Of ru-bies and
wan-dered on earth as the poor-est of them; But now He is
sin-ner by choice, and an al-ien by birth; But I've been a-
build-ing a pal-ace for me o-ver there; Tho' ex-iled from

dia-monds, of sil-ver and gold, His cof-fers are full, He has
plead-ing our par-don on high, That we may be His when He
dopt-ed, my name's writ-ten down, An heir to a man-sion, a
home, yet, still I may sing: All glo-ry to God, I'm a

Refrain

rich-es un-told.
comes by and by.
robe, and a crown.
child of the King.

I'm a child of the King, a child of the

King: With Je-sus my Sav-ior I'm a child of the King.

WORDS: Harriet E. Buell
MUSIC: John B. Sumner

BINGHAMTON

392 I Will Sing the Wondrous Story

While we were yet sinners, Christ died for us — Romans 5:8 KJV

1. I will sing the won - drous sto - ry Of the
2. I was lost, but Je - sus found me, Found the
3. I was bruised, but Je - sus healed me; Faint was
4. Days of dark - ness still come o'er me, Sor - row's
5. He will keep me till the riv - er Rolls its

Christ who died for me, How He left His home in
sheep that went a - stray, Threw His lov - ing arms a -
I from man - y a fall; Sight was gone, and fears pos -
paths I of - ten tread, But the Sav - ior still is
wa - ters at my feet; Then He'll bear me safe - ly

Refrain

glo - ry For the cross of Cal - va - ry.
round me, Drew me back in - to His way.
sessed me, But He freed me from them all.
with me; By His hand I'm safe - ly led.
o - ver, Where the loved ones I shall meet.

Yes, I'll

sing the won-drous sto - ry Of the

Yes, I'll sing the won-drous sto - ry

WORDS: Frances H. Rowley
MUSIC: Peter P. Bilhorn

WONDROUS STORY

I Will Sing the Wondrous Story

Christ who died for me, Sing it

Of the Christ who died for me,

with the saints in glo - ry, Gath - ered

Sing it with the saints in glo - ry,

by the crys - tal sea.

Gath - ered by the crys - tal sea, the crys - tal sea.

A man with leprosy came to him and begged him on his knees, "If you are willing, you can make me clean." Filled with compassion, Jesus reached out his hand and touched the man. "I am willing," he said. "Be clean!" Immediately the leprosy left him and he was cured. Jesus sent him away at once with a strong warning: "See that you don't tell this to anyone. But go, show yourself to the priest and offer the sacrifices that Moses commanded for your cleansing, as a testimony to them." Instead he went out and began to talk freely, spreading the news. As a result, Jesus could no longer enter a town openly but stayed outside in lonely places. Yet the people still came to him from everywhere.
(Adapted from Mark 1:40-45 KJV)

393 The Lord Will Make a Way Somehow

Your Father knoweth what thing ye have need of, before ye ask Him — Matthew 6:8 KJV

1. Like a ship that's tossed and driv-en, | Bat-tered by an an-gry
2. Try to do my best in ser-vice, Try to live the best I
3. Of-ten there's mis-un-der-stand-ing Out of all the good I

sea, When the storms of life are rag-ing And their
can, When I choose to do the right thing, Ev-il's
do, Go to friends for con-so-la-tion And I

fu-ry falls on me, I won-der what I have
pre-sent on ev-'ry hand, I look up and won-der
find them com-plain-ing, too, So man-y nights I toss in

done That makes this race so hard to run, Then I
why — That good for-tune pass me by, Then I
pain, Won-der-ing what the day will bring, But I

say to my soul, take cour-age, The Lord will make a way some-how.
say to my soul, be pa-tient, The Lord will make a way some-how.
say to my heart, don't wor-ry, The Lord will make a way some-how.

WORDS: Thomas A. Dorsey
MUSIC: Thomas A. Dorsey

The Lord Will Make a Way Somehow

394 We've Come a Long Way

Though I walk through the valley of the shadow of death, I will fear no evil — Psalm 23:4 KJV

Refrain

We've come a long way, Lord, __ A might-y long way, __

__ We've come a long way, Lord, __ A might-y long

way, __ We've borne our bur-dens in the heat of the

day, But we know the Lord has made the way, We've come a long

Fine

way, Lord, __ A might-y long way. __ 1. I've been in the

WORDS: Traditional; adapt. by Kenneth Morris
MUSIC: Traditional; arr. by Kenneth Morris
Adapt. and arr. © 1968 by Martin & Morris Music, Inc. Used by permission.

We've Come a Long Way

395 God Is So Good

O give thanks unto the Lord; for He is good — 1 Chronicles 16:34 KJV

Refrain

God is _____ so good to me, God is so good to me; I don't serve _____ Him as I should, I don't de - serve _____ all of this good; So man - y things are not as they should be, But God is so good to me. _____ *Fine*

WORDS: Doris Akers
MUSIC: Doris Akers; arr. by Thurston G. Frazier

God Is So Good

396 He Lifted Me

I will extol Thee, O Lord; for Thou hast lifted me up,
and hast not made my foes to rejoice over me — Psalm 30:1 KJV

1. In lov-ing-kind-ness Je-sus came My soul in mer-cy to re-claim, And from the depths of sin and shame Thru grace He lift-ed me. (He lift-ed me.)
2. He called me long be-fore I heard, Be-fore my sin-ful heart was stirred, But when I took Him at His word, For-giv'n, He lift-ed me. (He lift-ed me.)
3. His brow was pierced with many a thorn, His hands by cru-el nails were torn, When from my guilt and grief, for-lorn, In love He lift-ed me. (He lift-ed me.)
4. Now on a high-er plane I dwell, And with my soul I know 'tis well; Yet how or why, I can-not tell, He should have lift-ed me. (He lift-ed me.)

Refrain

From sink-ing sand He lift-ed me, With ten-der hand He lift-ed me; From

WORDS: Charles H. Gabriel
MUSIC: Charles H. Gabriel

HE LIFTED ME

He Lifted Me

shades of night   to plains of light,   O praise His name,   He   lift-ed me!

I Do, Don't You?   397

For I know whom I have believed — 2 Timothy 1:12 KJV

1. I know   a great Sav - ior,   I   do;   don't you?   I
2. I need   Him to   lead me,   I   do;   don't you? Heav'n's
3. I love   to be   near Him,   I   do;   don't you?   He
4. I want   Him to   use me,   I   do;   don't you?   For

live   by His fa - vor, I   do; don't you? For grace I im-plore Him, I
man - na to feed me, I   do; don't you? What-ev - er be - tide me, I
speaks and I hear Him, I   do; don't you? For me He is car - ing, The
serv - ice to choose me, I   do; don't you? I want Him to bless me, To

wor - ship be - fore Him, I   love and   a - dore Him, I   do; don't you?
need Him be - side me, In   mer - cy   to hide me, I   do; don't you?
cross I am bear-ing, I   love Him for shar-ing, I   do; don't you?
own and con-fess me, Com-plete-ly pos-sess me, I   do; don't you?

WORDS: Melville W. Miller
MUSIC: E. O. Excell

398 He Is So Precious to Me

There is none upon the earth that I desire beside Thee — Psalm 73:25 KJV

1. So pre-cious is Je-sus, my Sav-ior, my King,
2. He stood at my heart's door 'mid sun-shine and rain,
3. I stand on the moun-tain of bless-ing at last,
4. I praise Him be-cause He ap-point-ed a place

His praise all the day long with rap-ture I sing;
And pa-tient-ly wait-ed an en-trance to gain;
No cloud in the heav-ens a shad-ow to cast;
Where some day, thru faith in His won-der-ful grace,

To Him in my weak-ness for strength I can cling,
What shame that so long He en-treat-ed in vain,
His smile is up-on me, the val-ley is past,
I know I shall see Him—shall look on His face,

For He is so pre-cious to me.
For He is so pre-cious to me.
For He is so pre-cious to me.
For He is so pre-cious to me.

WORDS: Charles H. Gabriel
MUSIC: Charles H. Gabriel

PRECIOUS TO ME

He Is So Precious to Me

I will exalt you, O Lord, for you lifted me out of the depths and did not let my enemies gloat over me. O Lord my God, I called to you for help and you healed me. O Lord, you brought me up from the grave you spared me from going down into the pit. Sing to the Lord, you saints of his; praise his holy name. For his anger lasts only a moment, but his favor lasts a lifetime; weeping may remain for a night, but rejoicing comes in the morning. When I felt secure, I said, "I will never be shaken." O Lord, when you favored me, you made my mountain stand firm; but when you hid your face, I was dismayed. To you, O Lord, I called; to the Lord I cried for mercy: "What gain is there in my destruction, In my going down into the pit? Will the dust praise you? Will it proclaim your faithfulness? Hear, O Lord, and be merciful to me; O Lord, be my help." You turned my wailing into dancing; you removed my sackcloth and clothed me with joy, that my heart may sing to you and not be silent. O Lord my God, I will give you thanks forever.
(Adapted from Psalm 30:1-12 KJV)

399   I'm Going Through, Jesus

I rejoice therefore that I have confidence in you in all things — 2 Corinthians 7:16 KJV

1. Lord,   I   have start-ed   to   walk   in   the
2. Man-y   they   are   who   start   in   the
3. I'd   rath-er   walk   with   Je-sus   a-
4. O   broth-er, now   will   you   take   up   the

light   —   Shin-ing   up-on   me   from
race;   —   But   with   the   light   they re-
lone,   And   have   for   a   pil-low,   like
cross?   —   Give   up   the   world,   and

heav-en   so   bright;   I   bade the
fuse   to   keep   pace;   Oth-ers   ac-
Ja-cob,   a   stone,   Liv-ing   each
count   it   as   dross;   Sell   all   thou

world   and   its   fol-lies   a-dieu,   I've
cept   it   be-cause   it   is   new,   But
mo-ment   with   His   face   in   view,   Than
hast,   and   give   to   the   poor,   Then

WORDS: Unknown
MUSIC: Unknown

I'm Going Through, Jesus

start - ed in, Je - sus, and I'm go - ing through.
not ver - y man - y ex - pect to go through.
shrink from my path-way and fail to go through.
go thru with Je - sus and those who en - dure.

Refrain

I'm go - ing through, yes, I'm go - ing through;

I'll pay the price, what - ev - er oth - ers do;

I'll take the way with the Lord's de - spis - ed few.

I'm go - ing through, Je - sus, I'm go - ing through. A - men.

400   The Haven of Rest

God is our refuge and strength, a very present help in trouble — Psalm 46:1   KJV

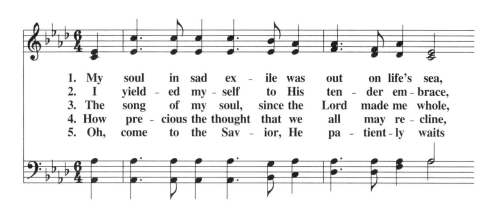

1. My   soul   in   sad   ex - ile   was   out   on   life's   sea,
2. I   yield - ed   my - self   to   His   ten - der   em - brace,
3. The   song   of   my   soul,   since   the   Lord   made   me   whole,
4. How   pre - cious   the   thought   that   we   all   may   re - cline,
5. Oh,   come   to   the   Sav - ior,   He   pa - tient - ly   waits

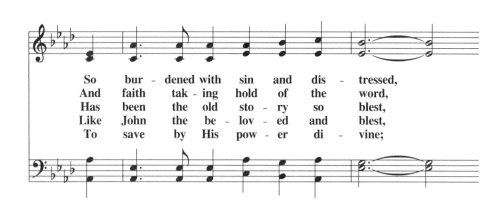

So   bur - dened   with   sin   and   dis - tressed,
And   faith   tak - ing   hold   of   the   word,
Has   been   the   old   sto - ry   so   blest,
Like   John   the   be - lov - ed   and   blest,
To   save   by   His   pow - er   di - vine;

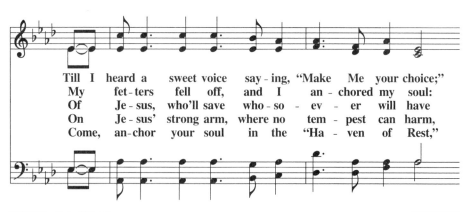

Till I   heard a   sweet voice   say - ing,   "Make   Me   your   choice;"
My   fet - ters   fell   off,   and   I   an - chored   my   soul:
Of   Je - sus,   who'll   save   who - so - ev - er   will   have
On   Je - sus'   strong   arm,   where   no   tem - pest   can   harm,
Come,   an - chor   your   soul   in   the   "Ha - ven   of   Rest,"

WORDS: H. L. Gilmour   GOODSHIP
MUSIC: George D. Moore

The "Haven of Rest"

401 God's Wonderful Grace Is Sufficient for Me

My grace is sufficient for thee — 2 Corinthians 12:9 KJV

1. My soul is at peace as on-ward I trod, For
2. The de-mons of hell their darts at me cast; I'll
3. And when I have sailed life's jour-ney at last, And

I can re-ly on the prom-ise of God; He
have no fear, for He'll hold me fast; No
safe in heav'n's har-bor my an-chor is cast; The

gave me His word when He set me free, "My
harm can be-fall while His face I see, His
theme of my praise for-ev-er shall be God's

won-der-ful grace is suf-fi-cient for thee."
won-der-ful grace is suf-fi-cient for thee.
won-der-ful grace is suf-fi-cient for thee.

WORDS: Kenneth Morris
MUSIC: Kenneth Morris
© 1942 by Kenneth Morris. Used by permission.

God's Wonderful Grace Is Sufficient for Me

402 Through It All

Yea, though I walk through the valley of the shadow of death,
I will fear no evil — Psalm 23:4 KJV

1. I've had man - y tears and sor - rows, I've had ques-tions for
2. I've been to lots of plac - es, And I've seen a lot
3. I thank God for the moun-tains, And I thank Him for

to - mor-row, There've been times I did-n't know right from
of fac - es, There've been times I felt so all a-
the val-leys, I thank Him for the storms He brought me

wrong; But in ev - 'ry sit - u -
lone; But in my lone - ly
through; For if I'd nev - er

a - tion God gave bless - ed con - so - la - tion That my
hours, Yes, those pre - cious lone - ly hours Je - sus
had a prob - lem I would-n't know that He could solve them, I'd

WORDS: Andraé Crouch
MUSIC: Andraé Crouch

Through It All

tri - als come to on - ly make me strong.
let me know that I was His own.
nev - er know what faith in God could do.

Refrain

Through it all, _____ Through it all, _____ I've

learned to trust in Je - sus, I've learned to trust in God;

Through it all, _____ Through it all, _____ I've

learned to de - pend up - on His Word. _____

403 Wonderful Peace

Peace I leave with you, my peace I give unto you — John 14:27 KJV

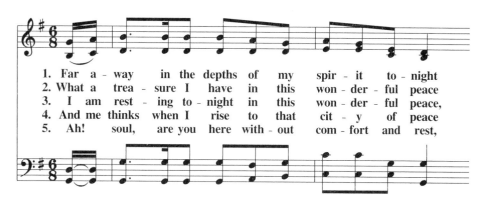

1. Far a - way in the depths of my spir - it to - night
2. What a trea - sure I have in this won - der - ful peace
3. I am rest - ing to - night in this won - der - ful peace,
4. And me thinks when I rise to that cit - y of peace
5. Ah! soul, are you here with - out com - fort and rest,

Rolls a mel - o - dy sweet - er than psalm;
Bur - ied deep in the heart of my soul,
Rest - ing sweet - ly in Je - sus' con - trol,
Where the Au - thor of peace I shall see,
March-ing down the rough path - way of time?

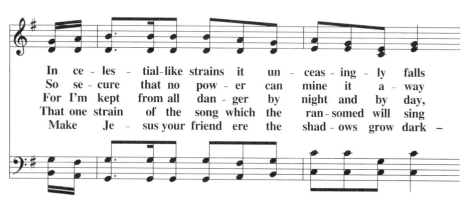

In ce - les - tial-like strains it un - ceas - ing - ly falls
So se - cure that no pow - er can mine it a - way
For I'm kept from all dan - ger by night and by day,
That one strain of the song which the ran - somed will sing
Make Je - sus your friend ere the shad - ows grow dark –

WORDS: W. D. Cornell
MUSIC: W. G. Cooper

WONDERFUL PEACE

Wonderful Peace

O'er my soul like an in - fi - nite calm.
While the years of e - ter - ni - ty roll.
And His glo - ry is flood - ing my soul.
In that heav - en - ly king - dom shall be:
O ac - cept this sweet peace so sub - lime!

Refrain

Peace, peace! won - der-ful peace, Com-ing down from the Fa - ther a -

bove, Sweep o - ver my spir - it for -

ev - er, I pray, In fath - om-less bil-lows of love.

404 Sweet Peace, the Gift of God's Love

Great shall be the peace of thy children — Isaiah 54:13 KJV

1. There comes to my heart one sweet strain, A glad and a joy-ous re-frain; I sing it a-gain and a-gain — Sweet peace, the gift of God's love.

2. Thru Christ on the cross peace was made, My debt by His death was all paid; No oth-er foun-da-tion is laid — For peace, the gift of God's love.

3. When Je-sus as Lord I had crowned, My heart with this peace did a-bound; In Him the rich bless-ing I found — Sweet peace, the gift of God's love.

4. In Je-sus for peace I a-bide, And as I keep close to His side, There's noth-ing but peace doth be-tide — Sweet peace, the gift of God's love.

Refrain

Peace, peace, sweet peace! Won-der-ful gift from a-

WORDS: Peter P Bilhorn
MUSIC: Peter P Bilhorn

SWEET PEACE

Sweet Peace, the Gift of God's Love

bove!   (a - bove!)   O   won - der-ful,   won - der - ful

peace!   Sweet peace,   the gift of God's love!

The mountains shall bring peace to the people, and the little hills, by righteousness. He shall judge the poor of the people, he shall save the children of the needy, and shall break in pieces the oppressor. They shall fear thee as long as the sun and moon endure, throughout all generations. He shall come down like rain upon the mown grass: as showers that water the earth. In his days shall the righteous flourish; and abundance of peace so long as the moon endureth. He shall have dominion also from sea to sea, and from the river unto the ends of the earth. They that dwell in the wilderness shall bow before him; and his enemies shall lick the dust. The kings of Tarshish and of the isles shall bring presents: the kings of Sheba and Seba shall offer gifts. Yea, all kings shall fall down before him: all nations shall serve him. For he shall deliver the needy when he crieth; the poor also, and him that hath no helper. He shall spare the poor and needy, and shall save the souls of the needy. He shall redeem their soul from deceit and violence: and precious shall their blood be in his sight. And he shall live, and to him shall be given of the gold of Sheba: prayer also shall be made for him continually; and daily shall he be praised. There shall be an handful of corn in the earth upon the top of the mountains; the fruit thereof shall shake like Lebanon: and they of the city shall flourish like grass of the earth. His name shall endure for ever. (Psalm 72:3-17 KJV)

405   Sweeter Than the Day Before

And my spirit hath rejoiced in God my Savior — Luke 1:47 KJV

Ev-'ry-day with Je-sus, Sweet-er than the day be-fore; Ev-'ry-day with Je-sus I love Him more and more; Je-sus saves and keeps me, He's the one that I a - dore; Ev-'ry-day is sweet - er, Sweet-er than the day be - fore.

WORDS: Unknown
MUSIC: Unknown; arr. by Kenneth Morris
Arr. © 1961 by Martin & Morris, Inc. Used by permission.

Sweeter Than the Day Before

406 The Last Mile of the Way

I have finished my course, I have kept the faith — 2 Timothy 4:7 KJV

1. If I walk in the path-way of du-ty, If I work till the close of the day; I shall see the great King in His beau-ty When I've gone the last mile of the way.

2. If for Christ I pro-claim the glad sto-ry, If I seek for His sheep gone a-stray; I am sure He will show me His glo-ry When I've gone the last mile of the way.

3. Here the dear-est of ties we must sev-er, Tears of sor-row are seen ev-'ry day; But no sick-ness, no sigh-ing for-ev-er When I've gone the last mile of the way.

4. And if here I have earn-est-ly striv-en, And have tried all His will to o-bey; 'Twill en-hance all the rap-ture of heav-en When I've gone the last mile of the way.

WORDS: Johnson Oatman, Jr.
MUSIC: Wm. Edie Marks

The Last Mile of the Way

Refrain

When I've gone the last mile of the way,   I will
mile, the last mile of the way,

rest at the close of the day,   And I
close, at the close of the day,

know there are joys that a - wait me   When I've

gone the last mile of the way.

407 I Heard the Voice of Jesus Say

Come unto me … and I will give you rest — Matthew 11:28 KJV

1. I heard the voice of Je - sus say, "Come
2. I heard the voice of Je - sus say, "Be -
3. I heard the voice of Je - sus say, "I

un - to Me and rest, Lay down, thou wea - ry
hold, I free - ly give The liv - ing wa - ter;
am this dark world's Light, Look un - to Me; thy

one, lay down Thy head up - on My breast!"
thirst - y one, Stoop down, and drink, and live!"
morn shall rise, And all thy day be bright!"

I came to Je - sus as I was, Wea -
I came to Je - sus, and I drank, Of
I looked to Je - sus, and I found In

WORDS: Horatius Bonar
MUSIC: Old English Aire

I Heard the Voice of Jesus Say

ry,   and   worn,   and   sad;   I   found   in   Him   a
that   life - giv - ing   stream;   My thirst was quenched, my
Him   my   Star,   my   Sun;   And in   that   light   of

rest - ing   place,   And   He   has made   me   glad.
soul   re -   vived,   And   now   I   live   in   Him.
life   I'll   walk   Till   trav - 'ling days   are   done.

Ho, every one that thirsteth, come ye to the waters, and he that hath no money; come ye, buy, and eat; yea, come, buy wine and milk without money and without price. Wherefore do ye spend money for that which is not bread? and your labour for that which satisfieth not? Hearken diligently unto me, and eat ye that which is good, and let your soul delight itself in fatness. Incline your ear, and come unto me: hear, and your soul shall live; and I will make an everlasting covenant with you, even the sure mercies of David. Behold, I have given him for a witness to the people, a leader and commander to the people. Behold, thou shalt call a nation that thou knowest not, and nations that knew not thee shall run unto thee because of the Lord thy God, and for the Holy One of Israel; for he hath glorified thee. Seek ye the Lord while he may be found, call ye upon him while he is near: Let the wicked forsake his way, and the unrighteous man his thoughts: and let him return unto the Lord, and he will have mercy upon him; and to our God, for he will abundantly pardon. (Isaiah 55:1-7 KJV)

408 Precious Memories

The memory of the just is blessed — Proverbs 10:7 KJV

1. Pre - cious mem-'ries, un - seen an - gels,
2. Pre - cious fa - ther, lov - ing moth - er,
3. As I trav - el on life's path-way,

Sent from some-where to my soul;
Fly a - cross the lone - ly years;
Know not what the years may hold;

How they lin - ger,
And old home scenes
As I pon - der,

ev - er near me, And the sa - cred past un - fold.
of my child-hood In fond mem - o - ry ap - pear.
hope grows fond - er, Pre - cious mem-'ries flood my soul.

Refrain

Pre-cious mem-'ries, how they lin-ger, How they ev-er flood my soul;

In the still-ness of the mid-night, Pre-cious, sa-cred scenes un-fold.

WORDS: J. B. F. Wright and Lonnie B. Combs
MUSIC: J. B. F. Wright

Stand Up, Stand Up for Jesus   **409**

For by faith ye stand — 2 Corinthians 1:24 KJV

1. Stand up, stand up for Je - sus, Ye sol - diers of the cross!
2. Stand up, stand up for Je - sus, The trum - pet call o - bey;
3. Stand up, stand up for Je - sus, Stand in His strength a - lone;
4. Stand up, stand up for Je - sus, The strife will not be long;

Lift high His roy - al ban - ner — It must not suf - fer loss.
Forth to the might - y con - flict In this His glo - rious day.
The arm of flesh will fail you — Ye dare not trust your own.
This day the noise of bat - tle — The next, the vic - tor's song.

From vic - t'ry un - to vic - t'ry His ar - my shall He lead,
Ye that are men now serve Him A - gainst un-num-bered foes;
Put on the gos - pel ar - mor, Each piece put on with prayer;
To him that o - ver - com - eth A crown of life shall be:

Till ev - 'ry foe is van-quished And Christ is Lord in - deed.
Let cour - age rise with dan - ger And strength to strength op - pose.
Where du - ty calls or dan - ger, Be nev - er want - ing there.
He with the King of Glo - ry Shall reign e - ter - nal - ly.

WORDS: George Duffield, Jr.   WEBB
MUSIC: George J. Webb

410 Take the Name of Jesus with You

Whatsoever ye do in word or deed, do all in the name of the Lord — Colossians 3:17 KJV

1. Take the name of Je-sus with you, Child of sor-row and of
2. Take the name of Je-sus ev - er, As a shield from ev - 'ry
3. O the pre-cious name of Je - sus! How it thrills our souls with
4. At the name of Je-sus bow - ing, Fall-ing pros-trate at His

woe; It will joy and com - fort give you –
snare; If temp - ta - tions 'round you gath - er,
joy, When His lov - ing arms re - ceive us
feet, King of kings in heav'n we'll crown Him

Refrain

Take it then wher - e'er you go.
Breathe that ho - ly name in prayer. Pre-cious name,
And His songs our tongues em - ploy!
When our jour - ney is com-plete. pre-cious name,

O how sweet! Hope of earth and joy of heav'n; Pre-cious
sweet, how sweet!

name, O how sweet! Hope of earth and joy of heav'n.
pre-cious name, sweet, how sweet!

WORDS: Lydia Baxter
MUSIC: William H. Doane

PRECIOUS NAME

Throw Out the Life-Line 411

Be ye all of one mind, having compassion one of another — 1 Peter 3:8 KJV

1. Throw out the Life-Line a - cross the dark wave! There is a broth - er whom some - one should save – Some-bod - y's broth-er! O who then will dare To throw out the Life-Line, his per - il to share?

2. Throw out the Life-Line with hand quick and strong – Why do you tar - ry, why lin - ger so long? See, he is sink-ing! O has - ten to - day, And out with the Life-Boat! a - way, then, a - way!

3. Throw out the Life-Line to dan - ger-fraught men, Sink-ing in an - guish where you've nev - er been; Winds of temp - ta - tion and bil - lows of woe Will soon hurl them out where the dark wa-ters flow.

4. Soon will the sea - son of res - cue be o'er, Soon will they drift to e - ter - ni - ty's shore; Haste then, my broth - er – no time for de - lay, But throw out the Life-Line and save them to - day.

Refrain

Throw out the Life-Line! Throw out the Life-Line! Some-one is drift-ing a-way;

Some - one is sink-ing to - day.

WORDS: Edward S. Ufford
MUSIC: Edward S. Ufford

LIFELINE

412 To the Ends of the Earth

Here am I, send me — Isaiah 6:8 KJV

Unison

1. To - day   I hear the help-less cries   of   chil - dren suf - f'ring
2. To - day   I see the bro - ken lives   of   peo - ple in   de -

pain,   Chil-dren who've not felt   the touch
spair,   Peo - ple who've not known God's love,

the Great Phy-si - cian brings.   To - day   I feel the hurt in -
who nev - er felt His care.   To - day   I know that I should

side   of   per - sons hat - ing life,   Per-sons who've not
go   to   peo - ple ev - 'ry - where,   Peo - ple who've not

WORDS: Ed Seabough
MUSIC: Bill Cates

To the Ends of the Earth

413 Share His Love

A true witness delivereth souls — Proverbs 14:25 KJV

1. The love of God is broad - er than earth's vast ex - panse, __
2. All those who have trust - ed in God's on - ly Son, __
3. We show the love of God each day we live, __

'Tis deep - er and wid - er than the sea. _____
And hold this pre-cious treas-ure in their hearts, ___
Re - veal Christ's pres-ence in our lives; ___

Love reach-es out to all to bring a - bun - dant life, __
Seek ways to make it known to all who need to know _
And how the Ho - ly Spir - it guides us day by day, __

For God so loved the world His on - ly Son He gave.
That God so loved the world His on - ly Son He gave.
For God so loved the world His on - ly Son He gave.

WORDS: William J. Reynolds
MUSIC: William J. Reynolds
© Copyright 1973 Broadman Press (SESAC). All rights reserved.

SULLIVAN

Share His Love

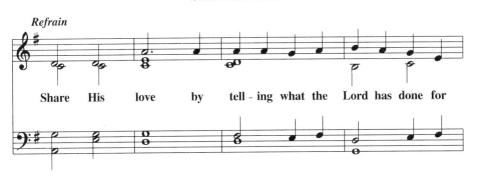

Refrain

Share His love by tell - ing what the Lord has done for

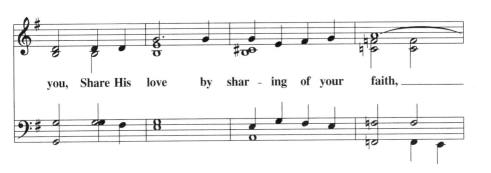

you, Share His love by shar - ing of your faith, ____

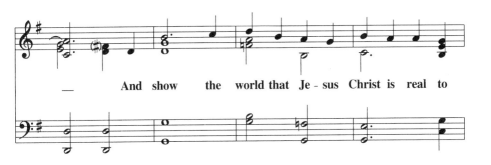

___ And show the world that Je - sus Christ is real to

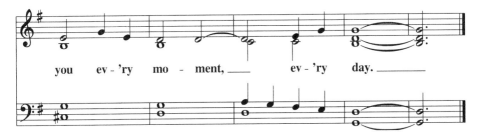

you ev - 'ry mo - ment, ___ ev - 'ry day. ____

414   Rescue the Perishing

The Lord is not willing that any should perish, but that all should come to repentance — 2 Peter 3:9 KJV

1. Res - cue the per - ish - ing, care for the dy - ing,
2. Though they are slight-ing Him, still He is wait - ing,
3. Down in the hu - man heart, crushed by the tempt - er,
4. Res - cue the per - ish - ing, du - ty de-mands it –

Snatch them in pit - y from sin and the grave;
Wait - ing the pen - i - tent child to re - ceive;
Feel - ings lie bur - ied that grace can re - store;
Strength for thy la - bor the Lord will pro - vide;

Weep o'er the err - ing one, lift up the fall - en,
Plead with them ear - nest - ly, plead with them gen - tly,
Touched by a lov - ing heart, wak - ened by kind - ness,
Back to the nar - row way pa - tient - ly win them,

Refrain

Tell them of Je - sus, the might - y to save.
He will for - give if they on - ly be - lieve.   Res-cue the per-ish-ing,
Chords that are bro - ken will vi - brate once more.
Tell the poor wan-d'rer a Sav - ior has died.

Care for the dy - ing; Je - sus is mer-ci - ful, Je - sus will save.

WORDS: Fanny J. Crosby
MUSIC: William H. Doane

RESCUE

Lead On, O King Eternal   415

He will be our guide even unto death — Psalm 48:14 KJV

1. Lead on, O King E - ter - nal, The day of march has come!
2. Lead on, O King E - ter - nal, Till sin's fierce wars shall cease
3. Lead on, O King E - ter - nal, We fol - low not with fears!

Hence-forth in fields of con - quest Thy tents shall be our home;
And ho - li - ness shall whis - per The sweet A - men of peace;
For glad-ness breaks like morn - ing Wher-e'er Thy face ap - pears;

Thru days of prep - a - ra - tion Thy grace has made us strong,
For not with swords loud clash - ing Nor roll of stir-ring drums –
Thy cross is lift - ed o'er us – We jour-ney in its light:

And now, O King E - ter - nal, We lift our bat - tle song.
With deeds of love and mer - cy The heav'n-ly king-dom comes.
The crown a - waits the con - quest; Lead on, O God of might.

WORDS: Ernest W. Shurtleff
MUSIC: Henry T. Smart

LANCASHIRE

416   We've a Story to Tell

These things speak, and exhort — Titus 2:15 KJV

1. We've a sto - ry to tell to the na - tions
2. We've a song to be sung to the na - tions
3. We've a mes - sage to give to the na - tions –
4. We've a Sav - ior to show to the na - tions

That shall turn their hearts to the right,
That shall lift their hearts to the Lord,
That the Lord who reign - eth a - bove
Who the path of sor - row hath trod,

A sto - ry of truth and mer - cy,
A song that shall con - quer e - vil
Hath sent us His Son to save us
That all of the world's great peo - ples

A sto - ry of peace and light,
And shat - ter the spear and sword,
And show us that God is love,
Might come to the truth of God,

WORDS: H. Ernest Nichol
MUSIC: H. Ernest Nichol

MESSAGE

We've a Story to Tell

A   sto - ry   of peace   and   light.
And   shat - ter the spear and   sword.
And   show   us   that God   is   love.
Might come   to   the truth   of   God.

Refrain

For the dark - ness shall turn   to   dawn - ing, And the

dawn - ing to noon - day bright,   And Christ's great king - dom shall

come   to   earth, The   king - dom of love   and   light.

417 Pass It On

Love one another; as I have loved you — John 13:34 KJV

Unison

1. It on - ly takes a spark to get a fire
2. What a won - drous time is spring when all the trees are
3. I wish for you, my friend, this hap - pi - ness that

go - ing, _____ And soon all those a - round can
bud - ding, _____ The birds be - gin to sing, the
I've found, _____ You can de - pend on Him, it

warm up in its glow - ing; _____ That's how it is with
flow - ers start their bloom - ing; _____ That's how it is with
mat - ters not where you're bound; _____ I'll shout it from the

God's love; Once you've ex - per - i - enced it you
God's love; Once you've ex - per - i - enced it you
moun - tain - top, I want my world to know: The

WORDS: Kurt Kaiser
MUSIC: Kurt Kaiser
© 1969 Bud John Songs, Inc. (ASCAP)

PASS IT ON

Pass It On

spread His love to ev - 'ry - one; You want to pass it on. _
want to sing, it's fresh like spring; You want to pass it on. _
Lord of love has come to me, I want to pass it on. _

1, 2   **3**

I'll shout it from the

moun-tain-top, I want my world to know: The Lord of love has

come to me, I want to pass it on. _____

418   Jesus Saves!

Christ Jesus came into the world to save sinners — 1 Timothy 1:15 KJV

1. We have heard the joy-ful sound – Je-sus saves! Je-sus saves!
2. Waft it on the roll-ing tide – Je-sus saves! Je-sus saves!
3. Sing a-bove the bat-tle strife – Je-sus saves! Je-sus saves!
4. Give the winds a might-y voice – Je-sus saves! Je-sus saves!

Spread the tid-ings all a-round – Je-sus saves! Je-sus saves!
Tell to sin-ners far and wide – Je-sus saves! Je-sus saves!
By His death and end-less life – Je-sus saves! Je-sus saves!
Let the na-tions now re-joice – Je-sus saves! Je-sus saves!

Bear the news to ev-'ry land, Climb the steeps and cross the waves;
Sing, ye is-lands of the sea! Ech-o back, ye o-cean caves!
Sing it soft-ly thru the gloom, When the heart for mer-cy craves;
Shout sal-va-tion full and free, High-est hills and deep-est caves;

On-ward! 'tis our Lord's com-mand – Je-sus saves! Je-sus saves!
Earth shall keep her ju-bi-lee – Je-sus saves! Je-sus saves!
Sing in tri-umph o'er the tomb – Je-sus saves! Je-sus saves!
This our song of vic-to-ry – Je-sus saves! Je-sus saves!

WORDS: Priscilla J. Owens
MUSIC: William J. Kirkpatrick

JESUS SAVES

Let the Lower Lights Be Burning   419

Ye are the light of the world — Matthew 5:14 KJV

1. Bright-ly beams our Fa-ther's mer-cy From His light-house ev - er -
2. Dark the night of sin has set-tled, Loud the an - gry bil-lows
3. Trim your fee - ble lamp, my broth-er! Some poor sail - or tem-pest-

more, But to us He gives the keep-ing Of the
roar; Ea - ger eyes are watch-ing, long-ing, For the
tossed, Try - ing now to make the har - bor, In the

Refrain

lights a - long the shore.
lights a - long the shore. Let the low - er lights be
dark-ness may be lost.

burn-ing! Send a gleam a - cross the wave! Some poor

faint - ing, strug-gling sea-man You may res-cue, you may save.

WORDS: Philip P. Bliss
MUSIC: Philip P. Bliss

LOWER LIGHTS

420   Lift Him Up

And I, if I be lifted up from the earth, I'll draw all men unto me — John 12:32 KJV

1. How to reach the mass - es, men of ev - 'ry birth,
2. Oh! the world is hun - gry for the Liv - ing Bread,
3. Don't ex - alt the preach-er, don't ex - alt the pew,
4. Lift Him up by liv - ing as a Chris-tian ought,

For an an - swer Je - sus gave the key:
Lift the Sav - ior up for them to see;
Preach the Gos - pel sim - ple, full and free;
Let the world in you the Sav - ior see;

"And I, if I be lift - ed up from the earth,
Trust Him, and do not doubt the words that He said,
Prove Him, and you will find that prom - ise is true,
Then men will glad - ly fol - low Him who once taught,

Will draw all men un - to Me."
"I'll draw all men un - to Me."
"I'll draw all men un - to Me."
"I'll draw all men un - to Me."

WORDS: Johnson Oatman, Jr.
MUSIC: B. B. Beall

Lift Him Up

Refrain

Lift Him up,   Lift Him up,
Lift the pre - cious Sav - ior up, Lift the pre - cious Sav - ior up,

Still He speaks from e - ter - ni - ty:

"And I, if I be lift - ed up from the earth,

Will draw all men un - to Me."

421 Set My Soul Afire

But His word was in mine heart as a burning fire — Jeremiah 20:9 KJV

1. Set my soul a - fire, Lord, for Thy ho - ly Word,
2. Set my soul a - fire, Lord, for the lost in sin,
3. Set my soul a - fire, Lord, in my dai - ly life,

Burn it deep with - in me, let Thy voice be heard;
Give to me a pas - sion as I seek to win;
Far too long I've wan - dered in this day of strife;

Mil - lions grope in dark - ness in this day and hour,
Help me not to fal - ter, nev - er let me fail,
Noth - ing else will mat - ter but to live for Thee,

I will be a wit - ness, fill me with Thy pow'r.
Fill me with Thy Spir - it, let Thy will pre - vail.
I will be a wit - ness, for Christ lives in me.

WORDS: Gene Bartlett
MUSIC: Gene Bartlett

SCALES

Set My Soul Afire

Refrain

Set my soul a - fire, Lord, set my soul a - fire,

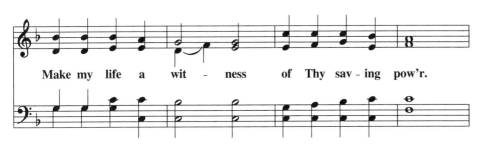

Make my life a wit - ness of Thy sav - ing pow'r.

Mil - lions grope in dark - ness, wait - ing for Thy Word,

Set my soul a - fire, Lord, set my soul a - fire.

422 O Zion, Haste

For thou shalt be His witness unto all men — Acts 22:15 KJV

1. O Zi - on, haste, thy mis - sion high ful - fill - ing,
2. Be - hold how man - y thou-sands still are ly - ing
3. Pro - claim to ev - 'ry peo - ple, tongue and na - tion
4. Give of thy sons to bear the mes - sage glo - rious,

To tell to all the world that God is Light; That He who
Bound in the dark - some pris - on house of sin, With none to
That God in whom they live and move is Love; Tell how He
Give of thy wealth to speed them on their way; Pour out thy

made all na - tions is not will - ing One soul should per - ish,
tell them of the Sav - ior's dy - ing Or of the life He
stooped to save His lost cre - a - tion And died on earth that
soul for them in prayer vic - to - rious, And all thou spend - est

lost in shades of night.
died for them to win.
we might live a - bove.
Je - sus will re - pay.

Refrain

Pub - lish glad ti - dings, Ti - dings of

peace, Ti - dings of Je - sus — Re - demp-tion and re - lease.

WORDS: Mary Ann Thomson
MUSIC: James Walch

TIDINGS

To Worship, Work and Witness 423

Yea, I will praise Him among the multitude — Psalm 109:30 KJV

1. To wor-ship, work, and wit-ness, The Good News spread a-broad,
2. Be thine thy Mas-ter's pur-pose To seek and save the lost,
3. Be thou to Christ His bod-y, Hold fast to Christ thy Head;
4. Head of the Church, in-spire us To have in us Thy mind,

We mag-ni-fy Thy mis-sion, Church of the liv-ing God;
To ran-som those in bond-age, To dare not count the cost;
Be thou Christ's o-pen let-ter By all men to be read;
To hum-bly wait Thy guid-ance, Thy joy in serv-ing find.

The Fa-ther's new cre-a-tion Thru Je-sus Christ His Son, The
To love and lift the low-ly, To heed the pris-'ner's groan, To
Be thou Christ's ho-ly tem-ple, Him-self the cor-ner-stone; Be
Be-stow the Spir-it's grace-gifts To serve the com-mon good, While

Spir-it has em-pow-ered To do as Christ has done.
take up oth-ers' bur-dens And bear them as thine own.
thou Christ's liv-ing al-tar Where-on His love is shown.
help-ing each the oth-er To love thy broth-er-hood. A-men.

WORDS: Henry Lyle Lambdin
MUSIC: George J. Webb

WEBB

424 I Love to Tell the Story

And tell them how great things the Lord hath done for thee — Mark 5:19 KJV

1. I love to tell the sto - ry Of un - seen things a -
2. I love to tell the sto - ry – More won - der - ful it
3. I love to tell the sto - ry – 'Tis pleas - ant to re -
4. I love to tell the sto - ry, For those who know it

bove, Of Je - sus and His glo - ry, Of
seems Than all the gold - en fan - cies Of
peat What seems, each time I tell it, More
best Seem hun - ger - ing and thirst - ing To

Je - sus and His love; I love to tell the
all our gold - en dreams; I love to tell the
won - der - ful - ly sweet; I love to tell the
hear it like the rest; And when in scenes of

sto - ry Be - cause I know 'tis true, It
sto - ry – It did so much for me, And
sto - ry For some have nev - er heard The
glo - ry I sing the new, new song, 'Twill

WORDS: A. Catherine Hankey
MUSIC: William G. Fischer

HANKEY

I Love to Tell the Story

sat - is - fied my long - ings As noth - ing else can do.
that is just the rea - son I tell it now to thee.
mes - sage of sal - va - tion From God's own ho - ly Word.
be the old, old sto - ry That I have loved so long.

Refrain

I love to tell the sto - ry! 'Twill be my theme in glo - ry –

To tell the old, old sto - ry of Je - sus and His love.

When the demons came out of the man, they went into the pigs, and the herd rushed down the steep bank into the lake and was drowned. When those tending the pigs saw what had happened, they ran off and reported this in the town and countryside, and the people went out to see what had happened. When they came to Jesus, they found the man from whom the demons had gone out, sitting at Jesus' feet, dressed and in his right mind; and they were afraid. Those who had seen it told the people how the demon-possessed man had been cured. Then all the people of the region of the Gadarenes asked Jesus to leave them, because they were overcome with fear. So he got into the boat and left. The man from whom the demons had gone out begged to go with him, but Jesus sent him away, saying, "Return home and tell how much God has done for you." So the man went away and told all over town how much Jesus had done for him. (Adapted from Luke 8:33-39 KJV)

425   Loyalty to Christ

My heart is fixed, O God, my heart is fixed; I will sing and give praise — Psalm 57:7 KJV

1. From o - ver hill and plain   There comes the sig - nal strain –
2. O hear, ye brave, the sound   That moves the earth a - round –
3. Come, join our loy - al throng –   We'll rout the gi - ant wrong –
4. The strength of youth we lay   At Je - sus' feet to - day –

'Tis loy - al - ty, loy - al - ty, loy - al - ty to Christ;
'Tis loy - al - ty, loy - al - ty, loy - al - ty to Christ;
'Tis loy - al - ty, loy - al - ty, loy - al - ty to Christ;
'Tis loy - al - ty, loy - al - ty, loy - al - ty to Christ;

Its mu - sic rolls a - long,   The hills take up the song,
A - rise to dare and do,   Ring out the watch-word true,
Where Sa - tan's ban-ners float   We'll send the bu - gle note,
His gos - pel we'll pro - claim   Thru - out the world's do - main,

Of loy - al - ty, loy - al - ty, yes, loy - al - ty to Christ.
Of loy - al - ty, loy - al - ty, yes, loy - al - ty to Christ.
Of loy - al - ty, loy - al - ty, yes, loy - al - ty to Christ.
Of loy - al - ty, loy - al - ty, yes, loy - al - ty to Christ.

WORDS: E. Taylor Cassel   LAMBDIN
MUSIC: Flora H. Cassel

Loyalty to Christ

426 Glorious Things of Thee Are Spoken

Glorious things are spoken of Thee, O city of God — Psalm 87:3 KJV

1. Glo - rious things of Thee are spo - ken,
2. See, the streams of liv - ing wa - ters,
3. Round each hab - i - ta - tion hov - 'ring,

Zi - on, cit - y of our God; He whose word can -
Spring - ing from e - ter - nal Love, Well sup - ply thy
See the cloud and fire ap - pear For a glo - ry

not be bro - ken Formed thee for His own a - bode.
sons and daugh-ters, And all fear of want re - move.
and a cov - 'ring, Show - ing that the Lord is near!

On the Rock of A - ges found-ed What can shake thy
Who can faint while such a riv - er Ev - er flows their
Glo-rious things of thee are spo - ken, Zi - on, cit - y

WORDS: John Newton
MUSIC: Franz Joseph Haydn

AUSTRIAN HYMN

Glorious Things of Thee Are Spoken

sure | re - pose? | With | sal - va - tion's | wall | sur - round - ed,
thirst | t'as - suage? | Grace | which, like | the | Lord, | the | Giv - er,
of | our | God; | He | whose word | can - not | be | bro - ken

Thou | may'st | smile | at | all | thy | foes.
Nev - er | fails | from | age | to | age!
Formed | thee | for | His | own | a - bode!

I will speak of the glorious honour of thy majesty, and of thy wondrous works. And men shall speak of the might of thy terrible acts: and I will declare thy greatness. They shall abundantly utter the memory of thy great goodness, and shall sing of thy righteousness. The Lord is gracious, and full of compassion; slow to anger, and of great mercy. The Lord is good to all: and his tender mercies are over all his works. All thy works shall praise thee, O Lord; and thy saints shall bless thee. They shall speak of the glory of thy kingdom, and talk of thy power; To make known to the sons of men his mighty acts, and the glorious majesty of his kingdom. (Psalm 145:5-12 KJV)

427 Onward, Christian Soldiers

Thou therefore endure hardness, as a good soldier of Jesus Christ — 2 Timothy 2:3 KJV

1. On-ward, Chris-tian sol - diers, March-ing as to war,
2. At the sign of tri - umph Sa - tan's host doth flee;
3. Like a might - y ar - my Moves the Church of God;
4. On-ward, then, ye peo - ple, Join our hap - py throng;

With the cross of Je - sus Go - ing on be - fore!
On, then, Chris-tian sol - diers, On to vic - to - ry!
Broth-ers, we are tread - ing Where the saints have trod.
Blend with ours your voic - es In the tri - umph song.

Christ, the roy - al Mas - ter, Leads a - gainst the foe;
Hell's foun - da - tions quiv - er At the shout of praise;
We are not di - vid - ed, All one bod - y we –
Glo - ry, laud and hon - or Un - to Christ the King –

For-ward in - to bat - tle See His ban - ner go!
Broth-ers, lift your voic - es, Loud your an-thems raise!
One in hope and doc - trine, One in char - i - ty.
This thru count-less a - ges Men and an - gels sing.

WORDS: Sabine Baring-Gould
MUSIC: Arthur S. Sullivan

ST. GERTRUDE

Onward, Christian Soldiers

Finally, be strong in the Lord and in his mighty power. Put on the full armor of God so that you can take your stand against the devil's schemes. For our struggle is not against flesh and blood, but against the rulers, against the authorities, against the powers of this dark world and against the spiritual forces of evil in the heavenly realms. Therefore put on the full armor of God, so that when the day of evil comes, you may be able to stand your ground, and after you have done everything, to stand. Stand firm then, with the belt of truth buckled around your waist, with the breastplate of righteousness in place, and with your feet fitted with the readiness that comes from the gospel of peace. In addition to all this, take up the shield of faith, with which you can extinguish all the flaming arrows of the evil one. Take the helmet of salvation and the sword of the Spirit, which is the word of God. (Adapted from Ephesians 6:10-17 KJV)

428   To the Work!

And be strong, all ye people of the land, saith the Lord, and work — Haggai 2:4 KJV

1. To the work! to the work! we are ser - vants of God,
2. To the work! to the work! let the hun - gry be fed,
3. To the work! to the work! there is la - bor for all,
4. To the work! to the work! in the strength of the Lord,

Let us fol - low the path that our Mas - ter has trod;
To the foun - tain of life let the wea - ry be led;
For the king - dom of dark - ness and er - ror shall fall;
And a robe and a crown shall our la - bor re-ward

With the balm of His coun - sel our strength to re - new,
In the cross and its ban - ner our glo - ry shall be,
And the name of Je - ho - vah ex - alt - ed shall be
When the home of the faith - ful our dwell - ing shall be

Let us do with our might what our hands find to do.
While we her - ald the ti - dings, "Sal - va - tion is free!"
In the loud swell-ing cho - rus, "Sal - va - tion is free!"
And we shout with the ran - somed, "Sal - va - tion is free!"

WORDS: Fanny J. Crosby
MUSIC: William H. Doane

TOILING ON

To the Work!

Toil - ing on,   toil - ing on,   Toil - ing
on,   toil - ing on;   Let us hope,   let us
watch,   And   la - bor till the Mas - ter comes.

The Spirit of the Lord God is upon me; because the Lord hath anointed me to preach good tidings unto the meek; he hath sent me to bind up the brokenhearted, to proclaim liberty to the captives, and the opening of the prison to them that are bound; To proclaim the acceptable year of the Lord, and the day of vengeance of our God; to comfort all that mourn; To appoint unto them that mourn in Zion, to give unto them beauty for ashes, the oil of joy for mourning, the garment of praise for the spirit of heaviness; that they might be called trees of righteousness, the planting of the Lord, that he might be glorified. (Isaiah 61:1-3 KJV)

429 Bringing in the Sheaves

Declare His works with rejoicing — Psalm 107:22 KJV

1. Sow-ing in the morn - ing, sow-ing seeds of kind - ness,
2. Sow-ing in the sun - shine, sow-ing in the shad - ows,
3. Go-ing forth with weep - ing, sow-ing for the Mas - ter,

Sow - ing in the noon - tide and the dew - y eve,
Fear - ing nei - ther clouds nor win - ter's chill - ing breeze;
Though the loss sus-tained our spir - it of - ten grieves;

Wait - ing for the har - vest and the time of reap - ing –
By and by the har - vest and the la - bor end - ed –
When our weep - ing's o - ver He will bid us wel - come –

We shall come re - joic - ing, bring-ing in the sheaves.
We shall come re - joic - ing, bring-ing in the sheaves.
We shall come re - joic - ing, bring-ing in the sheaves.

WORDS: Knowles Shaw
MUSIC: George A. Minor

HARVEST

Bringing in the Sheaves

430 Send the Light!

The people that walked in darkness have seen a great light — Isaiah 9:2 KJV

1. There's a call comes ring - ing o'er the rest - less wave,
2. We have heard the Mac - e - do - nian call to - day,
3. Let us pray that grace may ev - 'ry - where a - bound,
4. Let us not grow wea - ry in the work of love,

"Send the light! Send the light!"
"Send the light! Send the light!"
Send the light! Send the light!
Send the light! Send the light!

"Send the light! Send the light!"

There are souls to res - cue, there are souls to save,
And a gold - en of - f'ring at the cross we lay,
And a Christ - like spir - it ev - 'ry - where be found,
Let us gath - er jew - els for a crown a - bove,

Refrain

Send the light! Send the light!

Send the light! Send the light!

WORDS: Charles H. Gabriel
MUSIC: Charles H. Gabriel

McCABE

Send the Light!

During the night Paul had a vision of a man of Macedonia standing and begging him, "Come over to Macedonia and help us." After Paul had seen the vision, we got ready at once to leave for Macedonia, concluding that God had called us to preach the gospel to them. From Troas we put out to sea and sailed straight for Samothracia, and the next day on to Neapolis. From there we traveled to Philippi, a Roman colony and the leading city of that district of Macedonia. And we stayed there several days. On the Sabbath we went outside the city gate to the river, where we expected to find a place of prayer. We sat down and began to speak to the women who had gathered there. One of those listening was a woman named Lydia, a dealer in purple cloth from the city of Thyatira, who was a worshiper of God. The Lord opened her heart to respond to Paul's message. When she and the members of her household were baptized, she invited us to her home. "If you consider me a believer in the Lord," she said, "come and stay at my house." And she persuaded us.
(Adapted from Acts 16:9-15 KJV)

431 More About Jesus

Grow in grace, and in the knowledge of our Lord and Savior Jesus Christ — 2 Peter 3:18 KJV

1. More a-bout Je - sus would I know, More of His grace to
2. More a-bout Je - sus let me learn, More of His ho - ly
3. More a-bout Je - sus in His Word, Hold - ing com-mun - ion
4. More a-bout Je - sus on His throne, Rich - es in glo - ry

oth - ers show, More of His sav - ing full - ness see,
will dis - cern; Spir - it of God, my teach - er be,
with my Lord, Hear - ing His voice in ev - 'ry line,
all His own, More of His king - dom's sure in - crease,

Refrain

More of His love who died for me.
Show - ing the things of Christ to me.
Mak - ing each faith - ful say - ing mine. More, more a-bout
More of His com - ing, Prince of Peace.

Je - sus, More, more a-bout Je - sus; More of His sav - ing

full - ness see, More of His love who died for me.

WORDS: Eliza E. Hewitt
MUSIC: John R. Sweney

SWENEY

I Gave My Life for Thee

432

*Greater love hath no man than this,
that a man lay down his life for his friends* — John 15:13 KJV

1. I gave My life for thee, My pre-cious blood I shed,
2. My Fa-ther's house of light, My glo-ry - cir - cled throne
3. I suf-fered much for thee, More than thy tongue can tell,
4. And I have brought to thee, Down from My home a - bove,

That thou might'st ran-somed be, And quick - ened from the dead;
I left, for earth - ly night, For wan-d'rings sad and lone;
Of bit - t'rest ag - o - ny, To res - cue thee from hell;
Sal - va - tion full and free, My par - don and My love;

I gave, I gave My life for thee – What hast thou giv'n for Me?
I left, I left it all for thee – Hast thou left aught for Me?
I've borne, I've borne it all for thee – What hast thou borne for Me?
I bring, I bring rich gifts to thee – What hast thou brought to Me?

I gave, I gave My life for thee – What hast thou giv'n for Me?
I left, I left it all for thee – Hast thou left aught for Me?
I've borne, I've borne it all for thee – What hast thou borne for Me?
I bring, I bring rich gifts to thee – What hast thou brought to Me?

WORDS: Frances R. Havergal
MUSIC: Philip P. Bliss

KENOSIS

433 I Am on the Battlefield for My Lord

That he may please Him who hath chosen him to be a soldier — 2 Timothy 2:4 KJV

I am on the bat-tle-field for my Lord, I'm on the bat-tle-field for my Lord; And I prom-ised Him that I would serve Him till I die. I'm on the bat-tle-field for my Lord.

1. I was a-lone and i-dle, I was a sin-ner, too; I heard a voice from heav-en, "Say, there is work to do." I

2. I left my friends and kin-dred Bound for the Prom-ised Land, The grace of God up-on me, The Bi-ble in my hand; In

3. Now when I met my Sav-ior, I met Him with a smile, He healed my wound-ed spir-it, And owned me as His child. A-

WORDS: Sylvana Bell and E. V. Banks
MUSIC: Sylvana Bell and E. V. Banks; arr. by Thomas A. Dorsey

I Am on the Battlefield for My Lord

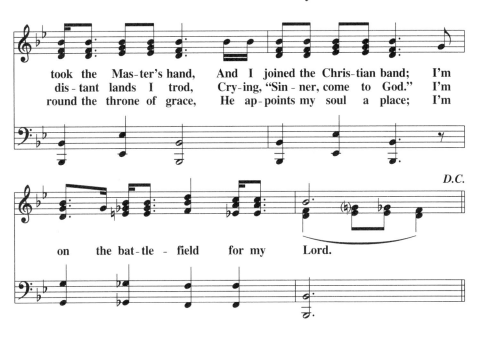

took the Mas-ter's hand, And I joined the Chris-tian band; I'm
dis-tant lands I trod, Cry-ing, "Sin-ner, come to God." I'm
round the throne of grace, He ap-points my soul a place; I'm

D.C.

on the bat-tle-field for my Lord.

Rise Up, O Men of God   434

A good man obtaineth favor of the Lord — Proverbs 12:2 KJV

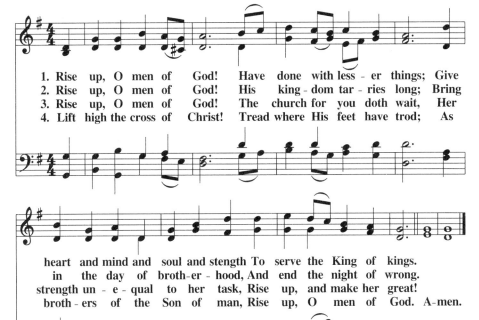

1. Rise up, O men of God! Have done with less-er things; Give
2. Rise up, O men of God! His king-dom tar-ries long; Bring
3. Rise up, O men of God! The church for you doth wait, Her
4. Lift high the cross of Christ! Tread where His feet have trod; As

heart and mind and soul and stength To serve the King of kings.
in the day of broth-er-hood, And end the night of wrong.
strength un-e-qual to her task, Rise up, and make her great!
broth-ers of the Son of man, Rise up, O men of God. A-men.

WORDS: William P. Merrill
MUSIC: Aaron Williams

ST. THOMAS

435 Reach Out and Touch

Inasmuch as ye have done it unto one of the least of these — Matthew 25:40 KJV

1. Reach out and touch a soul that is hun-gry; Reach out and touch a spir-it in de-spair; Reach out and touch a life torn and dirt-y, A man who is lone-ly – If you care! Reach out and touch that neigh-bor who hates you; Reach out and touch that stran-ger who meets you; Reach out and

2. Reach out and touch a friend who is wea-ry; Reach out and touch a seek-er un-a-ware; Reach out and touch, though touch-ing means los-ing A part of your own self – If you dare! Reach out and give your love to the love-less; Reach out and make a home for the home-less; Reach out and

WORDS: Charles F. Brown
MUSIC: Charles F. Brown

REACH OUT

Reach Out and Touch

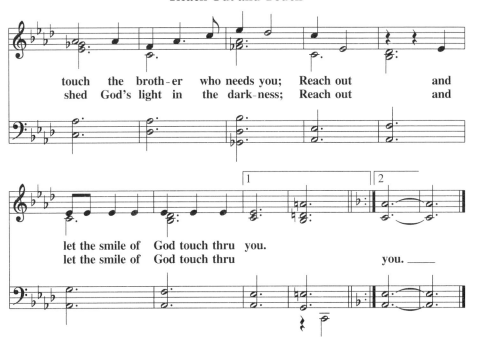

touch   the   broth-er   who needs you;   Reach out   and
shed   God's light in   the dark-ness;   Reach out   and

let the smile of   God touch thru   you.
let the smile of   God touch thru   you. ___

A Charge to Keep I Have   436

It is required in stewards, that a man be found faithful — 1 Corinthians 4:2   KJV

1. A   charge to keep I   have,   A   God to glo - ri - fy,   Who
2. To   serve the pres - ent   age,   My   call-ing to ful - fill,   O
3. Arm   me with jeal - ous   care,   As   in Thy sight to   live,   And
4. Help   me to watch and   pray,   And   on Thy - self re - ly,   By

gave His Son my   soul   to   save,   And   fit   it   for   the   sky.
may it   all my pow'rs en - gage   To   do   my   Mas - ter's   will.
O   Thy ser - vant, Lord, pre - pare   A   strict   ac - count   to   give.
faith as-sured I   will   o - bey,   For   I   shall   nev - er   die.

WORDS: Charles Wesley   LABAN
MUSIC: Lowell Mason

437 Make Me a Blessing

And thou shalt be a blessing — Genesis 12:2 KJV

Slowly

1. Out in the high-ways and by - ways of life, Man - y are
2. Tell the sweet sto - ry of Christ and His love, Tell of His
3. Give as 'twas giv - en to you in your need, Love as the

wea - ry and sad; Car - ry the sun-shine where
are wea - ry and sad;
pow'r to for - give; Oth - ers will trust Him if
His pow'r to for - give;
Mas - ter loved you; Be to the help-less a
The Mas - ter loved you;

rit.

dark-ness is rife, Mak-ing the sor - row - ing glad.
on - ly you prove True, ev - 'ry mo-ment you live.
help - er in - deed, Un - to your mis-sion be true.

Refrain
Men or Unison   *Women*

Make me a bless - ing, Make me a bless - ing,

WORDS: Ira B. Wilson
MUSIC: George S. Schuler

SCHULER

Make Me a Blessing

438 Our Best

To obey is better than sacrifice — 1 Samuel 15:22 KJV

1. Hear ye the Mas-ter's call, "Give me thy best!" For, be it
2. Wait not for men to laud, Heed not their slight; Win - ning the
3. Night soon comes on a - pace, Day has - tens by; Work-man and

great or small, That is His test. Do then the best you can,
smile of God Brings its de - light! Aid - ing the good and true
work must face Test - ing on high. Oh, may we in that day

Not for re - ward, Not for the praise of man, But for the Lord.
Ne'er goes un - blest, All that we think or do, Be it the best.
Find rest, sweet rest, Which God has prom-ised those Who do their best.

Refrain

Ev - 'ry work for Je - sus will be blest, But He

asks from ev-'ry - one his best. Our tal-ents may be few,

WORDS: S. C. Kirk
MUSIC: Grant Colfax Tullar

TULLAR

Our Best

These may be small, But un - to Him is due our best, our all.

Ready 439

Speak, Lord, for thy servant heareth — 1 Samuel 3:10 KJV

1. Read-y to suf-fer grief or pain, Read-y to stand the test;
2. Read-y to go, read-y to bear, Read-y to watch and pray;
3. Read-y to speak, read-y to think, Read-y with heart and mind;
4. Read-y to speak, read-y to warn, Read-y o'er souls to yearn;

Read-y to stay at home and send Oth-ers if He sees best.
Read-y to stand a - side and give Till He shall clear the way.
Read-y to stand where He sees fit, Read-y His will to find.
Read-y in life or read-y in death, Read-y for His re - turn.

Refrain

Read-y to go, read-y to stay, Read-y my place to fill;

Read-y for serv-ice low-ly or great, Read-y to do His will.

WORDS: A. C. Palmer
MUSIC: Charles D. Tillman

TILLMAN

440 Let Me Touch Him

If I may but touch His garment — Matthew 9:21 KJV

1. Let me touch Him, let me touch Je - sus. _____ Let me
2. I was stray - ing so far from Je - sus. _____ I was
3. There's a riv - er, a riv - er flow - ing, _____ From with -

touch Him as He pass - es by; _____ Then when I shall reach
lone - ly, had no peace with - in; _____ Then the hand of my
in and to cleanse my soul; _____ And the flow sets my

out to oth - ers, _____ They shall know Him, they shall live and not
Sav - ior touched me, _____ Now I'm reach - ing to oth - ers in
life to glow - ing. _____ Ho - ly Spir - it, more than sil - ver and

Refrain

die. _____
sin. _____ Oh, to be His hand ex - tend - ed, _____ Reach - ing
gold. _____

out to the op - pressed; _____ Let me touch Him, let me touch

WORDS: V. B. Ellis
MUSIC: V. B. Ellis

Let Me Touch Him

Je - sus, _____ So that oth-ers may know and be blessed. _____

Here Am I, Send Me   441

Then said I, "Here am I; send me" — Isaiah 6:8 KJV

Moderato

1. Hark! the voice of Je - sus call-ing, "Who will go and work to-day?
2. Let none hear you i - dly say-ing, "There is noth - ing I can do;"
3. Take the task He gives you glad-ly, Let His work your pleas-ure be;

Fields are white, the har-vest wait-ing; Who will bear the sheaves a - way?"
While the souls of men are dy - ing, And the Mas - ter calls for you.
An - swer quick - ly when He call-eth, "Here am I, send me, send me."

Refrain

Loud and long the Mas-ter call-eth, Rich re-ward He of - fers free;

Who will an - swer, glad - ly say-ing, "Here am I, send me, send me."

WORDS: Daniel March
MUSIC: J. C. Lenderman

442 People to People

And ye shall be witnesses unto Me — Acts 1:8 KJV

Unison

1. How do you share the love of Je - sus with a lone-ly man? ___
2. How do you tell a dy - ing man a - bout e - ter-nal life? ___
3. How do you tell a love-less world that God Him-self is love? ___

How do you tell a hun - gry man a-bout the Bread of Life? ___
How do you tell an or - phan child a-bout the Fa-ther's love? ___
How do you help a man who's down to lift his eyes a - bove? ___

How do you tell a thirst - y man a - bout the Liv - ing Wa - ter of the
How do you tell a man who's poor a - bout the won-drous rich - es of the
How do you tell a bleed - ing man a - bout the heal - ing pow - er of the

Lord? ___ How do you tell him of His Word? ___
Lord? ___ How do you tell him of His Word? ___
Lord? ___ How do you tell him of His Word? ___

WORDS: William J. Reynolds
MUSIC: William J. Reynolds
WASHBURN

People to People

Refrain

Peo-ple who know go to peo-ple who need to know Je - sus; _____

Peo-ple who love go to peo-ple a - lone with-out Je - sus; _____

_____ For there are peo-ple who need to see, peo-ple who need to love,

peo-ple who need to know God's re-deem-ing love. Peo-ple who see go to

those who are blind with-out Je - sus, _____ And this is peo-ple to peo - ple,

yes, peo-ple to peo - ple, All shar-ing to - geth - er God's love.

443 If Jesus Goes with Me

Let him deny himself, and take up his cross and follow Me — Matthew 16:24 KJV

1. It may be in the val - ley, where count - less dan - gers hide;
2. It may be I must car - ry the bless - ed word of life
3. But if it be my por - tion to bear my cross at home,
4. It is not mine to ques - tion the judg-ments of my Lord,

It may be in the sun - shine that I, in peace a - bide;
A - cross the burn - ing des - erts to those in sin - ful strife;
While oth - ers bear their bur - dens be - yond the bil - low's foam,
It is but mine to fol - low the lead - ings of His word;

But this one thing I know – if it be dark or fair,
And though it be my lot to bear my col - ors there,
I'll prove my faith in Him – con - fess His judg-ments fair,
But if to go or stay, or wheth - er here or there,

If Je - sus is with me, I'll go an - y - where!
If Je - sus goes with me, I'll go an - y - where!
And if He stays with me, I'll go an - y - where!
I'll be, with my Sav - ior, con - tent an - y - where!

WORD: C. Austin Miles
MUSIC: C. Austin Miles

If Jesus Goes with Me

Refrain

If Je - sus goes with me, I'll go
go, I'll go
An - y - where!

'Tis heav-en to me, Wher-e'er I may be, If He is there!

I count it a priv - i - lege here
here His cross, His cross, His
His cross to bear;
cross to bear;

If Je - sus goes with me, I'll go An - y - where!

444 Count on Me

That our God would count you worthy of this calling — 2 Thessalonians 1:11 KJV

1. The Lord has need of work-ers, to till His field to-day,
2. I count on Thee dear Mas-ter, for cleans-ing in the blood,
3. Now gird me for the bat-tle when e-vil pow'rs op-pose,
4. I'll bear an-oth-er's bur-den a-long a lone-ly way,

So kind-ly He has led me to walk in wis-dom's way;
For con-stant streams of bless-ing, a nev-er fail-ing flood;
And give me faith and cour-age to con-quer o'er Thy foes;
Or teach that bur-den bear-er with con-fi-dence to pray;

I pray for grace to help me with all my heart to say,
To ev-er new fru-i-tion, I see Thy mer-cies bud,
I pledge Thee my al-le-giance, my soul no oth-er knows,
In serv-ice ev-er loy-al, at home or far a-way,

Refrain

O bless-ed Sav-ior, count on me. Count on me, count on me, For
lov-ing-heart-ed serv-ice glad and free; Yes, count on me,

WORDS: E. E. Hewitt
MUSIC: J. Lincoln Hall

Count on Me

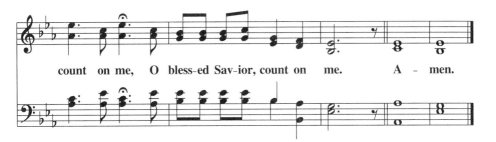

count on me, O bless-ed Sav-ior, count on me. A - men.

O Master, Let Me Walk with Thee 445

And they shall walk, and not faint — Isaiah 40:31 KJV

1. O Mas-ter, let me walk with Thee In low-ly paths of serv-ice free; Tell me Thy se-cret — help me bear The strain of toil, the fret of care.
2. Help me the slow of heart to move By some clear, win-ning word of love; Teach me the way-ward feet to stay, And guide them in the home-ward way.
3. Teach me Thy pa-tience! still with Thee In clos-er, dear-er com-pa-ny, In work that keeps faith sweet and strong, In trust that tri-umphs o-ver wrong.
4. In hope that sends a shin-ing ray Far down the fu-ture's broad-'ning way, In peace that on-ly Thou canst give, With Thee, O Mas-ter, let me live.

WORDS: Washington Gladden
MUSIC: H. Percy Smith

MARYTON

446 Give of Your Best to the Master

Neglect not the gift that is in thee — 1 Timothy 4:14 KJV

1. Give of your best to the Mas - ter, Give of the strength of your youth; _____ Throw your soul's fresh, glow - ing ar - dor In - to the bat - tle for truth. _____ Je - sus has set the ex - am - ple — Daunt-less was
2. Give of your best to the Mas - ter, Give Him first place in your heart; _____ Give Him first place in your serv - ice, Con - se - crate ev - 'ry part. _____ Give, and to you shall be giv - en — God His be -
3. Give of your best to the Mas - ter, Nought else is wor - thy His love; _____ He gave Him - self for your ran - som, Gave up His glo - ry a - bove: _____ Laid down His life with - out mur - mur, You from sin's

WORDS: Howard B. Grose
MUSIC: Charlotte A. Barnard

BARNARD

Give of Your Best to the Master

447 It Pays to Serve Jesus

For it is He that giveth thee power to get wealth — Deuteronomy 8:18 KJV

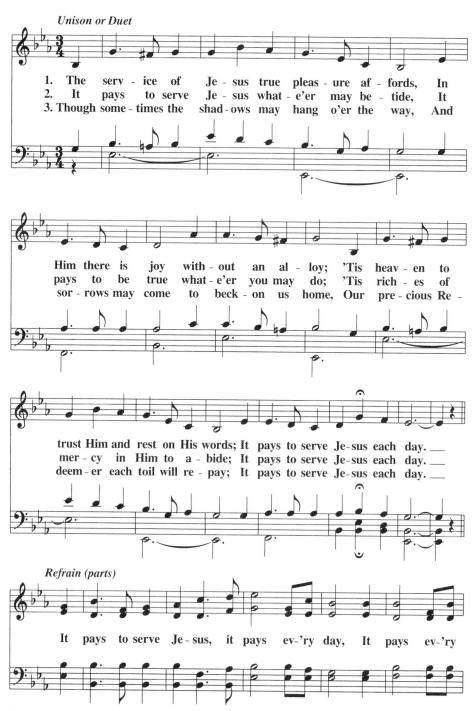

Unison or Duet

1. The serv-ice of Je-sus true pleas-ure af-fords, In
2. It pays to serve Je-sus what-e'er may be-tide, It
3. Though some-times the shad-ows may hang o'er the way, And

Him there is joy with-out an al-loy; 'Tis heav-en to
pays to be true what-e'er you may do; 'Tis rich-es of
sor-rows may come to beck-on us home, Our pre-cious Re-

trust Him and rest on His words; It pays to serve Je-sus each day. __
mer-cy in Him to a-bide; It pays to serve Je-sus each day. __
deem-er each toil will re-pay; It pays to serve Je-sus each day. __

Refrain (parts)

It pays to serve Je-sus, it pays ev-'ry day, It pays ev-'ry

WORDS: Frank C. Huston
MUSIC: Frank C. Huston

It Pays to Serve Jesus

step of the way; _____
step, ev - 'ry step of the way;
Tho' the path-way to glo - ry may

some-times be drear, You'll be hap-py each step of the way. ____

Keep Me True   448

Let us draw near with a true heart — Hebrews 10:22 KJV

Unison

Keep me true, Lord Je - sus, keep me true, Keep me

true, Lord Je-sus, keep me true, There's a race that must be run, There's a

vic-t'ry to be won, Ev-'ry hour by Thy pow'r keep me true.

449 Use Me, O Lord

Serve the Lord with fear — Psalm 2:11 KJV

1. For Thee, dear Lord, a cross I'll bear, And I'll
2. Dear Lord, you've done so much for me, Man-y
3. Not for fame or name that the world might see, But the

go an-y-time an-y-where; I'll not fal-ter from the
things the world can't see; In my heart I yearn Thy
glo-ry be all for Thee; Lord, I'll be true, give me

weight of woe, If you'll lead me, dear Lord, I'll go.
love to re-turn, For Thee, Lord, the fire burns.
work to do, And I'll run all the way for you.

Refrain

Use me, Lord, use me for Thy glo-ry,

Use me, Lord, help me tell love's sto-ry; O use me,
Make my will o-bey,

WORDS: Virgie Carrington DeWitty
MUSIC: Virgie Carrington DeWitty; based on the tune MAITLAND by George N. Allen
© 1947 Virgie C. DeWitty

Use Me, O Lord

Lord,
I'll go all the way,
Use me, O Lord, I pray.

Let There Be Light 450

O send out Thy light and Thy truth; let them lead me — Psalm 43:3 KJV

1. Let there be light, Lord God of hosts, Let there be
2. With-in our pas - sioned hearts in - still The calm that
3. Give us the peace of vi - sion clear To see our
4. Let woe and waste of war - fare cease, That use - ful

wis - dom on the earth! Let broad hu - man - i - ty have
en - deth strain and strife; Make us Thy min - is - ters of
broth - ers' good our own, To joy and suf - fer not a -
la - bor yet may build Its homes with love and laugh - ter

birth; Let there be deeds in - stead of boasts.
life; Purge us from lusts that curse and kill.
lone - The love that cast - eth out all fear!
filled; God, give Thy way - ward chil - dren peace!

WORDS: William M. Vories
MUSIC: William Boyd

PENTECOST

451 Work, for the Night is Coming

I must work the works of Him that sent me, while it is day — John 9:4 KJV

1. Work, for the night is com - ing, Work thru the morn-ing hours;
2. Work, for the night is com - ing, Work thru the sun ny noon;
3. Work, for the night is com - ing, Un - der the sun - set skies;

Work while the dew is spark - ling, Work 'mid spring-ing flow'rs.
Fill bright - est hours with la - bor — Rest comes sure and soon.
While their bright tints are glow - ing, Work, for day - light flies.

Work when the day grows bright - er, Work in the glow-ing sun;
Give ev - 'ry fly - ing min - ute Some-thing to keep in store;
Work till the last beam fad - eth, Fad - eth to shine no more;

Work, for the night is com _ ing, When man's work is done.
Work, for the night is com _ ing, When man works no more.
Work, while the night is dark _ 'ning, When man's work is o'er.

WORDS: Annie L. Coghill
MUSIC: Lowell Mason

WORK SONG

Ring Out the Old, Ring In the New 452

If any man be in Christ Jesus, he is a new creature — 2 Corinthians 5:17 KJV

1. Ring out the old, ring in the new, Ring,
2. Ring out a slow - ly dy - ing cause, And
3. Ring out old shapes of foul dis - ease, Ring
4. Ring in the val - iant man and free, The

hap - py bells a - cross the snow: The
an - cient forms of par - ty strife; Ring
out the nar - r'wing lust of gold; Ring
larg - er heart, the kind - lier hand; Ring

year is go - ing, let him go; Ring
in the no - bler modes of life, With
out the thou - sand wars of old, Ring
out the dark - ness of the land, Ring

out the false, ring in the true.
sweet - er man - ners, pur - er laws.
in the thou - sand years of peace.
in the Christ that is to be. A - men.

WORDS: Alfred Tennyson
MUSIC: John Baptiste Calkin

WALTHAM

453 Another Year Is Dawning

Thy years are throughout all generations — Psalm 102:24 KJV

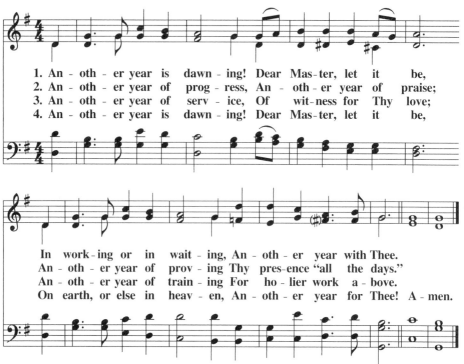

1. An - oth - er year is dawn - ing! Dear Mas-ter, let it be,
2. An - oth - er year of prog - ress, An - oth - er year of praise;
3. An - oth - er year of serv - ice, Of wit-ness for Thy love;
4. An - oth - er year is dawn - ing! Dear Mas-ter, let it be,

In work-ing or in wait - ing, An - oth - er year with Thee.
An - oth - er year of prov - ing Thy pres-ence "all the days."
An - oth - er year of train - ing For ho - lier work a - bove.
On earth, or else in heav - en, An - oth - er year for Thee! A - men.

WORDS: Frances R. Havergal
MUSIC: Friedrich von Flotow

Praise ye the Lord. Praise the Lord, O my soul. While I live will I praise the Lord: I will sing praises unto my God while I have any being. Put not your trust in princes, nor in the son of man, in whom there is no help. His breath goeth forth, he returneth to his earth; in that very day his thoughts perish. Happy is he that hath the God of Jacob for his help, whose hope is in the Lord his God: Which made heaven, and earth, the sea, and all that therein is: which keepeth truth forever: Which executeth judgment for the oppressed: which giveth food to the hungry. The Lord looseth the prisoners: The Lord openeth the eyes of the blind: the Lord raiseth them that are bowed down: the Lord loveth the righteous: The Lord preserveth the strangers; he relieveth the fatherless and widow: but the way of the wicked he turneth upside down. The Lord shall reign forever, even thy God, O Zion, unto all generations. Praise ye the Lord. (Psalm 146:1-10 KJV)

America, the Beautiful 454

And be ye saved, all the ends of the earth — Isaiah 45:22 KJV

1. O beau-ti-ful for spa-cious skies, For am-ber waves of grain,
2. O beau-ti-ful for pil-grim feet, Whose stern, im-pas-sioned stress
3. O beau-ti-ful for he-roes proved In lib-er-at-ing strife,
4. O beau-ti-ful for pa-triot dream That sees, be-yond the years,

For pur-ple moun-tain maj-es-ties A-bove the fruit-ed plain!
A thor-ough-fare for free-dom beat A-cross the wil-der-ness!
Who more than self their coun-try loved And mer-cy more than life!
Thine al-a-bas-ter cit-ies gleam – Un-dimmed by hu-man tears!

A-mer-i-ca! A-mer-i-ca! God shed His grace on thee,
A-mer-i-ca! A-mer-i-ca! God mend thine ev-'ry flaw,
A-mer-i-ca! A-mer-i-ca! May God thy gold re-fine,
A-mer-i-ca! A-mer-i-ca! God shed His grace on thee,

And crown thy good with broth-er-hood From sea to shin-ing sea.
Con-firm thy soul in self-con-trol, Thy lib-er-ty in law.
Till all suc-cess be no-ble-ness, And ev-'ry gain di-vine.
And crown thy good with broth-er-hood From sea to shin-ing sea.

WORDS: Katharine Lee Bates
MUSIC: Samuel A. Ward

MATERNA

455 Battle Hymn of the Republic

Surely I come quickly — Revelation 22:20 KJV

1. Mine eyes have seen the glo - ry of the com - ing of the Lord,
2. I have seen Him in the watch-fires of a hun-dred cir-cling camps,
3. He has sound-ed forth the trum - pet that shall nev - er sound re - treat,
4. In the beau - ty of the lil - ies Christ was born a - cross the sea,

He is tram-pling out the vin-tage where the grapes of wrath are stored;
They have build - ed Him an al - tar in the eve-ning dews and damps;
He is sift - ing out the hearts of men be - fore His judg-ment seat;
With a glo - ry in His bos - om that trans - fig - ures you and me;

He hath loosed the fate - ful light-ning of His ter - ri - ble swift sword – His
I can read His right-eous sen-tence by the dim and flar - ing lamps – His
O be swift, my soul, to an - swer Him, be ju - bi-lant, my feet! Our
As He died to make men ho - ly, let us die to make men free, While

Refrain

truth is march-ing on.
day is march-ing on.
God is march-ing on.
God is march-ing on.

Glo-ry! glo-ry, hal-le - lu-jah! Glo-ry! glo-ry, hal-le-

WORDS: Julia Ward Howe
MUSIC: William Steffe

BATTLE HYMN

Battle Hymn of the Republic

lu - jah! Glo - ry! glo-ry, hal-le - lu - jah! His truth is march-ing on.

My Country, 'Tis of Thee 456

To set at liberty them that are bruised — Luke 4:18 KJV

1. My coun - try, 'tis of thee, Sweet land of lib - er - ty,
2. My na - tive coun - try, thee, Land of the no - ble free,
3. Let mu - sic swell the breeze, And ring from all the trees
4. Our fa - thers' God, to Thee, Au - thor of lib - er - ty,

Of thee I sing: Land where my fa - thers died, Land of the
Thy name I love: I love thy rocks and rills, Thy woods and
Sweet free-dom's song: Let mor - tal tongues a - wake, Let all that
To Thee we sing: Long may our land be bright With free-dom's

pil - grims' pride, From ev - 'ry moun-tain side Let free-dom ring!
tem - pled hills; My heart with rap - ture thrills Like that a - bove.
breathe par - take; Let rocks their si - lence break, The sound pro-long.
ho - ly light; Pro-tect us by Thy might, Great God, our King!

WORDS: Samuel Francis Smith
MUSIC: From *Thesaurus Musicus*, 1744

AMERICA

457 Lift Every Voice and Sing

National Negro Hymn

Ethiopia shall soon stretch out her hands unto God — Psalm 68:31 KJV

1. Lift ev-'ry voice and sing, till earth and heav - en
2. Ston-y the road we trod, bit - ter the chast - 'ning
3. God of our wea - ry years, God of our si - lent

ring, Ring with the har - mo - nies of lib - er -
rod, Felt in the days when hope un - born had
tears, Thou who hast brought us thus far on the

ty; Let our re - joic - ing rise high as the lis - t'ning
died; Yet with a stead - y beat, have not our wea - ry
way; Thou who hast by Thy might led us in - to the

skies, Let it re - sound loud as the roll - ing sea.
feet Come to the place for which our fa - thers sighed?
light, Keep us for - ev - er in the path, we pray.

WORDS: James Weldon Johnson
MUSIC: R. Rosamond Johnson
LIFT EVERY VOICE

Lift Every Voice and Sing

458   The Star-Spangled Banner

Live as free men ... live as servants of God — 1 Peter 2:16 KJV

1. O say, can you see, by the dawn's ear - ly light,
2. O thus be it ev - er, when free men shall stand

What so proud - ly we hailed at the twi-light's last gleam-ing,
Be - tween their loved homes and the war's des - o - la - tion!

Whose broad stripes and bright stars, through the per - il - ous fight,
Blest with vic - t'ry and peace, may the heav'n res-cued land

O'er the ram - parts we watched, were so gal - lant - ly stream-ing?
Praise the Pow'r that hath made and pre-served us a na - tion!

WORDS: Francis Scott Key
MUSIC: Origin unknown; attr. to John Stafford Smith

NATIONAL ANTHEM

The Star-Spangled Banner

459 God of Our Fathers

Blessed be the Lord God of our fathers — Ezra 7:27 KJV

Trumpets, before each stanza

1. God of our fa-thers, whose al-might-y
2. Thy love di-vine hath led us in the
3. From war's a-larms, from dead-ly pes-ti-
4. Re-fresh Thy peo-ple on their toil-some

hand   Leads forth in beau-ty all the star-ry band
past,   In this free land by Thee our lot is cast;
lence,   Be Thy strong arm our ev-er-sure de-fense;
way,   Lead us from night to nev-er-end-ing day;

Of shin-ing worlds in splen-dor thru the skies,
Be Thou our rul - er, guard-ian, guide, and stay,
Thy true re - li - gion in our hearts in-crease,
Fill all our lives with love and grace di - vine,

Our grate-ful songs be-fore Thy throne a - rise.
Thy word our law, Thy paths our cho-sen way.
Thy boun-teous good - ness nour-ish us in peace.
And glo-ry, laud, and praise be ev-er Thine!

WORDS: Daniel C. Roberts
MUSIC: George W. Warren

NATIONAL HYMN

God Bless America

460

He will be our guide, even unto death — Psalm 48:14 KJV

God bless A - mer-i - ca, ___ Land that I love; ___ Stand be -
side her ___ and guide her ___ Thru the night with a light from a -
bove. _ From the moun-tains ___ To the prai- ries, ___ To the
From the moun-tains To the prai-ries, To the
o - ceans ___ white with foam, ___ God bless A -
mer-i - ca, ___ My home sweet home, ___ home. ___

WORDS: Irving Berlin
MUSIC: Irving Berlin

GOD BLESS AMERICA

461 Day Is Dying in the West

Even the night shall be light about me — Psalm 139:11 KJV

1. Day is dy - ing in the west, Heav'n is touch - ing
2. Lord of life, be - neath the dome Of the u - ni -
3. While the deep - 'ning shad - ows fall, Heart of Love, en -
4. When for - ev - er from our sight Pass the stars, the

earth with rest; Wait and wor-ship while the night Sets her eve - ning
verse, Thy home, Gath - er us, who seek Thy face, To the fold of
fold - ing all, Thru the glo - ry and the grace Of the stars that
day, the night, Lord of an - gels, on our eyes Let e - ter - nal

Refrain

lamps a - light Thru all the sky.
Thy em - brace, For Thou art nigh.
veil Thy face, Our hearts as - cend.
morn - ing rise, And shad - ows end!

Ho - ly, Ho - ly,

Ho - ly, Lord God of Hosts! Heav'n and earth are full of Thee!

WORDS: Mary A. Lathbury
MUSIC: William F. Sherwin

CHAUTAUQUA

Day Is Dying in the West

Heav'n and earth are prais-ing Thee, O Lord Most High!

Now the Day Is Over 462

Weeping may endure for a night,
but joy cometh in the morning — Psalm 30:5 KJV

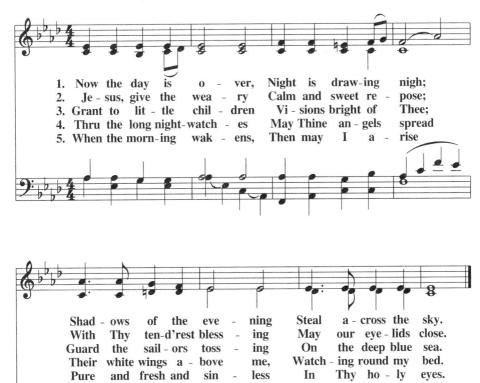

1. Now the day is o - ver, Night is draw-ing nigh;
2. Je - sus, give the wea - ry Calm and sweet re - pose;
3. Grant to lit - tle chil - dren Vi - sions bright of Thee;
4. Thru the long night-watch - es May Thine an - gels spread
5. When the morn-ing wak - ens, Then may I a - rise

Shad - ows of the eve - ning Steal a - cross the sky.
With Thy ten-d'rest bless - ing May our eye - lids close.
Guard the sail - ors toss - ing On the deep blue sea.
Their white wings a - bove me, Watch - ing round my bed.
Pure and fresh and sin - less In Thy ho - ly eyes.

1. eve-ning Steal a - cross the sky.

WORDS: Sabine Baring-Gould
MUSIC: Joseph Barnby

MERRIAL

463   I'll Be Singing Up There

It shall blossom abundantly, and rejoice even with joy and singing — Isaiah 35:2 KJV

Refrain

I'll be sing-ing up there,
up, sing-ing up there,

I'll be sing-ing up there, Oh!
yes, sing-ing up there,

come on up to bright glo - ry,

I'll be sing-ing up there.
1. If you miss me
2. If you miss me
3. If you miss me
4. If you miss me

WORDS: Unknown
MUSIC: Unknown; arr. by W. O. Hoyle, Lillian Bowles, and W. Webb

I'll Be Singing Up There

sing - ing down here, If you miss me
pray - ing down here, If you miss me
walk - ing down here, If you miss me
shout - ing down here, If you miss me

sing - ing down here, Oh, come on up to bright
pray - ing down here, Oh, come on up to bright
walk - ing down here, Oh, come on up to bright
shout - ing down here, Oh, come on up to bright

glo - ry, You'll find me sing - ing up there.
glo - ry, You'll find me pray - ing up there.
glo - ry, You'll find me walk - ing up there.
glo - ry, You'll find me shout - ing up there.

464 Where We'll Never Grow Old

And lo, I am with you always, even unto the end of the world — Matthew 28:20 KJV

1. I have heard of a land on the far - a - way strand,
2. In that beau - ti - ful home where we'll nev - er-more roam,
3. When our work here is done and the life crown is won,

'Tis a beau - ti - ful home of the soul;
We shall be in the sweet by and by;
And our trou - bles and tri - als are o'er,

Built by Je - sus on high, there we nev - er shall die,
Hap-py praise to the King thru e - ter - nit - ty sing,
All our sor - row will end, and our voic - es will blend

'Tis a land where we nev - er grow old.
'Tis a land where we nev - er shall die.
With the loved ones who've gone on be - fore.

WORDS: James C. Moore
MUSIC: James C. Moore

Where We'll Never Grow Old

And he carried me away in the Spirit to a mountain great and high, and showed me the Holy City, Jerusalem, coming down out of heaven from God. It shone with the glory of God, and its brilliance was like that of a very precious jewel, like a jasper, clear as crystal. It had a great, high wall with twelve gates, and with twelve angels at the gates. On the gates were written the names of the twelve tribes of Israel. There were three gates on the east, three on the north, three on the south and three on the west. The wall of the city had twelve foundations, and on them were the names of the twelve apostles of the Lamb. The angel who talked with me had a measuring rod of gold to measure the city, its gates and its walls. The city was laid out like a square, as long as it was wide. He measured the city with the rod and found it to be 12,000 stadia in length, and as wide and high as it is long. He measured its wall and it was 144 cubits thick, by man's measurement, which the angel was using. The wall was made of jasper, and the city of pure gold, as pure as glass.

(Adapted from Revelation 21:10-18 KJV)

465   I'll Fly Away

Be thou faithful unto death, and I will give thee a crown of life — Revelation 2:10 KJV

1. Some glad morn - ing when this life is o'er,
2. When the shad - ows of this life have grown,
3. Just a few more wea - ry days and then,

I'll (fly a-way,) fly a-way, (fly a-way,)   To a home on
I'll (fly a-way,) fly a-way, (fly a-way,)   Like a bird from
I'll (fly a-way,) fly a-way, (fly a-way,)   To a land where

God's ce - les - tial shore,   I'll (fly a-way,) fly a -
pris - on bars has flown,   I'll (fly a-way,) fly a -
joys shall nev - er end,   I'll (fly a-way,) fly a -

Refrain

way, (fly a-way,)
way, (fly a-way,)   I'll (fly a-way,) fly a -
way, (fly a-way,)

WORDS: Albert E. Brumley
MUSIC: Albert E. Brumley; arr. by L. M. Bowles and Theo. R. Frye

I'll Fly Away

way, oh glo - ry, I'll (fly a - way,) fly a - way. (In the morn - ing.)

When I die, hal - le - lu - jah, by and by,

I'll (fly a - way,) fly a - way, (fly a - way.)

But I would not have you to be ignorant, brethren, concerning them which are asleep, that ye sorrow not, even as others which have no hope. For if we believe that Jesus died and rose again, even so them also which sleep in Jesus will God bring with him.For this we say unto you by the word of the Lord, that we which are alive and remain unto the coming of the Lord shall not prevent them which are asleep. For the Lord himself shall descend from heaven with a shout, with the voice of the archangel, and with the trump of God: and the dead in Christ shall rise first: Then we which are alive and remain shall be caught up together with them in the clouds, to meet the Lord in the air: and so shall we ever be with the Lord. Wherefore comfort one another with these words.
(1 Thessolonians 4:13-18 KJV)

466 He Understands, He'll Say, "Well Done"

Well done, thou good and faithful servant — Matthew 25:21 KJV

1. If when you give the best of your
2. Mis - un - der - stood, the Sav - ior of
3. If when this life of la - bor is
4. But if you try and fail in your

serv - ice, Tell - ing the world that the Sav - ior is
sin - ners, Hung on the cross; He was God's on - ly
end - ed, And the re - ward of the race you have
try - ing, Hands sore and scarred from the work you've be -

come; Be not dis - mayed when men don't be -
Son; Oh! hear Him call - ing His Fa - ther
run; Oh! the sweet rest pre - pared for the
gun; Take up your cross, run quick - ly to

lieve you; He un - der - stands; He'll say, "Well done."
in Heav'n, "Not my will, but Thine be done."
faith - ful, Will be His blest and fi - nal "Well done."
meet Him; He'll un - der - stand, He'll say, "Well done."

WORDS: Lucie E. Campbell
MUSIC: Lucie E. Campbell

He Understands, He'll Say, "Well Done"

Again, it will be like a man going on a journey, who called his servants and entrusted his property to them. To one he gave five talents of money, to another two talents, and to another one talent, each according to his ability. Then he went on his journey. The man who had received the five talents went at once and put his money to work and gained five more. So also, the one with the two talents gained two more. But the man who had received the one talent went off, dug a hole in the ground and hid his master's money. After a long time the master of those servants returned and settled accounts with them. The man who had received the five talents brought the other five. "Master," he said, "you entrusted me with five talents. See, I have gained five more." His master replied, "Well done, good and faithful servant! You have been faithful with a few things; I will put you in charge of many things. Come and share your master's happiness!" (Adapted from Matthew 25:14-21 KJV)

467   Face to Face

For now we see through a glass, darkly; but then face to face — 1 Corinthians 13:12 KJV

1. Face to face with Christ, my Sav - ior,
2. On - ly faint - ly now I see Him,
3. What re - joic - ing in His pres - ence,
4. Face to face – oh, bliss - ful mo - ment!

Face to face – what will it be, When with rap-ture I be -
With the dark - ling veil be - tween, But a bless-ed day is
When are ban - ished grief and pain; When the crook-ed ways are
Face to face – to see and know; Face to face with my Re -

hold Him, Je - sus Christ who died for me.
com - ing, When His glo - ry shall be seen.
straight - ened, And the dark things shall be plain.
deem - er, Je - sus Christ who loves me so.

Refrain

Face to face I shall be - hold Him, Far be-yond the star-ry sky;

Face to face in all His glo - ry, I shall see Him by and by!

WORDS: Carrie E. Breck
MUSIC: Grant Colfax Tullar

FACE TO FACE

When We All Get to Heaven

468

And so shall we ever be with the Lord — 1 Thessalonians 4:17 KJV

1. Sing the won-drous love of Je - sus, Sing His mer - cy
2. While we walk the pil - grim path-way Clouds will o - ver -
3. Let us then be true and faith - ful, Trust-ing, serv - ing
4. On - ward to the prize be - fore us! Soon His beau - ty

and His grace; In the man - sions bright and bless - ed
spread the sky; But when trav - 'ling days are o - ver
ev - 'ry day; Just one glimpse of Him in glo - ry
we'll be - hold; Soon the pearl - y gates will o - pen —

Refrain

He'll pre - pare for us a place.
Not a shad - ow, not a sigh. When we all get to
Will the toils of life re - pay. When we all
We shall tread the streets of gold.

heav - en, What a day of re-joic-ing that will be! When we
What a day of re - joic-ing that will be!

all see Je - sus, We'll sing and shout the vic-to - ry!
When we all shout, and shout the vic-to-ry!

WORDS: Eliza E. Hewitt
MUSIC: Emily D. Wilson

HEAVEN

469   Just Over in the Glory Land

We are ... willing ... to be absent from the body,
and to be present with the Lord — 2 Corinthians 5:8 KJV

1. I've a home pre-pared where the saints a - bide, Just o-ver in the glo-ry land; And I long to be by my Sav-ior's side, Just o-ver in the glo-ry land.

2. I am on my way to those man-sions fair, Just o-ver in the glo-ry land; There to sing God's praise, and His glo-ry share, Just o-ver in the glo-ry land.

3. What a joy-ful thought that my Lord I'll see, Just o-ver in the glo-ry land; And with kin-dred saved, there for-ev-er be, Just o-ver in the glo-ry land.

4. With the blood-washed throng I will shout and sing, Just o-ver in the glo-ry land; Glad ho-san-nas to Christ, the Lord and King, Just o-ver in the glo-ry land.

Refrain

Just o - ver in the glo-ry land, I'll join the hap-py
Just o - ver, o-ver in the glo-ry land, I'll join, yes, join the hap-py

WORDS: James W. Acuff
MUSIC: Emmet S. Dean

Just Over in the Glory Land

an - gel band, Just   o - ver in the glo - ry   land;   Just
an - gel band,   Just

o   -   ver in the glo - ry   land, There   with   the might-y
o - ver,   o - ver in the   glo - ry   land, There   with, yes, with the might-y

host   I'll   stand, Just   o - ver   in the   glo - ry   land.
host   I'll   stand,

Now we know that if the earthly tent we live in is destroyed, we have a building from God, an eternal house in heaven, not built by human hands. Meanwhile we groan, longing to be clothed with our heavenly dwelling, because when we are clothed, we will not be found naked. For while we are in this tent, we groan and are burdened, because we do not wish to be unclothed but to be clothed with our heavenly dwelling, so that what is mortal may be swallowed up by life. Now it is God who has made us for this very purpose and has given us the Spirit as a deposit, guaranteeing what is to come. Therefore we are always confident and know that as long as we are at home in the body we are away from the Lord. We live by faith, not by sight. We are confident, I say, and would prefer to be away from the body and at home with the Lord.
(Adapted from 2 Corinthians 5:1-8 KJV)

470 God Shall Wipe All Tears Away

And there shall be no more death, neither sorrow, nor crying — Revelation 21:4 KJV

1. Tho' the clouds may hov-er o'er us, There's a
2. No more sor-row, no more weep-ing, Peace and
3. Ev-'ry care will be for-got-ten, All our
4. O, the joy of meet-ing Je-sus, Mor-tal

bright and gold-en ray, It's the prom-ise that in
joy shall hold full sway, For be-side life's crys-tal
bur-dens we shall lay, Safe with-in the walls of
tongue can-not por-tray, But we know when we be-

Refrain

heav-en God shall wipe all tears a-way.
riv-er God shall wipe all tears a-way.
jas-per God shall wipe all tears a-way.   When we reach
hold Him God shall wipe all tears a-way.

that bless-ed home-land, Where 'tis ev-er-last-ing day, On that

bright e-ter-nal morn-ing God shall wipe all tears a-way.

WORDS: Antonio L. Haskell
MUSIC: Antonio L. Haskell

Beyond the Sunset

471

But ye are come unto Mount Zion,
and unto the city of the living God — Hebrews 12:22 KJV

1. Be - yond the sun - set, O bliss - ful morn - ing, When with our Sav - ior heav'n is be - gun. Earth's toil - ing end - ed, O glo - rious dawn - ing; Be-yond the sun - set, when day is done.

2. Be - yond the sun - set, no clouds will gath - er, No storms will threat - en, no fears an - noy; O day of glad - ness, O day un - end - ing, Be-yond the sun - set, e - ter - nal joy!

3. Be - yond the sun - set, a hand will guide me To God, the Fa - ther, whom I a - dore; His glo - rious pres - ence, His words of wel - come, Will be my por - tion on that fair shore.

4. Be - yond the sun - set, O glad re - un - ion, With our dear loved ones who've gone be - fore; In that fair home - land we'll know no part - ing, Be-yond the sun - set for - ev - er - more!

WORDS: Virgil P. Brock
MUSIC: Blanche Kerr Brock
SUNSET

472 On Jordan's Stormy Banks

A land which the Lord thy God careth for — Deuteronomy 11:12 KJV

1. On Jordan's storm-y banks I stand And cast a wish-ful eye To Canaan's fair and happy land, Where my possessions lie.
2. All o'er those wide-extend-ed plains Shines one e-ter-nal day; There God the Son for-ever reigns And scatters night away.
3. No chill-ing winds nor poi-s'nous breath Can reach that health-ful shore; Sick-ness and sor-row, pain and death Are felt and feared no more.
4. When shall I reach that happy place And be for-ev-er blest? Fa-ther's face And in His bos-om rest?

Refrain

I am bound for the prom-ised land, I am

WORDS: Samuel Stennett
MUSIC: American folk tune; arr. by Rigdon M. McIntosh

PROMISED LAND

On Jordan's Stormy Banks

bound for the prom-ised land; O who will come and
go with me? I am bound for the prom-ised land.

And it came to pass, when all the people were clean passed over Jordan, that the Lord spake unto Joshua, saying, "Take you twelve men out of the people, out of every tribe a man, And command ye them, saying, 'Take you hence out of the midst of Jordan, out of the place where the priests' feet stood firm, twelve stones, and ye shall carry them over with you, and leave them in the lodging place, where ye shall lodge this night.'" Then Joshua called the twelve men, whom he had prepared of the children of Israel, out of every tribe a man: And Joshua said unto them, "Pass over before the ark of the Lord your God into the midst of Jordan, and take you up every man of you a stone upon his shoulder, according unto the number of tribes of the children of Israel: That this may be a sign among you, that when your children ask their fathers in time to come, saying, 'What mean ye by these stones?' Then ye shall answer them, 'That the waters of Jordan were cut off before the ark of the covenant of the Lord; when it passed over Jordan, the waters of Jordan were cut off: and these stones shall be for a memorial unto the children of Israel for ever.'"
(Joshua 4:1-7 KJV)

473 I Bowed on My Knees and Cried "Holy"

Holy, Holy, Holy is the Lord of hosts — Isaiah 6:3 KJV

Unison

1. I dreamed of that cit - y called Glo - ry, _____ so
2. I thought when I en - tered that cit - y, _____ my
3. I thought when I saw my dear Sav - ior, _____ there

bright and so fair, _____ When I en-tered the gate I cried,
loved ones knew me well, _____ They showed me all thru
seat - ed on His throne, _____ Oh, the won - der that He could

"Ho - ly," _____ the an - gels all wel comed me - there. _____ They
heav-en, _____ the scenes are too num-'rous to tell. _____ I
love me, _____ and call me His ver - y own. _____ I

led me from man - sion to man - sion, _____ and, oh, the
saw A-br'ham, I - saac, and Ja - cob, _____ Mark, Luke, and
bowed down and wor-shipped this Sav - ior, _____ my friend of

WORDS: Nettie Dudley Washington
MUSIC: E. M. Dudley Cantwell

I Bowed on My Knees and Cried "Holy"

sights I saw; _____ But I said, "I want to see
Tim - o - thy; _____ But I said, "Let me bow down and
Cal - va - ry; _____ And I want - ed to praise Him for -

Je - sus, _____ the One who died for all." _____
wor - ship _____ the One who died for me." _____
ev - er _____ for sav - ing one like me. _____

Refrain

Then I fell on my knees and cried, "Ho - ly," ___ "Ho - ly," ___
"Ho - ly,"

"Ho - ly, Ho - ly,"

"Ho - ly," _____ I fell at His feet and sang, "Glo - ry, _____
"Ho - ly," "Glo - ry,"

1, 2 *3*

glo - ry to the Son of God." ___ Son of God." _____
God, of God."

474 Life's Railway to Heaven

And the Lord shall guide thee continually — Isaiah 58:11 KJV

Unison or Two-part

1. Life is like a moun-tain rail - road, With an en - gi - neer that's brave; We must make the run suc - cess-ful, From the cra - dle to the grave; Watch the curves, the fills, the tun - nels; Nev - er fal - ter, nev - er

2. You will roll up grades of tri - al; You will cross the bridge of strife; See that Christ is your con - duc-tor On this light - ning train of life; Al - ways mind - ful of ob - struc - tion, Do your du - ty, nev - er

3. You will oft - en find ob - struc - tions; Look for storms of wind and rain; On a fill, or curve, or tres - tle, They will al - most ditch your train; Put your trust a - lone in Je - sus; Nev - er fal - ter, nev - er

4. As you roll a - cross the tres - tle, Span-ning Jor - dan's swell - ing tide, You be - hold the Un - ion De - pot In - to which your train will glide; There you'll meet the Su-p'rin-tend - ent, God the Fa - ther, God the

WORDS: M. E. Abbey
MUSIC: Charlie D. Tillman

Life's Railway to Heaven

475 Goin' Home

And there shall be no more death, neither sorrow, nor crying — Revelation 21:4 KJV

1. Go - in' home, go - in' home, I'm a - go - in' home;
2. Morn - ing star lights the way, Rest - less dream all done;

Qui - et - like, some still day, I'm just go - in' home.
Shad - ows gone, break of day, Real life just be - gun.

It's not far, just close by, Through an o - pen door;
There's no break, there's no end, Just a - liv - ing on;

Work all done, care laid by, going to fear no more.
Wide a - wake, with a smile go - ing on and on.

Moth - er's there ex - pect - ing me, Fa - ther's wait - ing, too;
Go - in' home, go - in' home, I'm just go - in' home,

WORDS: William Arms Fisher
MUSIC: Antonin Dvorak
Words © 1922 Oliver Ditson Co., renewed Theodore Presser Co.

Goin' Home

Lots of folk gath-ered there, All the friends I knew.
It's not far, just close by Through an o-pen door.

Soon and Very Soon 476

Surely I come quickly — Revelation 22:20 KJV

1. Soon and ver-y soon, we are going to see the King;
2. No more cry-ing there, we are going to see the King;
3. No more dy-ing there, we are going to see the King;

Soon and ver-y soon, we are going to see the King;
No more cry-ing there, we are going to see the King;
No more dy-ing there, we are going to see the King;

Soon and ver-y soon, we are going to see the King;
No more cry-ing there, we are going to see the King; Hal-le-
No more dy-ing there, we are going to see the King;

lu - jah! Hal-le-lu - jah! We're going to see the King.

WORDS: Andraé Crouch
MUSIC: Andraé Crouch

477 The Unclouded Day

Even a morning without clouds — 2 Samuel 23:4 KJV

1. O they tell me of a home far be - yond the skies,
2. O they tell me of a home where my friends have gone,
3. O they tell me of a King in His beau - ty there,
4. O they tell me that He smiles on His chil - dren there,

O they tell me of a home far a - way;
O they tell me of that land far a - way,
And they tell me that mine eyes shall be - hold
And His smile drives their sor - rows all a - way;

O they tell me of a home where no storm - clouds rise,
Where the tree of life in e - ter - nal bloom
Where He sits on the throne that is whit - er than snow,
And they tell me that no tears ev - er come a - gain,

O they tell me of an un - cloud - ed day.
Sheds its fra - grance thru the un - cloud - ed day.
In the cit - y that is made of gold.
In that love - ly land of un - cloud - ed day.

WORDS: Rev. J. K. Alwood
MUSIC: Rev. J. K. Alwood

THE UNCLOUDED DAY

The Unclouded Day

Then I saw a new heaven and a new earth, for the first heaven and the first earth had passed away, and there was no longer any sea. I saw the Holy City, the new Jerusalem, coming down out of heaven from God, prepared as a bride beautifully dressed for her husband. And I heard a loud voice from the throne saying, "Now the dwelling of God is with men, and he will live with them. They will be his people, and God himself will be with them and be their God. He will wipe every tear from their eyes. There will be no more death or mourning or crying or pain, for the old order of things has passed away." He who was seated on the throne said, "I am making everything new!" Then he said, "Write this down, for these words are trustworthy and true." He said to me, "It is done. I am the Alpha and the Omega, the Beginning and the End. To him who is thirsty I will give to drink without cost from the spring of the water of life. He who overcomes will inherit all this, and I will be his God and he will be my son." (Adapted from Revelation 21:1-7 KJV)

478　In My Home Over There

For He hath prepared for them a city — Hebrews 11:16 KJV

1. When my work on earth is done, At the set-ting of the
2. When I reach my jour-ney's end, And I bid fare-well to
3. Just a few more years I know, And my wea-ry soul must

sun, I am go-ing to my home o-ver there.
men, I will seek e-ter-nal rest from all care.
go To a land with neith-er bur-dens or care,

— I will walk the gold-en stair, And be free from ev-'ry
You can look for me to go To that oth-er gold-en
For be-yond the stars a-bove, Where I'll dwell in peace and

care, I'll be hap-py in my home o-ver there.
shore, And be hap-py in my home o-ver there.
love, I'll be hap-py in my home o-ver there.

WORDS: H. J. Ford
MUSIC: H. J. Ford; arr. by Roberta Martin
© 1946 by H. J. Ford. Used by permission.

In My Home Over There

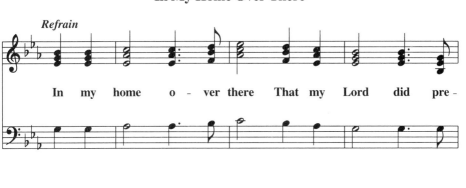

In my home o - ver there That my Lord did pre-

pare, There is peace, there is joy ev-'ry - where. ___

___ I will see His face so fair, and a star - ry crown I'll

wear; I'll be hap-py in my home o - ver there. ___

479 When I Can Read My Title Clear

If our earthly house … were dissolved, we have a building of God — 2 Corinthians 5:1 KJV

1. When I can read my ti - tle clear To man-sions in the skies,
2. Should earth a - gainst my soul en - gage, And fi - ery darts be hurled,
3. Let cares, like a wild de-luge come, And storms of sor - row fall!
4. There shall I bathe my wea-ry soul In seas of heav'n-ly rest,

I'll bid fare-well to ev - 'ry fear And wipe my weep - ing eyes.
Then I can smile at Sa - tan's rage And face a frown - ing world.
May I but safe - ly reach my home, My God, my heav'n, my all.
And not a wave of trou - ble roll A - cross my peace - ful breast.

And wipe my weep - ing eyes, And wipe my weep - ing eyes,
And face a frown - ing world, And face a frown - ing world,
My God, my heav'n, my all, My God, my heav'n, my all,
A - cross my peace - ful breast, A - cross my peace - ful breast,

I'll bid fare-well to ev - 'ry fear And wipe my weep - ing eyes.
Then I can smile at Sa - tan's rage And face a frown - ing world.
May I but safe - ly reach my home, My God, my heav'n, my all.
And not a wave of trou - ble roll A - cross my peace - ful breast.

WORDS: Isaac Watts
MUSIC: Attr. to Joseph C. Lowry, 19th cent.

PISGAH

There's a Great Day Coming 480

Be ye therefore ready — Luke 12:40 KJV

1. There's a great day com-ing, A great day com-ing, There's a
2. There's a bright day com-ing, A bright day com-ing, There's a
3. There's a sad day com-ing, A sad day com-ing, There's a

great day com-ing by and by, When the saints and the sin-ners shall be
bright day com-ing by and by, But its bright-ness shall on-ly come to
sad day com-ing by and by, When the sin-ner shall hear His doom, "De-

part-ed right and left, Are you read-y for that day to come?
them that love the Lord, Are you read-y for that day to come?
part, I know ye not!" Are you read-y for that day to come?

Refrain

Are you read-y? Are you read-y? Are you read-y for the judg-ment day?

Are you read-y? Are you read-y? for the judg-ment day?

WORDS: Will L. Thompson
MUSIC: Will L. Thompson

481 When the Roll Is Called Up Yonder

And it shall come to pass ... that the great trumpet shall be blown — Isaiah 27:13 KJV

1. When the trum - pet of the Lord shall sound and
2. On that bright and cloud - less morn - ing when the
3. Let us la - bor for the Mas - ter from the

time shall be no more, And the morn-ing breaks e - ter - nal, bright and
dead in Christ shall rise, And the glo - ry of His res - ur - rec - tion
dawn till set - ting sun, Let us talk of all His won-drous love and

fair – When the saved of earth shall gath - er o - ver
share – When His cho - sen ones shall gath - er to their
care; Then when all of life is o - ver and our

on the oth - er shore, And the roll is called up yon-der, I'll be there!
home be-yond the skies, And the roll is called up yon-der, I'll be there!
work on earth is done, And the roll is called up yon-der, I'll be there!

WORDS: James M. Black
MUSIC: James M. Black

ROLL CALL

When the Roll Is Called Up Yonder

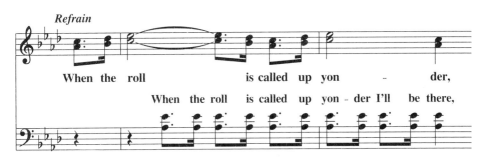

When the roll is called up yon - der,
When the roll is called up yon - der I'll be there,

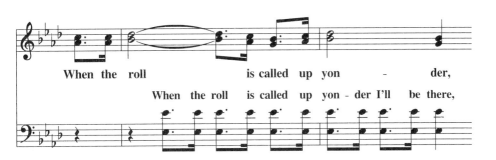

When the roll is called up yon - der,
When the roll is called up yon - der I'll be there,

When the roll is called up yon - der,
When the roll is called up yon - der

When the roll is called up yon - der, I'll be there!

482   Safe in the Arms of Jesus

Thou wilt keep him in perfect peace whose mind is stayed on Thee — Isaiah 26:3 KJV

1. Safe in the arms of Je - sus, Safe on His gen - tle breast,
2. Safe in the arms of Je - sus, Safe from cor - rod - ing care,
3. Je - sus, my heart's dear ref - uge, Je - sus has died for me;

There by His love o'er - shad - ed, Sweet-ly my soul shall rest.
Safe from the world's temp - ta - tions, Sin can-not harm me there.
Firm on the Rock of A - ges, Ev - er my trust shall be.

Hark! 'tis the voice of an - gels, Borne in a song to me,
Free from the blight of sor - row, Free from my doubts and fears;
Here let me wait with pa - tience, Wait till the night is o'er;

O - ver the fields of glo - ry, O - ver the jas - per sea.
On - ly a few more tri - als, On - ly a few more tears!
Wait till I see the morn - ing Break on the gold - en shore.

WORDS: Fanny J. Crosby
MUSIC: William H. Doane

Safe in the Arms of Jesus

Refrain

Safe in the arms of Je - sus, Safe on His gen - tle breast,

There by His love o'er - shad - ed, Sweet-ly my soul shall rest.

And the same day, when the even was come, he saith unto them, Let us pass over unto the other side. And when they had sent away the multitude, they took him even as he was in the ship. And there were also with him other little ships. And there arose a great storm of wind, and the waves beat into the ship, so that it was now full. And he was in the hinder part of the ship, asleep on a pillow: and they awake him, and say unto him, Master, carest thou not that we perish? And he arose, and rebuked the wind, and said unto the sea, Peace, be still. And the wind ceased, and there was a great calm. And he said unto them, Why are ye so fearful? How is it that ye have no faith? And they feared exceedingly, and said one to another, What manner of man is this, that even the wind and the sea obey him. (Mark 4:35-41 KJV)

483 Lead Me Gently Home, Father

Lead me in a plain path — Psalm 27:11 KJV

Unison or Two-part

1. Lead me gen-tly home, Fa-ther, Lead me gen - tly home,
2. Lead me gen-tly home, Fa-ther, Lead me gen - tly home,
3. Lead me gen-tly home, Fa-ther, Lead me gen - tly home,

When life's toils are end - ed, and part - ing days have come;
In life's dark-est hours, Fa-ther, when life's trou-bles come;
In temp - ta-tion's hour, Fa-ther, when sore tri - als come;

Sin no more shall tempt me, Ne'er from Thee I'll roam,
Keep my feet from wan - d'ring, Lest from Thee I roam,
Be Thou near to keep me, Take me as Thine own,

If Thou'lt on - ly lead me, Fa-ther, Lead me gen-tly home.
Lest I fall up-on the way-side, Lead me gen-tly home.
For I can-not live with-out Thee, Lead me gen-tly home.

WORDS: Will L. Thompson
MUSIC: Will L. Thompson

Lead Me Gently Home, Father

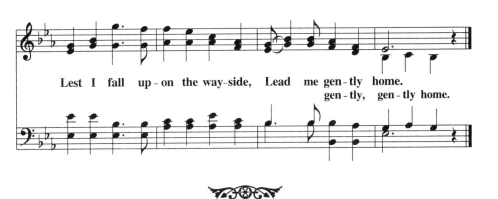

The Lord is my shepherd, I shall not want. He maketh me to lie down in green pastures, he leadeth me beside the still waters, He restoreth my soul: he leadeth me in the paths of righteousness for his name's sake. Yea, though I walk through the valley of the shadow of death, I will fear no evil: for thou art with me; thy rod and thy staff they comfort me. Thou preparest a table before me in the presence of mine enemies: thou anointest my head with oil; my cup runneth over. Surely goodness and mercy shall follow me all the days of my life: and I will dwell in the house of the Lord forever. (Psalm 23 KJV)

484 Sweet By and By

The things which God hath prepared for them that love Him — 1 Corinthians 2:9 KJV

1. There's a land that is fair-er than day, And by faith we can see it a-
2. We shall sing on that beau-ti-ful shore The me-lo-di-ous songs of the
3. To our boun-ti-ful Fa-ther a-bove We will of-fer our trib-ute of

far, For the Fa-ther waits o-ver the way To pre-
blest; And our spir-its shall sor-row no more — Not a
praise, For the glo-ri-ous gift of His love And the

Refrain

pare us a dwell-ing-place there. In the sweet by and
sigh for the bless-ing of rest. In the sweet by and
bless-ings that hal-low our days. In the sweet by and

by, We shall meet on that beau-ti-ful shore; In the
by, by and by, shore, by and by;

sweet by and by, We shall meet on that beau-ti-ful shore.
In the sweet by and by, by and by,

WORDS: Sanford F. Bennett
MUSIC: Joseph P. Webster

SWEET BY AND BY

Every Time I Feel the Spirit   485

And they were filled with the Holy Spirit, and began to speak with other tongues,
as the Spirit gave them utterance — Acts 2:4 KJV

Ev - 'ry time I feel the Spir - it mov - ing
in my heart, I will pray. Ev - 'ry
time I feel the Spir - it mov - ing in my heart, I will

Fine *Unison*

pray.

1. On the moun - tain my Lord
2. All a - round me looked so
3. Jor - dan riv - er chil - ly and

D.C. al Fine

spoke,	Out His mouth came	fire and smoke.
fine,	Asked my Lord if	all was mine.
cold,	Chills the bod - y	but not the soul.

WORDS: Traditional Spiritual
MUSIC: Traditional Spiritual

486   Oh, Freedom

And where the Spirit of the Lord is, there is liberty — 2 Corinthians 3:17 KJV

1. Oh, free-dom! Oh, free-dom! Oh,
2. No more moan-ing, No more moan-ing, No more
3. There'll be sing-ing, There'll be sing-ing, There'll be
4. There'll be shout-ing, There'll be shout-ing, There'll be
5. There'll be pray-ing, There'll be pray-ing, There'll be

free-dom ov-er me! ___ And be-fore I'd be a slave, I'll be
moan-ing ov-er me! ___ And be-fore I'd be a slave, I'll be
sing-ing ov-er me! ___ And be-fore I'd be a slave, I'll be
shout-ing ov-er me! ___ And be-fore I'd be a slave, I'll be
pray-ing ov-er me! ___ And be-fore I'd be a slave, I'll be

bur-ied in my grave, And go home to my Lord and be free.

WORDS: African-American spiritual
MUSIC: African-American spiritual; arr. by Paul Abels

487   Great Day! Great Day!

Build Thou the walls of Jerusalem — Psalm 51:18 KJV

Refrain

Great day! Great day, the right-eous march-ing. Great

WORDS: African-American spiritual
MUSIC: African-American spiritual

Great Day! Great Day!

488   Over My Head

If I ascend up into heaven, Thou art there — Psalm 139:8 KJV

Refrain

O-ver my head   I see trou-ble in the air,

O-ver my head   I see trou-ble in the air,

O-ver my head   I see trou-ble in the air,

There must be   a   God   some - where.

WORDS: African-American spiritual
MUSIC: African-American spiritual; arr. by Kenneth Morris

Over My Head

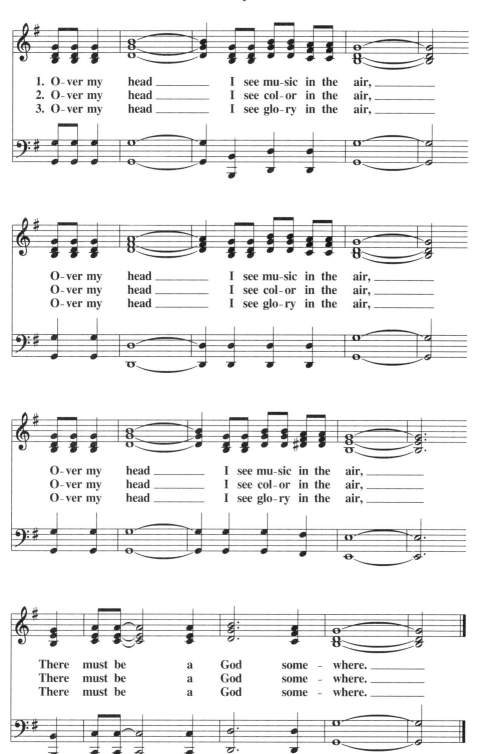

1. O- ver my head _____ I see mu-sic in the air, _____
2. O- ver my head _____ I see col- or in the air, _____
3. O- ver my head _____ I see glo- ry in the air, _____

O- ver my head _____ I see mu-sic in the air, _____
O- ver my head _____ I see col- or in the air, _____
O- ver my head _____ I see glo- ry in the air, _____

O- ver my head _____ I see mu-sic in the air, _____
O- ver my head _____ I see col- or in the air, _____
O- ver my head _____ I see glo- ry in the air, _____

There must be a God some - where. _____
There must be a God some - where. _____
There must be a God some - where. _____

489 Balm in Gilead

Is there no balm in Gilead, is there no physician there?
Why then is not the health of the daughter of my people recovered — Jeremiah 8:22 KJV

There is a balm in Gil-e-ad to make the wound-ed whole, _____ There is a balm in Gil-e-ad to heal the sin-sick soul

Fine

1. Some-times I feel dis-cour-aged, And think my work's in vain, But then the Ho-ly Spir-it Re-vives my soul a-gain. _____
2. Don't ev-er feel dis-cour-aged, For Je-sus is your friend, And if you look for knowl-edge, He'll ne'er re-fuse to lend. _____
3. If you can't preach like Pe-ter, If you can't pray like Paul, Just tell the love of Je-sus, And say He died for all. _____

D.C.

WORDS: African-American spiritual
MUSIC: African-American spiritual

BALM IN GILEAD

Go Down, Moses

490

Thus saith the Lord, "Let my people go" — Exodus 8:1 KJV

1. When Is-rael was in E-gypt's land, Let my peo-ple go;
2. "Thus saith the Lord," bold Mo-ses said, Let my peo-ple go;
3. No more shall they in bond-age toil, Let my peo-ple go;

Op-pressed so hard they could not stand, Let my peo-ple go.
"If not, I'll smite your first-born dead," Let my peo-ple go.
Let them come out with E-gypt's spoil, Let my peo-ple go.

Refrain

Go down Mo-ses, 'Way down in E-gypt's land.
Go down, go down, Mo-ses,

Go down, go down, Mo-ses,

Tell old Pha-roah, Let my peo-ple go.

WORDS: African-American spiritual
MUSIC: African-American spiritual

TUBMAN

491 Deep River

Then had thy peace been as a river — Isaiah 48:18 KJV

Deep riv - er, my home is o - ver Jor - dan,
Deep, deep

Fine

Deep riv - er, Lord, I want to cross o - ver in - to camp-ground.
Deep, deep

O don't you want to go to that gos - pel feast, That prom - ised

land where all is peace, O don't you want to go to that

D.C. al Fine

prom - ised land, that land where all is peace?

WORDS: African-American spiritual
MUSIC: African-American spiritual

Soon-a Will Be Done

492

Unto Thee lift I up mine eyes — Psalm 123:1 KJV

Refrain

Soon-a will be done a-with the trou-bles of the world, Trou-bles of the world, The trou-bles of the world, Soon-a will be done a-with the trou - bles of the world, Goin' home to live with God.

Fine

1. No more weep-ing and a - wail - ing, No more weep-ing and a - wail - ing,
2. I want t'meet my moth-er, I want t'meet my moth-er,
3. I want t'meet my Je - sus, I want t'meet my Je - sus,

D.C. al Fine

No more weep-ing and a - wail - ing, I'm goin' to live with God.
I want t'meet my moth - er, I'm goin' to live with God.
I want t'meet my Je - sus, I'm goin' to live with God.

WORDS: African-American spiritual
MUSIC: African-American spiritual

493 Some O' These Days

He ... shall doubtless come again with rejoicing — Psalm 126:6 KJV

1. I'm goin' t' sit down at the wel-come ta - ble,
2. I'm goin' t' feast on milk and hon - ey,
3. I'm goin' t' sing and nev-er get tired,
4. I'm goin' t' tell God all of my trou - bles,
5. I'm goin' t' tell God how you treat me,
6. God's goin' t' set this world on fire,
7. God's goin' t' stop that long-tongue li - ar,

I'm goin' t' sit down at the wel - come
I'm goin' t' feast on milk and
I'm goin' t' sing and nev - er get
I'm goin' t' tell God all of my
I'm goin' t' tell God how you
God's goin' t' set this world on
God's goin' t' stop that long - tongue

ta - ble, Some o' these days, (Hal - le - lu - jah,)
hon - ey, Some o' these days, (Hal - le - lu - jah,)
tired, Some o' these days, (Hal - le - lu - jah,)
trou - bles, Some o' these days, (Hal - le - lu - jah,)
treat me, Some o' these days, (Hal - le - lu - jah,)
fire, Some o' these days, (Hal - le - lu - jah,)
li - ar, Some o' these days, (Hal - le - lu - jah,)

WORDS: African-American spiritual
MUSIC: African-American spiritual; arr. by Phil V. S. Lindsley

Some O' These Days

494   Wade in the Water

Lo, he cometh forth to the water — Exodus 8:20 KJV

Refrain

Wade in the wa - ter, (chil - dren,) Wade in the wa - ter, chil - dren, Wade in the wa - ter, God's a - goin' to trou - ble the wa - ter. O wa - ter.

Leader

1. See that host all dressed in white,
2. See that band all dressed in red,
3. Look o - ver yon - der, what do I see?
4. If you don't be - lieve I've been re - deemed,

Hmm,

WORDS: African-American spiritual
MUSIC: African-American spiritual

Wade in the Water

God's a - goin' to trou - ble the wa - ter; The
God's a - goin' to trou - ble the wa - ter; Looks
God's a - goin' to trou - ble the wa - ter; The
God's a - goin' to trou - ble the wa - ter; Just

hmm, ___

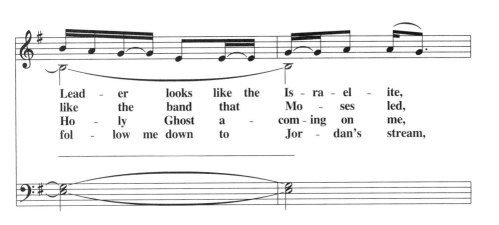

Lead - er looks like the Is - ra - el - ite,
like the band that Mo - ses led,
Ho - ly Ghost a - com - ing on me,
fol - low me down to Jor - dan's stream,

God's a - goin' to trou - ble the wa - ter.
God's a - goin' to trou - ble the wa - ter.
God's a - goin' to trou - ble the wa - ter.
God's a - goin' to trou - ble the wa - ter.

495   He Is King of Kings

Which in His times, He shall show, who is the blessed and only Potentate,
the King of kings, and Lord of lords; who only hath immortality — 1 Timothy 6:15-16 KJV

He is   King of kings, He is Lord of lords;   Je-sus Christ, the first and last

1-3 no man   works like   Him.   He   is   **2** no man   works like   Him.   *Fine*

He   built His throne up   in   the   air,   no man works like Him;   And

D.S.
called the saints from ev - ry - where,   no man works like Him.   He   is

WORDS: African-American spiritual
WORDS: African-American spiritual

Standin' in the Need of Prayer   496

Pray ye to the Lord for me — Acts 8:24 KJV

1. Not my broth-er, nor my sis-ter, but it's me, O Lord,
2. Not the preach-er, nor the dea-con, but it's me, O Lord,
3. Not my fa-ther, nor my moth-er, but it's me, O Lord,
4. Not the stran-ger, nor my neigh-bor, but it's me, O Lord,

Stand-in' in the need of prayer; Not my broth-er, nor my sis-ter, but it's
Stand-in' in the need of prayer; Not the preach-er, nor the dea-con, but it's
Stand-in' in the need of prayer; Not my fa-ther, nor my moth-er, but it's
Stand-in' in the need of prayer; Not the stran-ger, nor my neigh-bor, but it's

me, O Lord, Stand-in' in the need of prayer.

Refrain

It's me, (It's me,) it's me, O Lord, Stand-in' in the need of prayer;

It's me, (It's me,) it's me, O Lord, Stand-in' in the need of prayer.

WORDS: African-American spiritual
MUSIC: African-American spiritual

PENITENT

497 Ezekiel Saw the Wheel

*And their appearance and their work was as it were
a wheel in the middle of a wheel — Ezekial 1:16 KJV*

E - ze - kiel saw the wheel 'Way up in the mid - dle of the air, E - ze - kiel saw the wheel 'Way in the mid-dle of the air. The big wheel run by faith, The lit - tle wheel run by the grace of God, A

WORDS: Traditional Spiritual
MUSIC: Traditional Spiritual

Ezekiel Saw the Wheel

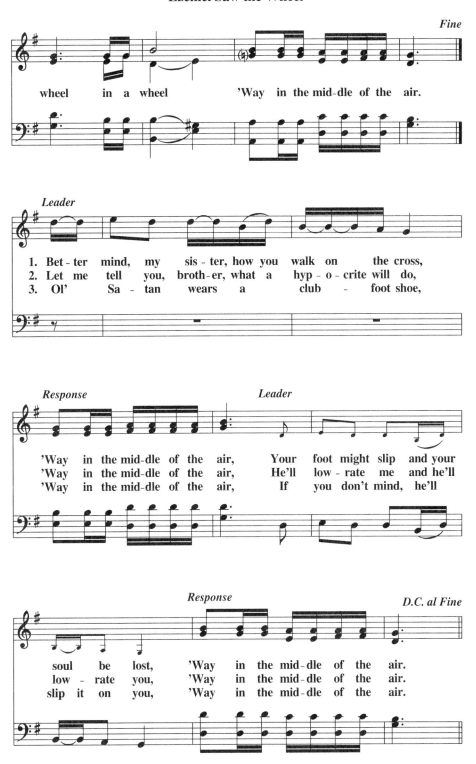

498 Swing Low

Who maketh the clouds His chariot — Psalm 104:3 KJV

WORDS: African-American spiritual
MUSIC: African-American spiritual; adapt. by John W. Work, Jr. and Frederick J. Work

SWING LOW

My Lord, What a Morning

499

The Lord Himself shall descend from heaven …
with the trump of God — 1 Thessalonians 4:16 KJV

Refrain

My Lord, what a morn-ing, My Lord, what a morn-ing,

Fine

My Lord, what a morn-ing, When the stars be-gin to fall.

1. You'll hear the trum - pet sound,
2. You'll hear the sin - ner mourn, To wake the
3. You'll hear the Chris - tian shout,

na - tions un - der - ground, Look-ing to my God's right

parts

D.C. al Fine

hand, When the stars be - gin to fall.

WORDS: African-American spiritual
MUSIC: African-American spiritual; arr. by David Hugh Jones

500 Walk with Me

But if we walk in the light, as He is in the light — 1 John 1:7 KJV

Refrain

I want Je - sus to walk with me, I want Je - sus to walk with me, (with me,) All a - long my pil - grim jour-ney, I want Je - sus to walk with me. *Fine*

1. In my tri - als, walk with me, walk with me, In my tri - als, walk with me, walk with me, When the shades of life are fall-ing, Lord, I want Je - sus to walk with me.
2. In my sor - rows, walk with me, walk with me, In my sor-rows, walk with me, walk with me, When my heart with - in is ach-ing, Lord, I want Je - sus to walk with me.
3. In my trou - bles, walk with me, walk with me, In my trou-bles, walk with me, walk with me, When my life be - comes a bur-den, Lord, I want Je - sus to walk with me.

D.C.

WORDS: African-American spiritual
MUSIC: African-American spiritual

SOJOURNER

We Shall Overcome 501

Live in peace; and the God of love and peace shall be with you — 2 Corinthians 13:11 KJV

1. __ We shall o - ver - come, __ We shall o - ver -
2. __ We'll walk hand in hand, __ We'll walk hand in
3. __ We shall all be free, __ We shall all be
4. __ We shall live in peace, __ We shall live in
5. The Lord will see us through, The Lord will see us

come, __ We shall o - ver - come some
hand, __ We'll walk hand in hand some
free, __ We shall all be free some
peace, __ We shall live in peace some
through, The Lord will see us through some

day; _____ Oh, deep in my heart I do be -
day; _____ Oh, deep in my heart I do be -
day; _____ Oh, deep in my heart I do be -
day; _____ Oh, deep in my heart I do be -
day; _____ Oh, deep in my heart I do be -

lieve, __ We shall o - ver - come some day.
lieve, __ We'll walk hand in hand some day.
lieve, __ We shall all be free some day.
lieve, __ We shall live in peace some day.
lieve, The Lord will see us through some day.

WORDS: African-American spiritual
MUSIC: African-American spiritual; arr. by Allen Tuten

MARTIN

502   Hear Me Praying

Hear my cry, O God; attend unto my prayer — Psalm 61:1 KJV

Lord, oh, hear me pray - ing, Lord, oh, hear me pray - ing, Lord, oh, hear me pray - ing; I

want to be more ho - ly ev - 'ry day, oh, ev - 'ry day.

Solo

1. Like   Pe-ter when you said   to   him, __   Like
2. Like   Pe-ter when you said   to   him, __   Like
3. Like   the   Bap-tist when you said, __   Like

(Choir)

ev - 'ry day. _____

   __   Feed   my sheep, __
   I   build   my church __
   I   am   a   voice __

WORDS: Traditional
MUSIC: Traditional

Hear Me Praying

503

Amen!

And in Him, Amen, unto the glory of God — 2 Corinthians 1:20 KJV

WORDS: Rev. B. H. Hogan
MUSIC: Rev. B. H. Hogan and Laura B. Davis; arr. by E. Edwin Young

Amen!

Solo

1. The Lord is my Shep-herd, He leads me day by
2. John on the Isle of Pat-mos, Looked o - ver in the glo - ry
3. I would not be a de - ceiv - er, I'll tell you the rea - son
4. When I was a sin - ner, A sin - ner just like
5. Some - times my way is cloud-ed, My path - way all con -

Hum _____ Hum _____

day, He feeds me when I'm hun - gry, And
land; He heard the an - gels sing - ing, And
why: I'm a - fraid my Lord might call me And I
you, I came to the Lord in re - pent - ance, I be -
fused; I set my face to-ward heav - en, De -

Hum _____ Hum __

D.C. al Fine

hears me when I pray.
shout-ing Hal - le - lu - jah! A - men.
would-n't be read - y to die.
lieved till I came thru.
ter - mined to go thru.

D.C. al Fine

Ev - 'ry - bod - y said,

504 On My Journey Home

And he that seeketh findeth — Luke 11:10 KJV

Refrain

My Lord, I'm on my jour-ney, My Lord, I'm on my jour-ney,

Fine

My Lord, I'm on my jour-ney, On my jour-ney home.

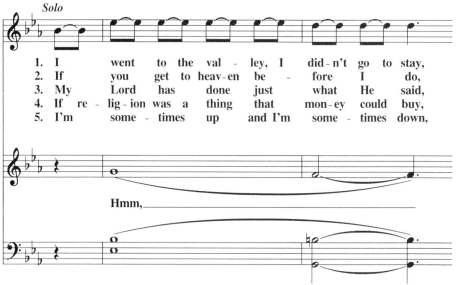

Solo

1. I went to the val - ley, I did-n't go to stay,
2. If you get to heav-en be - fore I do,
3. My Lord has done just what He said,
4. If re - lig-ion was a thing that mon-ey could buy,
5. I'm some - times up and I'm some - times down,

Hmm,

WORDS: Rev. B. H. Hogan
MUSIC: Rev. B. H. Hogan and Laura B. Davis; arr. by E. Edwin Young

On My Journey Home

505   Steal Away to Jesus!

The voice of Thy thunder was in the heaven — Psalm 77:18 KJV

Refrain

Steal a - way, steal a - way, steal a - way to Je - sus! Steal a - way, steal a - way home, I ain't got long to stay here.

Fine

1. My Lord, He calls me, He calls me by the thun - der; The trum-pet sounds with - in my soul; I ain't got long to stay here.
2. Green trees are bend - ing, Poor sin - ners stand a - tremb - ling; The trum-pet sounds with - in my soul; I ain't got long to stay here.
3. My Lord, He calls me, He calls me by the light - ning; The trum-pet sounds with - in my soul; I ain't got long to stay here.

D.C.

WORDS: African-American spiritual
MUSIC: African-American spiritual

STEAL AWAY

Jesus Loves Me

506

Suffer the little children to come unto me — Mark 10:14 KJV

1. Je - sus loves me! this I know, For the Bi - ble tells me so;
2. Je - sus loves me! He who died Heav-en's gates to o - pen wide!
3. Je - sus loves me! loves me still, Tho' I'm ver - y weak and ill;
4. Je - sus loves me! He will stay Close be - side me all the way;

Lit - tle ones to Him be - long, They are weak, but He is strong.
He will wash a - way my sin, Let His lit - tle child come in.
From His shin - ing throne on high, Comes to watch me where I lie.
If I love Him when I die, He will take me home on high.

Refrain

Yes, Je - sus loves me, Yes, Je - sus loves me,

Yes, Je - sus loves me, The Bi - ble tells me so.

WORDS: Anna B. Warner
MUSIC: William B. Bradbury

CHINA

507 Jesus, Oh How I Love You

I will praise Thee, O Lord, with my whole heart;
I will show forth the marvelous works — Psalm 9:1 KJV

Je - sus, Oh, how I { love / praise / need } You!

Je - sus, Oh, how I { love / praise / need } You!

Je - sus, Oh, how I { love / praise / need } You! Ev - 'ry

Fine

day, all of the way, I love You.

WORDS: Norman L. Starks
MUSIC: Norman L. Starks

Do Lord, Do Remember Me 508

And he said unto Jesus, "Lord, remember me
when Thou comest into Thy kingdom" — Luke 23:42 KJV

1. Do   Lord,   do Lord,   Do   re-mem-ber   me.
2. When I'm   in   trou-ble,   Do   re-mem-ber   me.
3. When I'm   dy - in',   Do   re-mem-ber   me.
4. When this   world's on   fire,   Do   re-mem-ber   me.

Do   Lord,   do Lord,   Do   re-mem-ber   me,
When I'm   in   trou-ble,   Do   re-mem-ber   me,
When I'm   dy - in',   Do   re-mem-ber   me,
When this   world's on   fire,   Do   re-mem-ber   me,

Do   Lord,   do Lord,   Do   re-mem-ber   me,
When I'm   in   trou-ble,   Do   re-mem-ber   me,   O
When I'm   dy - in',   Do   re-mem-ber   me,
When this   world's on   fire,   Do   re-mem-ber   me,

do Lord,   re - mem - ber   me.

WORDS: Traditional Spiritual
MUSIC: Traditional Spiritual

509 Oh, Be Careful

Looking diligently lest any man fail of the grace of God — Hebrews 12:15 KJV

1. Oh, be care-ful, lit-tle eyes, what you see,
2. Oh, be care-ful, lit-tle ears, what you hear,
3. Oh, be care-ful, lit-tle tongue, what you say,
4. Oh, be care-ful, lit-tle hands, what you do,
5. Oh, be care-ful, lit-tle feet, where you go,

Oh, be care-ful, lit-tle eyes, what you see,
Oh, be care-ful, lit-tle ears, what you hear,
Oh, be care-ful, lit-tle tongue, what you say,
Oh, be care-ful, lit-tle hands, what you do,
Oh, be care-ful, lit-tle feet, where you go,

For the Fa-ther up a-bove Is look-ing down in love,
For the Fa-ther up a-bove Is look-ing down in love,
For the Fa-ther up a-bove Is look-ing down in love,
For the Fa-ther up a-bove Is look-ing down in love,
For the Fa-ther up a-bove Is look-ing down in love,

So be care-ful, lit-tle eyes, what you see.
So be care-ful, lit-tle ears, what you hear.
So be care-ful, lit-tle tongue, what you say.
So be care-ful, lit-tle hands, what you do.
So be care-ful, lit-tle feet, where you go.

WORDS: Unknown
MUSIC: Unknown

I'll Be a Sunbeam

510

Then shall the righteous shine forth as the sun — Matthew 13:43 KJV

1. Je - sus wants me for a sun - beam, To shine for Him each day;
2. Je - sus wants me to be lov - ing, And kind to all I see;
3. I will ask Je - sus to help me To keep my heart from sin,
4. I'll be a sun-beam for Je - sus; I can if I but try;

In ev - 'ry way try to please Him, At home, at school, at play.
Show-ing how pleas-ant and hap - py His lit - tle one can be.
Ev - er re - flect-ing His good - ness, And al - ways shine for Him.
Serv-ing Him mo-ment by mo - ment, Then live with Him on high.

Refrain

A sun - beam, a sun - beam, Je-sus wants me for a sun - beam;

A sun - beam, a sun - beam, I'll be a sun-beam for Him.

WORDS: Nellie Talbot
MUSIC: Edwin O. Excell

511   This Little Light of Mine

Let your light so shine before men…glorify your Father which is in heaven — Matthew 5:16 KJV

WORDS: African-American spiritual
MUSIC: African-American spiritual; arr. by Lillian M. Bowles
Arr. © 1934 by Lillian M. Bowles Music House. Used by permission.

LATTIMER

L-O-V-E, Love

512

For God so loved the world — John 3:16 KJV

1. I know the sweet-est lit-tle word, 'Tis L - O - V - E, love; The
2. It keeps me hap - py ev-'ry day, His L - O - V - E, love; It
3. It guides these lit - tle feet of mine, His L - O - V - E, love; It

sweet - est word man ev - er heard Is L - O - V - E, love.
makes me sing a - long the way, His L - O - V - E, love.
keeps them in the path di - vine, His L - O - V - E, love.

Refrain

God's L - O - V - E, love Is wid - er than the sea; It

reach-es all, yes, ev - en me; God's L - O - V - E, love.

WORDS: C. L. Dorris
MUSIC: R. J. Hughes

513 We've Got a Great Big Wonderful God

All Thy works shall praise Thee, O Lord,
and Thy saints shall bless Thee — Psalm 145:10 KJV

Unison or Two part

We've got a great big won-der-ful God, Great big won-der-ful

God. A God who's al-ways vic-to-ri-ous, al-ways watch-ing o-ver us,

Great big won-der-ful God. We've got a great big won-der-ful

God, Great big won-der-ful God. A God who loves ev-'ry one of us,

done so much for all of us, Great big won-der-ful God. He

WORDS: Tim Spencer
MUSIC: Tim Spencer

We've Got a Great Big Wonderful God

514 Praise Him, All Ye Little Children

Let everything that hath breath, praise the Lord — Psalm 150:6 KJV

1. Praise Him, praise Him, all ye lit-tle chil-dren,
2. Love Him, love Him, all ye lit-tle chil-dren,
3. Thank Him, thank Him, all ye lit-tle chil-dren,

God is love, God is love; Praise Him, praise Him,
God is love, God is love; Love Him, love Him,
God is love, God is love; Thank Him, thank Him,

all ye lit-tle chil-dren, God is love, God is love.
all ye lit-tle chil-dren, God is love, God is love.
all ye lit-tle chil-dren, God is love, God is love.

WORDS: Anonymous
MUSIC: Anonymous

GOD IS LOVE

515 Child's Morning Hymn

Giving thanks unto the Father — Colossians 1:12 KJV

1. Fa - ther, we thank Thee for the night,
2. Help us to do the things we should,

WORDS: Rebecca J. Weston
MUSIC: Daniel Batchellor

WE THANK THEE

Child's Morning Prayer

And for the pleas-ant morn - ing light; For rest and food and
To be to oth - ers kind and good; In all we do, in

lov - ing care, And all that makes the world so fair.
work or play, To love Thee bet - ter day by day.

Jesus Loves the Little Children   516

Those that seek Me early shall find Me — Proverbs 8:17 KJV

Je - sus loves the lit - tle chil - dren, All the chil-dren of the

world; Red and yel - low, black and white, They are

pre-cious in His sight; Je - sus loves the lit - tle chil-dren of the world.

WORDS: Anonymous
MUSIC: American folk hymn; arr. by George F. Root

517   I'm in the Lord's Army

And the armies in heaven followed Him upon white horses,
clothed in fine linen, white and clean — Revelation 19:14 KJV

WORDS: Traditional
MUSIC: Traditional

Arise, O Youth of God

518

Arise, call upon thy God — Jonah 1:6 KJV

1. A - rise, O youth of God! Have done with less - er things; Give
2. A - rise, O youth of God! His king - dom tar - ries long; Bring
3. A - rise, O youth of God! The Church for you doth wait; Her
4. Lift high, the cross of Christ! Tread where His feet have trod; Be

heart and soul and mind and strength To serve the King of kings.
in the day of joy and peace, And end the night of wrong.
strength shall make your spir - it strong; Her serv - ice make you great.
loy - al to the King of kings; March on, O youth of God!

Refrain

A - rise, A - rise, The Mas-ter calls for thee;

A - rise,

A - rise, A - rise,

A - rise, A-rise, O youth of God, March on to vic - to - ry!

WORDS: Wm. P. Merrill, alt. by B. B. McKinney
MUSIC: B. B. McKinney

519   Stand Still

Be still, and know that I am God — Psalm 46:10 KJV

1. Stand still and see the sal - va - tion of the Lord. Stand still and see His glo - ry. Stand still and know that I am God for the bat - tle is not yours, But Mine, said the Lord.

2. Oh Lord, my God, How ex - cel - lent is Thy name. I stand in praise be - fore Thee. And tho' a host en - camp a - round me, I nev - er have to fight nor fear, said the Lord.

3. Oh Lord, my God, How pow - er - ful is Thy name. An - gels bow down be - fore Thee. And tho' the world should come a - gainst me, there is no great - er pow'r nor might, said the Lord.

WORDS: Margaret Douroux
MUSIC: Margaret Douroux

Stand Still

520 Serve the Lord in Youth

Remember now thy Creator in the days of thy youth — Ecclesiastes 12:1 KJV

1. Serve the Lord in the days of youth, Learn His law and ac-
2. Give to Him what He gave to you, Bouy-ant strength and a
3. Serve Him then, ev-'ry youth-ful day, Choose His guid-ance with-

cept His truth; Sing His praise with a read-y tongue,
cour-age true; Ring-ing voic-es and eyes a-light,
out de-lay; Waste no part of these pre-cious years,

While the heart is young, While yet the heart is young.
Souls all pure and white, Un-stained and pure and white.
Youth soon dis-ap-pears, Too soon it dis-ap-pears.

Refrain (unison)

Serve the Lord in youth-ful days,

WORDS: Edith Sanford Tillotson
MUSIC: J. Lincoln Hall

Serve the Lord in Youth

521 Total Praise

Speaking to yourselves in psalms and hymns and spiritual songs,
singing and making melody in your heart to the Lord — Ephesians 5:19 KJV

Lord, I will lift mine eyes to the hills,

Know - ing my help is com - ing from You.

Your peace You give me in time of the storm;

You are the Source _ of my strength, You are the strength _

_ of my life. I lift my hands in to - tal

WORDS: Richard Smallwood
MUSIC: Richard Smallwood

Total Praise

522 Glorious Is the Name of Jesus

We love Him, because He first loved us — 1 John 4:19 KJV

Glo - rious is the name of Je - sus, Prais - es to His

name. Oh, glo - rious and righ - teous and

ho - ly is His name. Oh, glo - ri - ous

is His name. _____ I feel His pres-ence

WORDS: Robert J. Fryson
MUSIC: Robert J. Fryson

Glorious Is the Name of Jesus

in this place. His Spir - it has con - trol, Can't you

feel His warm em - brace and all the joy with-in your

soul? Oh, glo - ri - ous is His name. Oh,

glo - ri - ous is His name. _____

523   All Hail, Immanuel!

And they shall call His name, Emmanuel — Matthew 1:23 KJV

1. All hail to Thee, Im-man-u-el, We cast our crowns be-
2. All hail to Thee, Im-man-u-el, The ran - somed hosts sur-
3. All hail to Thee, Im-man-u-el, Our ris - en King and

                  1. cast our crowns be -

fore Thee; Let ev - 'ry heart o - bey Thy will, And
round Thee; And earth - ly mon-archs clam - or forth Their
Sav - ior! Thy foes are van-quished, and Thou art Om -

                  1. and

ev - 'ry voice a - dore Thee. In praise to Thee, our
Sov - 'reign King to crown Thee. While those re-deemed in
nip - o - tent for - ev - er. Death, sin and hell no

ev - 'ry voice a - dore Thee.

Sav - ior King, The vi - brant chords of Heav - en ring, And
a - ges gone, As - sem - bled 'round the great white throne, Break
long - er reign, And Sa - tan's pow'r is burst in twain; E -

WORDS: D. R. Van Sickle
MUSIC: Charles H. Gabriel

All Hail, Immanuel

All Hail, Immanuel!

All Hail, Immanuel

lords,   All   hail,   Im-man - u - el!   A - men.

God So Loved the World   524

He gave His only begotten Son — John 3:16 KJV

Andante ma non lento

God   so loved the   world, _____   God   so loved the

world, _____ that He   gave   His   on - ly   be - got - ten   Son, that
world,   that   He

who-so be - liev-eth, be - liev-eth in   Him   should not   per-ish,

WORDS: John 3:16
MUSIC: John Stainer

God So Loved the World

should not per-ish, but have ev-er last - ing life. For God

sent not His Son in - to the world to con - demn the world, God

sent not His Son in - to the world to con - demn the world;

But that the world thru Him might be sav - ed. God

so loved the world, ___ God so loved the world, ___ that He

world, that He

God So Loved the World

525 Why We Sing

Oh, sing unto the Lord a new song — Psalm 98:1 KJV

Some-one asked the ques-tion Why do we sing? When we lift our hands to Je-sus, what do we real - ly mean? Some-one may be won-der-ing, when we sing our song, at times we may be cry-ing, and noth-ing's real - ly wrong. I

Three-part harmony

WORDS: Kirk Franklin
MUSIC: Kirk Franklin
© Copyright 1992 Lilly Mack Music (BMI). Used by permission.

Why We Sing

526   Order My Steps

The steps of a good man are ordered by the Lord — Psalm 37:23 KJV

1. Or-der my steps in Your Word, dear Lord, _____
2. Hum-bly I ask Thee, teach me Your will, _____
3. Bri-dle my tongue, let my words ed-i-fy, Let the

Lead me, guide me, Show me the way,
While You are work-ing, help me be still. Tho'
words of my mouth be ac-cept-a-ble in Thy sight. Take

Send Your a-noint-ing, Fa-ther, I pray.
Sa-tan is bus-y, God is real! Or-der my steps in Your
charge of my thoughts, both day and night.

Word. Please, or-der my steps in Your Word. I want to walk

WORDS: Glenn Burleigh; based on Psalm 119:133
MUSIC: Glenn Burleigh
© Copyright 1998 Glenn Burleigh (Burleigh Inspirational Music).

Order My Steps

527   I'm So Glad I'm Saved

For with the heart man believeth unto righteousness;
and with the mouth confession is made unto salvation — Romans 10:10 KJV

1. I'm so glad I'm saved,   I'm so glad I'm saved,
2. I'm so glad I'm saved,   I'm so glad I'm saved,

I've been washed in the blood,   I've been washed in the blood
Je - sus lives in me,   Je - sus lives in me,

of the cru - ci - fied Lamb,   of the cru - ci - fied Lamb.
praise His ho - ly name,   praise His ho - ly name.

One day He touched me,   one day He touched me and

WORDS: Anderson T. Dailey
MUSIC: Anderson T. Dailey

I'm So Glad I'm Saved

I'm So Glad I'm Saved

Second time through, Choir should stop and repeat (chant) "So glad I'm saved" four times, each time should be louder. Then proceed to last measure, break between each word. Hold the word "saved" a long time with a high A♭.

You Can't Beat God Giving   528

And God is able to make all grace abound toward you — 2 Corinthians 9:8 KJV

Refrain

You can't beat God giv-ing, no mat-ter how you try, And
just as sure as you are liv-ing and the Lord is in heav-en on

WORDS: Doris Akers
MUSIC: Doris Akers

You Can't Beat God Giving

You Can't Beat God Giving

Stanzas - Solo

1. Should we re - ceive and nev - er give? The
2. He gives me health, He keeps me strong, He
3. He gave me peace, He made me whole, And

Ooo

Sav - ior died that we might live. His life on Cal - va - ry He
guides me when I would go wrong, He gives me ev - 'ry - thing
when in sin He saved my soul. And what I give would nev-er

Ooo _____ Ooo

You Can't Beat God Giving

glad - ly   gave,   our sin - ful   souls   to save.
that   I   need,   my   ev - 'ry   hun - ger feeds.
be com- pared with the bless-ing   that   I share.

Ooo   Ooo   Ooo

529 We've Come This Far by Faith

Now the just shall live by faith — Hebrews 10:38 KJV

We've come this far   by   faith   Lean-ing on the

Lord;   Trust-ing in His Ho - ly   Word,

WORDS: Albert A. Goodson
MUSIC: Albert A. Goodson; arr. by Thurston G. Frazier
© Copyright 1965 Rev. Albert A. Goodson, 3419 Montellono Ave., Palmdale, CA 93551

We've Come This Far by Faith

He's nev-er failed me yet. Oh, _____

_ Can't turn a-round, We've come this far by faith. *Fine*

Stanza

Don't be dis - cour - aged with
*Just the other day I heard a man say he didn't believe in God's Word;

trou - ble in your life. He'll bear your
I can say God has made a way, He's never failed me yet,

(sing both times)

bur-dens And move all mis-er - y and strife, That's why we've
Thank God, We've

*Optional recitation

530   Center of My Joy

I will greatly rejoice in the Lord, my soul shall be joyful in my God;
for He hath clothed me with the garments of salvation, He
hath covered me with the robe of righteousness — Isaiah 61:10 KJV

Je - sus, You're the cen - ter of my joy,

All that's good and per - fect comes from You.

You're the heart of my con - tent - ment, hope for all I do,

WORDS: Gloria Gaither, William J. Gaither, and Richard Smallwood
MUSIC: Gloria Gaither, William J. Gaither, and Richard Smallwood; arr. by Richard Smallwood

Center of My Joy

Je - sus, You're the cen - ter of my joy.

When I've lost my di - rec - tion, You're the
You are why I find pleas - ure in the

com - pass for my way, You're the
sim - ple things in life, You're the

fire and light when nights are long and cold. In
mu - sic in the mead - ows and the streams. The

Center of My Joy

Center of My Joy

joy. All that's good and per-fect comes from

You. You're the heart of my con-tent - ment,

hope for all I do. Je - sus, You're the cen-ter of my

1 joy.

2 joy.

531 Only What You Do for Christ Will Last

Except the Lord build the house, they labor in vain that build it — Psalm 127:1 KJV

1. You may build great ca-the-drals large or small,
2. You may seek earth-ly pow-er and fame,
3. Tho' your ar-mies may con-trol each hem-i-sphere,
4. Tho' your songs and prayers are heard and praised by man,

You can build sky-scrap-ers grand and tall,
The world might be im-pressed by your great name,
And your or-bits out in space cause men to cheer,
They've no mean-ing un-less you've been born a-gain,

You may con-quer all the fail-ures of the past, But
Soon the glo-ries of this life will all be past, But
Your sci-en-tif-ic knowl-edge may be vast, But
Sin-ner, heed these words, don't let this har-vest past, For

Refrain

on-ly what you do for Christ will last.
on-ly what you do for Christ will last.
on-ly what you do for Christ will last.
on-ly what you do for Christ will last.

Re-mem-ber on-ly what you

WORDS: Raymond Rasberry
MUSIC: Raymond Rasberry

Only What You Do for Christ Will Last

532   Christ Is All

For to me to live is Christ, and to die is gain — Phillippians 1:21 KJV

Slowly, with feeling

1. I don't pos - sess   hous - es   or   lands,   fine clothes or
2. There are some folks   who look and long   for   this world's
3. Yes, Christ is   all,   means more   to   me   than this world's

jewel - ry,   Sor - rows and cares   in   this old world, my lot seems to
rich - es,   There are some folk   who look for   pow'r,   po - si - tion
rich - es,   He   is   my sight,   my guid - ing   light   thru path - less

be,   But   I   have a   Christ who paid the price   way back on
too,   But   I   have a   Christ all   in my life,   this makes me
seas,   Yes, it's might - y   nice   to own a Christ who will my

Cal - v'ry,   And Christ is   all,   all and all   this world to   me.
hap - py,   For Christ is   all,   all and all   this world to   me.
friend be,   Yes, Christ is   all,   all and all   this world to   me.

WORDS: Kenneth Morris
MUSIC: Kenneth Morris

Christ Is All

533 We Shall Walk Through the Valley in Peace

Yea, though I walk through the valley of the shadow of death,
I will fear no evil — Psalm 23:4 KJV

1. There will be no sorrow there; There will be no sorrow there. If Jesus Himself shall be our Leader, We shall walk thru the valley in peace.

2. There will be no dying there; There will be no dying there. If Jesus Himself shall be our Leader, We shall walk thru the valley in peace.

WORDS: A. L. Hatter
MUSIC: A. L. Hatter

We Shall Walk Through the Valley in Peace

534 Old Ship of Zion!

Whosoever shall call upon the name of the Lord shall be saved — Romans 10:13 KJV

Slowly, ad lib

1. I was lost in sin and sor - row On an
2. I got up but hes - i - tat - ed Won-d'ring
3. Then I stepped a-board the ves - sel Thru the

Hum   Hum

isle in life's dark sea, When I saw far in the
who this friend could be, Tho' the waves were wild and
straights and thru the gorge, Man - y years it sailed the

Hum   Hum   Hum

dis - tance There a ship it seemed to be, Then I
dash-ing Seem-ing they would swal-low me, Then he
wa - ters Man - y souls have made the voyage, Then I

Hum   Hum   Hum

WORDS: Thomas A. Dorsey
MUSIC: Thomas A. Dorsey

Old Ship of Zion!

Old Ship of Zion!

The Broken Vessel 535

I am forgotten as a dead man out of mind: I am like a broken vessel — Psalm 31:12 KJV

Slowly (with easy moving tempo)

1. The Pot-ter saw a ves-sel _____ That was
(2. My) friend, if you're bro-ken _____ And

bro-ken by the wind and rain; _____ And He
shat-tered by the storms of life; _____ And have

sought with so much com-pas-sion _____ to make it
searched in vain for the an-swer _____ to all your

WORDS: Andraé Crouch
MUSIC: Andraé Crouch

The Broken Vessel

o - ver a - gain. _____ Oh! I   was   that
tur-moil and strife. _____ Just look   to   the

ves-sel _____ that no   one thought was good. _____
Sav-ior _____ Who now can set   you   free. _____

— I cried, "Lord, You're the Pot - ter and I am the
— And cry, "Lord, You're the Pot - ter and I am the

clay, Make me o - ver a - gain to - day." _____ Then
clay, Make me o - ver a - gain to - day." _____ Let

The Broken Vessel

536

Even Me

Oh that Thou wouldest bless me indeed ...
and that Thine hand might be with me ... and keep me — 1 Chronicles 4:10 KJV

WORDS: Unknown
MUSIC: Unknown; arr. by Roberta Martin

Even Me

537 He Knows Just How Much You Can Bear

He shall never suffer the righteous to be moved — Psalm 55:22 KJV

Slowly, with expression

1. We are our heav - en-ly Fa - ther's chil - dren
2. Think of the times you've asked the ques - tion
3. Just praise His name al - though you're bur - dened,

And we all know that He loves us one and all;
Down in your heart now just what shall I do?
For there are bless - ings He's be-stowed on you;

Yet there are times when we find we an - swer
Then you con - fide in your friends and loved ones
In ev - 'ry way we must nev - er doubt Him

An - oth - er's voice and call; If we are will - ing,
But they have trou - bles, too; There is a God who
These trials we must go thru; Try to en - dure a

WORDS: Roberta Martin
MUSIC: Roberta Martin
© Copyright 1941 Roberta Martin

He Knows Just How Much You Can Bear

He Knows Just How Much You Can Bear

this as - sur - ance: The heav-en - ly Fa - ther will

al-ways an-swer prayer and He knows, Yes, He knows

Just how much you can bear. bear.

538 My God Is Real
(Yes, God Is Real)

Let us draw near with a true heart in full assurance of faith — Hebrews 10:22 KJV

Slowly, with emphasis

1. There are some things   I may not know,   There are some
2. Some folk may doubt,   some folk may scorn,   All can de-
3. I can-not tell   just how you felt   When Je - sus

WORDS: Kenneth Morris
MUSIC: Kenneth Morris

My God Is Real (Yes, God Is Real)

539 Just to Behold His Face

And they shall see His face — Revelation 22:4 KJV

1. Not just to kneel with the an - gels, — Nor to see loved ones who've gone, — Not just to drink at the foun - tain Un - der the great white throne,

2. Not just to join in the cho - rus, And sing with those that are blest, And bathe my soul that is wea - ry In the sea of heav - en - ly rest,

3. Yes, I want to see Je - sus Who bore His cross in my stead; Who will - ing - ly suf - fered af - flic - tion With a crown of thorns on His head;

4. I'll bless the hand that guid - ed, — I'll bless the heart that planned, I'll not reat un - til I see Je - sus And He takes me by the hand;

WORDS: Derricks Jackson
MUSIC: Derricks Jackson; arr. by Lucie E. Campbell

Just to Behold His Face

540 The Lord's Prayer

After this manner therefore pray ye — Matthew 6:9 KJV

Our Fa - ther, __ which art in heav - en, ____ Hal-low-ed

be ____ Thy name. ____ Thy king-dom come,

Thy will be done on earth as it is in heav - en.

Give us this day our dai - ly bread, And for-give us our debts, as

WORDS: Matthew 6:9-13
MUSIC: Albert Hay Malotte; arr. by Donald P. Hustad

The Lord's Prayer

541 There'll Be Peace in the Valley for Me

Peace be with you all that are in Christ Jesus. Amen. — 1 Peter 5:14 KJV

Moderato

1. I am tir - ed and wea - ry, but I must toil on Till the Lord comes to call me a - way, _____ Where the morn - ing is bright and the Lamb is the light, And the
2. There the flow'rs will be bloom - ing, the grass will be green, And the skies will be clear and se - rene, _____ The sun ev - er shines, giv-ing one end-less beam, And no
3. There the bear will be gen - tle, the wolf will be tame, And the lion will lay down by the lamb, _____ The host from the wild will be led by a Child, I'll be
4. No head - aches or heart - aches or mis - un - der - stands, No con - fu - sion or trou - ble won't be, _____ No frowns to de - file, just a big end-less smile, There'll be

WORDS: Thomas A. Dorsey
MUSIC: Thomas A. Dorsey

There'll Be Peace in the Valley for Me

Refrain

night   is as   fair as   the   day. _____
clouds   there will   ev - er   be   seen. _____
changed   from the   crea-ture   I   am. _____
peace   and con - tent-ment   for   me. _____

There'll be

peace   in the val-ley   for   me   some - day,   There'll be peace   in the

val-ley   for   me.   I   pray no more sor-row and   sad-ness or   trou-ble will

be,   There'll be   peace   in the   val-ley   for   me. _____

542 My Desire

The desire of the righteous is only good — Proverbs 11:23 KJV

1. It's my de - sire to do some good thing ev-'ry day, It's my de-
(2. It's my de) - sire to teach some sin - ner how to pray, It's my de-

sire to help the fall - en by the way, It's my de -
sire to help some trav-'ler find the way, It's my de -

sire to bring back those who've gone a - stray, It's my de -
sire to lift up Je - sus ev - 'ry day, It's my de -

WORDS: Thomas A. Dorsey
MUSIC: Thomas A. Dorsey

My Desire

sire to be like the Lord. It's my de-sire to bring some wan-d'rer
sire to be like the Lord. It's my de-sire to see His face when

to the fold, It's my de - sire to shel - ter some-one
life is done, It's my de - sire to meet the Fa - ther

from the cold, It's my de-sire to do Thy will as I am told, It's my de-
and the Son, It's my de-sire to hear Him say, "My child well done," It's my de-

sire to be like my Lord. _____ 2. It's my de-
sire to be like my Lord. _____

543 May the Work I've Done Speak for Me

Let this mind be in you, which was also in Christ Jesus — Philippians 2:5 KJV

Slowly, with feeling

1. May the work I've done speak for me, May the
2. May the life I live speak for me, May the
3. May the serv'ce I give speak for me, May the

work I've done speak for me, When I'm
life I live speak for me, When the
serv'ce I give speak for me, When I've

rest - ing in my grave, there is noth-ing that can be said, May the
best I try to live, my mis - takes He will for-give, May the
done the best I can and my friends don't un - der-stand, May the

1, 2

work I've done speak for me. 2. May the
life I live speak for me. 3. May the
serv'ce I give speak for

WORDS: Sullivan Pugh
MUSIC: Sullivan Pugh; arr. by K. Morris

May the Work I've Done Speak for Me

544 Canaan

And [He] showed me the great city — Revelation 21:10 KJV

1. I am bound for Can-aan Land To that hap-py gold-en strand, There I shall re-ceive a bless-ing For the work I've done be-low. There I'll see my loved ones gone on To re-ceive their just re-ward; What a

2. Some are com-ing from the East, Some are com-ing from the West, For the're man-y ways to en-ter To that Ce-les-tial Home. Though you en-ter from the North, Though you en-ter from the South, You'll be

3. God the Fa-ther, Christ our Broth-er And the proph-ets all of old, All are wait-ing there to wel-come Me to that sweet hap-py land. I'll be glad to meet the Proph-ets And the oth-ers gone be-fore, But I

WORDS: Aaron Bush Windom
MUSIC: Aaron Bush Windom

Canaan

meet-ing that will be | On that bright Ce - les - tial Shore.
in the great re - un-ion | When we gath - er round the throne.
long to see my Sav-ior | Who has died to save us all.

Give Me a Clean Heart   545

Create in me a clean heart, O God — Psalm 51:10 KJV

Refrain

Give me a clean heart so I may serve Thee. Lord, fix my heart so that I may be

Give Me a Clean Heart

Give Me a Clean Heart

546 All Hail King Jesus

He is Lord of lords, and King of kings — Rev. 17:14 KJV

All hail King Je - sus. ___ All hail Em-man - u - el, ___ King of kings, Lord of lords, Bright Morn-ing Star. ___ And through-out e - ter - ni - ty, I'll sing His prais - es, ___ And I'll reign with Him through - out e - ter - ni - ty. ___

WORDS: Dave Moody
MUSIC: Dave Moody

What a Mighty God We Serve 547

The works of the Lord are great — Psalm 111:2 KJV

What a might - y God we serve. _____

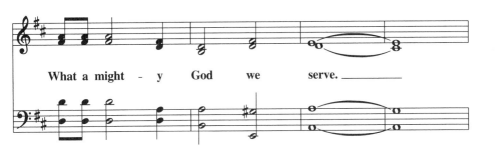

What a might - y God we serve. _____

An-gels bow be - fore Him, heav'n and earth a - dore Him;

What a might - y God we serve. _____

WORDS: Unknown
MUSIC: Unknown

548 One More Day

This is the day which the Lord hath made — Psalm 118:24 KJV

Unison or three-part

1. One more day, one more day. I thank God just for one more day. One more day, the Lord has made a way. I thank God just for one more day.

2. One more chance, one more chance. I thank God just for one more chance. One more chance to do the best I can. I thank God just for one more chance.

Time af-ter time, I start my day with a made up mind. I say in my heart,

3

WORDS: Margaret Douroux
MUSIC: Margaret Douroux
© 1993 Rev. Earl Pleasant Publications

One More Day

This is the day that I make a new start. But when the

end of the day has come and noth-ing for Him have I be-gun,

I be-gin to pray _____ for one more day.

One more day, the Lord has made a way.
One more chance to do the best I can.

I thank God just for one more day.
I thank God just for one more chance.

549 The Lord Is in His Holy Temple

Let all the earth keep silence before Him — Habakkuk 2:20 KJV

The Lord is in His ho-ly tem - ple, The

Lord is in His ho-ly tem - ple: Let all the earth keep

si - lence, Let all the earth keep si - lence be -

fore Him — Keep si - lence, keep

si - lence be - fore Him. A - men.

WORDS: Habakkuk 2:20
MUSIC: George F. Root

Almighty Father, Hear Our Prayer 550

Hear my prayer — Psalm 4:1 KJV

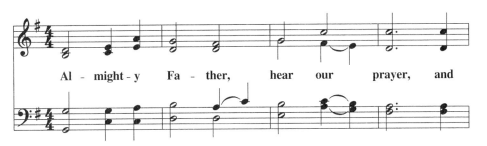

Al - might - y Fa - ther, hear our prayer, and

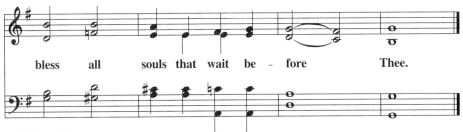

bless all souls that wait be - fore Thee.

WORDS: Unknown
MUSIC: Felix Mendelssohn

Hear Our Prayer, O Lord 551

O my God, incline Thine ear, and hear — Daniel 9:18 KJV

Hear our prayer, O Lord; hear our prayer, O Lord; In -

cline Thine ear to us and grant us Thy peace.

WORDS: George Whelpton
MUSIC: George Whelpton

552   Twofold Amen

A - men,   A - men.

DRESDEN AMEN

553   Threefold Amen

A - men,   A - men,   A -   men.

WORDS: Traditional
MUSIC: Traditional

554   Threefold Amen

A -   men,   A - men,   A -   men.

MUSIC: John Stainer

555   Fourfold Amen

A -   men,   A -   men,

Fourfold Amen

A - men, A - men.

Sevenfold Amen 556

dim. poco a poco e rit.

MUSIC: Peter C. Lutkin

557 The Lord Bless You and Keep You

The Lord make His face shine upon thee — Numbers 6:25 KJV

The Lord bless you and keep you; The Lord lift His coun-te-nance up-

on you, and give you peace,

and give you peace, and give you

The Lord make His

and give you peace; The Lord make His face to shine up-

peace; The Lord make His

And be gra - cious un-to you be gra-cious,

on you, And be gra-cious and be gra-cious,

WORDS: Numbers 6:24-26
MUSIC: Peter C. Lutkin

BENEDICTION

The Lord Bless You and Keep You

The Lord be gra-cious, gra-cious un - to you. A - men.

May the Grace of Christ Our Savior 558

The grace of our Lord Jesus Christ be with you all. Amen — Revelation 22:21 KJV

1. May the grace of Christ our Sav - ior, And the Fa - ther's
2. Thus may we a - bide in un - ion With each oth - er

bound - less love, With the Ho - ly Spir - it's fa - vor,
and the Lord, And pos - sess, in sweet com-mu - nion,

Rest up - on us from a - bove.
Joys which earth can - not af - ford. A - men.

WORDS: John Newton
MUSIC: Ludwig van Beethoven

SARDIS

559 Praise God, from Whom All Blessings Flow

Praise ye the Lord — Psalm 150:6 KJV

Slowly, with feeling

Praise God, from whom all bless - ings flow;

Praise Him, all crea - tures here be - low,

Praise Him, a - bove, ye heav'n - ly host;

Praise Fa - ther, Son, and Ho - ly Ghost.

WORDS: Thomas Ken, Isaac Watts and William Kethe
MUSIC: John Hatton; adapt. by Rev. George Coles; arr. by Roberta Martin

Praise God, from Whom All Blessings Flow

Peo - ple and realms of ev - 'ry tongue
Sing to the Lord with cheer - ful voice,

Dwell on His love with sweet - est song,
Come ye be - fore Him and re - joice,

To Him shall end - less pray'r be made,
All peo - ple that on earth do dwell,

And end - less prais - es crown His
Serve Him with mirth, His prais - es

head.
tell. A - men, A - men.

560 God Be with You

The Lord watch between me and thee — Genesis 31:49 KJV

1. God be with you till we meet a-gain, By His coun-sels guide, up-
2. God be with you till we meet a-gain, 'Neath His wings pro-tect-ing
3. God be with you till we meet a-gain, When life's per-ils thick con-
4. God be with you till we meet a-gain, Keep love's ban-ner float-ing

hold you, With His sheep se-cure-ly fold you –
hide you, Dai-ly man-na still pro-vide you –
found you, Put His arms un-fail-ing round you –
o'er you; Smite death's threat-'ning wave be-fore you –

Refrain

God be with you till we meet a-gain. Till we meet, till we

meet, Till we meet at Je-sus' feet, Till we
till we meet,

meet, till we meet – God be with you till we meet a-gain.

WORDS: Jeremiah E. Rankin
MUSIC: William G. Tomer

GOD BE WITH YOU

Till We Meet Again

561

May the Lord watch between me and thee,
when we are absent one from another — Genesis 31:49 KJV

May His peace be with you _ till we meet _ a -

gain. May His peace be with you _ till we meet _ a - gain.

Till we reach that dis - tant shore, _ And we'll

shed a tear no more, May He give you strength to en - dure _

_ till we meet _ a - gain. Till we meet a - gain.

WORDS: Kirk Franklin
MUSIC: Kirk Franklin

562
God the Creator
Genesis 1:1-5; 2:4-7; Psalm 33:6-9

Leader: In the beginning God created the heaven and the earth.

Congregation: And the earth was without form, and void; and darkness was upon the face of the deep. And the spirit of God moved upon the face of the waters.

And God said, Let there be light: and there was light.

And God saw the light, that it was good: and God divided the light from the darkness.

And God called the light Day, and the darkness he called Night. And the evening and the morning were the first day. *(Genesis 1:1-5)*

These are the generations of the heavens and of the earth when they were created, in the day that the Lord God made the earth and the heavens,

And every plant of the field before it was in the earth, and every herb of the field before it grew: for the Lord God had not caused it to rain upon the earth, and there was not a man to till the ground.

But there went up a mist from the earth, and watered the whole face of the ground.

And the Lord God formed man of the dust of the ground, and breathed into his nostrils the breath of life; and man became a living soul. *(Genesis 2:4-7)*

By the word of the Lord were the heavens made; and all the host of them by the breath of his mouth.

He gathereth the waters of the sea together as an heap: He layeth up the depth in storehouses.

Let all the earth fear the Lord: let all the inhabitants of the world stand in awe of him.

All: For he spake, and it was done; he commanded, and it stood fast. (*Psalm 33:6-9)*

563
God the Omnipotent
Isaiah 40:18, 21-31

Leader: To whom then will ye liken God? or what likeness will ye compare unto him? *(Isaiah 40:18)*

Congregation: Have ye not known? have ye not heard? hath it not been told you from the beginning? have ye not understood from the foundations of the earth?

It is he that sitteth upon the circle of the earth, and the inhabitants thereof are as grasshoppers; that stretcheth out the heavens as a curtain, and spreadeth them out as a tent to dwell in:

That bringeth the princes to nothing; he maketh the judges of the earth as vanity.

Yea, they shall not be planted; yea, they shall not be sown: yea, their stock shall not take root in the earth: and he shall also blow upon them, and they shall wither, and the whirlwind shall take them away as stubble.

To whom then will ye liken me, or shall I be equal? saith the Holy One.

Lift up your eyes on high, and behold who hath created these things, that bringeth out their host by number: he calleth them all by names by the greatness of his might, for that he is strong in power; not one faileth.

Why sayest thou, O Jacob, and speakest, O Israel, My way is hid from the Lord, and my judgment is passed over from my God?

Hast thou not known? hast thou not heard, that the everlasting God, the Lord, the Creator of the ends of the earth, fainteth not, neither is weary? there is no searching of his understanding.

He giveth power to the faint; and to them that have no might he increaseth strength.

Even the youths shall faint and be weary, and the young men shall utterly fall:

All: But they that wait upon the Lord shall renew their strength; they shall mount up with wings as eagles; they shall run, and not be weary; and they shall walk, and not faint. (*Isaiah 40:21-31*)

564
God the Omnipresent
Psalm 139:1-14, 23-24

Leader: O Lord, thou hast searched me, and known me.

Congregation: **Thou knowest my downsitting and mine uprising; thou understandest my thought afar off.**

Thou compassest my path and my lying down, and art acquainted with all my ways.

For there is not a word in my tongue, but, lo, O Lord, thou knowest it altogether.

Thou hast beset me behind and before, and laid thine hand upon me.

Such knowledge is too wonderful for me; it is high, I cannot attain unto it.

Whither shall I go from thy spirit? Or whither shall I flee from thy presence?

If I ascend up into heaven, thou art there: if I make my bed in hell, behold, thou art there.

If I take the wings of the morning, and dwell in the uttermost parts of the sea;

Even there shall thy hand lead me, and thy right hand shall hold me.

If I say, Surely the darkness shall cover me; even the night shall be light about me.

Yea, the darkness hideth not from thee; but the night shineth as the day: the darkness and the light are both alike to thee.

For thou hast possessed my reins: thou hast covered me in my mother's womb.

I will praise thee; for I am fearfully and wonderfully made: marvelous are thy works; and that my soul knoweth right well. (*Psalm 139:1-14*)

Search me, O God, and know my heart: try me, and know my thoughts:

All: **And see if there be any wicked way in me, and lead me in the way everlasting.** (*Psalm 139:23-24*)

565
God's Providential Care
Psalm 91

Leader: He that dwelleth in the secret place of the most High shall abide under the shadow of the Almighty.

Congregation: **I will say of the Lord, He is my refuge and my fortress: my God; in him will I trust.**

Surely he shall deliver thee from the snare of the fowler, and from the noisome pestilence.

He shall cover thee with his feathers, and under his wings shalt thou trust: his truth shall be thy shield and buckler.

(over)

Thou shalt not be afraid for the terror by night; nor for the arrow that flieth by day;

Nor for the pestilence that walketh in darkness; nor for the destruction that wasteth at noonday.

A thousand shall fall at thy side,and ten thousand at thy right hand; but it shall not come nigh thee.

Only with thine eyes shalt thou behold and see the reward of the wicked.

Because thou hast made the Lord, which is my refuge, even the most High, thy habitation;

There shall no evil befall thee, neither shall any plague come nigh thy dwelling.

For he shall give his angels charge over thee, to keep thee in all thy ways.

They shall bear thee up in their hands, lest thou dash thy foot against a stone.

Thou shalt tread upon the lion and adder: the young lion and the dragon shalt thou trample under feet.

Because he hath set his love upon me, therefore will I deliver him: I will set him on high, because he hath known my name.

He shall call upon me, and I will answer him: I will be with him in trouble; I will deliver him, and honour him.

All: **With long life will I satisfy him, and shew him my salvation.**

566
The Pre-existence of Jesus
John 1:1-14; 3:16-17

Leader: In the beginning was the Word, and the Word was with God, and the Word was God.

Congregation: **The same was in the beginning with God.**

All things were made by him; and without him was not any thing made that was made.

In him was life; and the life was the light of men.

And the light shineth in darkness; and the darkness comprehended it not.

There was a man sent from God, whose name was John.

The same came for a witness, to bear witness of the Light, that all men through him might believe.

He was not that Light, but was sent to bear witness of that Light.

That was the true Light, which lighteth every man that cometh into the world.

He was in the world, and the world was made by him, and the world knew him not.

He came unto his own, and his own received him not.

But as many as received him, to them gave he power to become the sons of God, even to them that believe on his name:

Which were born, not of blood, nor of the will of the flesh, nor of the will of man, but of God.

And the Word was made flesh, and dwelt among us, (and we beheld his glory, the glory as of the only begotten of the Father,) full of grace and truth. *(John 1:1-14)*

For God so loved the world, that he gave his only begotten Son, that whosoever believeth in him should not perish, but have everlasting life.

All: **For God sent not his Son into the world to condemn the world; but that the world through him might be saved.** *(John 3:16-17)*

567

The Birth of Jesus
Luke 2:7-20

Leader: And she brought forth her firstborn son, and wrapped him in swaddling clothes, and laid him in a manger; because there was no room for them in the inn.

Congregation: **And there were in the same country shepherds abiding in the field, keeping watch over their flock by night.**

And, lo, the angel of the Lord came upon them, and the glory of the Lord shone round about them: and they were sore afraid.

And the angel said unto them, Fear not: for, behold, I bring you good tidings of great joy, which shall be to all people.

For unto you is born this day in the city of David a Saviour, which is Christ the Lord.

And this shall be a sign unto you; Ye shall find the babe wrapped in swaddling clothes, lying in a manger.

And suddenly there was with the angel a multitude of the heavenly host praising God, and saying,

Glory to God in the highest and on earth peace, good will toward men.

And it came to pass, as the angels were gone away from them into heaven, the shepherds said one to another, Let us now go even unto Bethlehem, and see this thing which is come to pass, which the Lord hath made known unto us.

And they came with haste, and found Mary, and Joseph, and the babe lying in a manger.

And when they had seen it, they made known abroad the saying which was told them concerning this child.

And all they that heard it wondered at those things which were told them by the shepherds.

But Mary kept all these things, and pondered them in her heart.

All: **And the shepherds returned, glorifying and praising God for all the things that they had heard and seen, as it was told unto them.**

568

The Life and Ministry of Jesus
Luke 4:14-20; Matthew 4:23-25

Leader: And Jesus returned in the power of the Spirit into Galilee: and there went out a fame of him through all the region round about.

Congregation: **And he taught in their synagogues, being glorified of all.**

And he came to Nazareth, where he had been brought up: and, as his custom was, he went into the synagogue on the sabbath day, and stood up for to read.

And there was delivered unto him the book of the prophet Esaias. And when he had opened the book, he found the place where it was written,

The Spirit of the Lord is upon me, because he hath anointed me to preach the gospel to the poor; he hath sent me to heal the brokenhearted, to preach deliverance to the captives, and recovering of sight to the blind, to set at liberty them that are bruised,

(over)

To preach the acceptable year of the Lord.

And he closed the book, and he gave it again to the minister, and sat down. And the eyes of all them that were in the synagogue were fastened on him. *(Luke 4:14-20)*

And Jesus went about all Galilee, teaching in their synagogues, and preaching the gospel of the kingdom, and healing all manner of sickness and all manner of disease among the people.

And his fame went throughout all Syria: and they brought unto him all sick people that were taken with divers diseases and torments, and those which were possessed with devils, and those which were lunatic, and those that had the palsy; and he healed them.

All: And there followed him great multitudes of people from Galilee, and from Decapolis, and from Jerusalem, and from Judaea, and from beyond Jordan. *(Matthew 4:23-25)*

569

Palm Sunday

John 12:12, 13, 15; Mark 11:1-6,8, 10

Leader: On the next day much people that were come to the feast, when they heard that Jesus was coming to Jerusalem. (John 12:12)

Congregation: And when they came nigh to Jerusalem, unto Bethpage and Bethany, at the mount of Olives, he sendeth forth two of his disciples,

And saith unto them, Go your way into the village over against you: and as soon as ye be entered into it, ye shall find a colt tied, whereon never man sat; loose him, and bring him.

And if any man say unto you, Why do ye this? say ye that the Lord hath need of him; and straightway he will send him hither.

And they went their way, and found the colt tied by the door without in a place where two ways met; and they loose him.

And certain of them that stood there said unto them, What do ye, loosing the colt?

And they said unto them even as Jesus had commanded: and they let them go. *(Mark 11: 1-6)*

Fear not, daughter of Zion: behold, thy King cometh, sitting on an ass's colt. *(John 12:15)*

And many spread their garments in the way: and others cut down branches off the trees, and strawed them in the way. *(Mark 11:8)*

And went forth to meet him, and cried, Hosanna: Blessed is the King of Israel that cometh in the name of the Lord. *(John 12:13)*

All: Blessed be the kingdom of our father David, that cometh in the name of the Lord: Hosanna in the highest. *(Mark 11:10)*

570

The Crucifixion of Jesus

John 19:16-19; 23-30

Leader: Then delivered he him therefore unto them to be crucified. And they took Jesus, and led him away.

Congregation: And he bearing his cross went forth into a place called the place of a skull, which is called in the Hebrew Golgotha:

Where they crucified him, and two other with him, on either side one, and Jesus in the midst.

And Pilate wrote a title, and put it on the cross. And the writing was, JESUS OF NAZARETH THE KING OF THE JEWS. *(John 19:16-19)*

Then the soldiers, when they had crucified Jesus, took his garments, and made four parts, to every soldier a part; and also his coat: now the coat was without seam, woven from the top throughout.

They said therefore among themselves, Let us not rend it, but cast lots for it, whose it shall be: that the scripture might be fulfilled, which saith, They parted my raiment among them, and for my vesture they did cast lots. These things therefore the soldiers did.

Now there stood by the cross of Jesus his mother, and his mother's sister, Mary the wife of Cleophas, and Mary Magdalene.

When Jesus therefore saw his mother, and the disciple standing by, whom he loved, he saith unto his mother, Woman, behold thy son!

Then saith he to the disciple, Behold thy mother! And from that hour that disciple took her unto his own home.

After this, Jesus knowing that all things were now accomplished, that the scripture might be fulfilled, saith, I thirst.

Now there was set a vessel full of vinegar: and they filled a sponge with vinegar, and put it upon hyssop, and put it to his mouth.

All: When Jesus therefore had received the vinegar, he said, it is finished: and he bowed his head, and gave up the ghost. *(John 19:23-30)*

571
The Resurrection of Jesus
Matthew 28:1-10, 18-20

Leader: In the end of the sabbath, as it began to dawn toward the first day of the week, came Mary Magdalene and the other Mary to see the sepulchre.

Congregation: **And, behold, there was a great earthquake: for the angel of the Lord descended from heaven, and came and rolled back the stone from the door, and sat upon it.**

His countenance was like lightning, and his raiment white as snow:

And for fear of him the keepers did shake, and became as dead men.

And the angel answered and said unto the women, Fear not ye: for I know that ye seek Jesus, which was crucified.

He is not here: for he is risen, as he said. Come, see the place where the Lord lay.

And go quickly, and tell his disciples that he is risen from the dead; and, behold, he goeth before you into Galilee; there shall ye see him: lo, I have told you.

And they departed quickly from the sepulchre with fear and great joy; and did run to bring his disciples word.

And as they went to tell his disciples, behold, Jesus met them, saying, All hail. And they came and held him by the feet, and worshipped him.

Then said Jesus unto them, Be not afraid: go tell my brethren that they go into Galilee, and there shall they see me. *(Matthew 28:1-10)*

And Jesus came and spake unto them, saying, All power is given unto me in heaven and in earth. *(over)*

Go ye therefore, and teach all nations, baptizing them in the name of the Father, and of the Son, and of the Holy Ghost:

All: Teaching them to observe all things whatsoever I have commanded you: and, lo, I am with you always, even unto the end of the world. Amen. *(Matthew 28:18-20)*

572
The Promise of the Holy Spirit
John 14:15-26

Leader: If ye love me, keep my commandments.

Congregation: And I will pray the Father, and he shall give you another Comforter, that he may abide with you for ever;

Even the Spirit of truth; whom the world cannot receive, because it seeth him not, neither knoweth him: but ye know him; for he dwelleth with you, and shall be in you.

I will not leave you comfortless: I will come to you.

Yet a little while, and the world seeth me no more; but ye see me: because I live, ye shall live also.

At that day ye shall know that I am in my Father, and ye in me, and I in you.

He that hath my commandments, and keepeth them, he it is that loveth me: and he that loveth me shall be loved of my Father, and I will love him, and will manifest myself to him.

Judas saith unto him, not Iscariot, Lord, how is it that thou wilt manifest thyself unto us, and not unto the world?

Jesus answered and said unto him, If a man love me, he will keep my words: and my Father will love him, and we will come unto him, and make our abode with him.

He that loveth me not keepeth not my sayings: and the word which ye hear is not mine, but the Father's which sent me.

These things have I spoken unto you, being yet present with you.

All: But the Comforter, which is the Holy Ghost, whom the Father will send in my name, he shall teach you all things, and bring all things to your remembrance, whatsoever I have said unto you.

573

The Coming of the Holy Spirit
Acts 2:1-7; 10:44-48

Leader: And when the day of Pentecost was fully come, they were all with one accord in one place.

Congregation: And suddenly there came a sound from heaven as of a rushing mighty wind, and it filled all the house where they were sitting.

And there appeared unto them cloven tongues like as of fire, and it sat upon each of them.

And they were all filled with the Holy Ghost, and began to speak with other tongues, as the Spirit gave them utterance.

And there were dwelling at Jerusalem Jews, devout men, out of every nation under heaven.

Now when this was noised abroad, the multitude came together, and were confounded, because that every man heard them speak in his own language.

And they were all amazed and marvelled, saying one to another, Behold, are not all these which speak Galilaeans? *(Acts 2:1-7)*

While Peter yet spake these words, the Holy Ghost fell on all them which heard the word.

And they of the circumcision which believed were astonished, as many as came with Peter, because that on the Gentiles also was poured out the gift of the Holy Ghost.

For they heard them speak with tongues, and magnify God. Then answered Peter,

Can any man forbid water, that these should not be baptized, which have received the Holy Ghost as well as we?

All: **And he commanded them to be baptized in the name of the Lord. Then prayed they him to tarry certain days.** *(Acts 10:44-48)*

574
The Work of the Holy Spirit
John 16:5-15

Leader: But now I go my way to him that sent me; and none of you asketh me, Whither goest thou?

Congregation: **But because I have said these things unto you, sorrow hath filled your heart.**

Nevertheless I tell you the truth; It is expedient for you that I go away: for if I go not away, the Comforter will not come unto you; but if I depart, I will send him unto you.

And when he is come, he will reprove the world of sin, and of righteousness, and of judgment:

Of sin, because they believe not on me;

Of righteousness, because I go to my Father, and ye see me no more;

Of judgment, because the prince of this world is judged.

I have yet many things to say unto you, but ye cannot bear them now.

Howbeit when he, the Spirit of truth, is come, he will guide you into all truth: for he shall not speak of himself; but whatsoever he shall hear, that shall he speak: and he will show you things to come.

He shall glorify me: for he shall receive of mine, and shall show it unto you.

All: **All things that the Father hath are mine: therefore said I, that he shall take of mine, and shall show it unto you.**

575
The Christian Family
Ephesians 5:21-33; 6:1-4

Leader: Submitting yourselves one to another in the fear of God.

Congregation: **Wives, submit yourselves unto your own husbands, as unto the Lord.**

For the husband is the head of the wife, even as Christ is the head of the church: and he is the saviour of the body.

Therefore as the church is subject unto Christ, so let the wives be to their own husbands in everything.

Husbands, love your wives, even as Christ also loved the church, and gave himself for it;

That he might sanctify and cleanse it with the washing of water by the word,

That he might present it to himself a glorious church, not having spot, or wrinkle, or any such thing; but that it should be holy and without blemish.

(over)

So ought men to love their wives as their own bodies. He that loveth his wife loveth himself.

For no man ever yet hated his own flesh; but nourisheth and cherisheth it, even as the Lord the church:

For we are members of his body, of his flesh, and of his bones.

For this cause shall a man leave his father and mother, and shall be joined unto his wife, and they two shall be one flesh.

This is a great mystery: but I speak concerning Christ and the church.

Nevertheless let every one of you in particular so love his wife even as himself; and the wife see that she reverence her husband. *(Ephesians 5:21-33)*

Children, obey your parents in the Lord: for this is right.

Honour thy father and mother; which is the first commandment with promise;

That it may be well with thee, and thou mayest live long on the earth.

All: And, ye fathers, provoke not your children to wrath: but bring them up in the nurture and admonition of the Lord. *(Ephesians 6:1-4)*

576
Training in the Christian Home
Deuteronomy 6:1-7;
Proverbs 22:6; 2 Timothy 1:5-6

Leader: Now these are the commandments, the statutes, and the judgments, which the Lord your God commanded to teach you, that ye might do them in the land whither ye go to possess it:

Congregation: That thou mightest fear the Lord thy God, to keep all his statutes and his commandments, which I command thee, thou, and thy son, and thy son's son all the days of thy life; and that thy days may be prolonged.

Hear therefore, O Israel, and observe to do it; that it may be well with thee, and that ye may increase mightily, as the Lord God of thy fathers hath promised thee, in the land that floweth with milk and honey.

Hear, O Israel: the Lord our God is one Lord:

And thou shalt love the Lord thy God with all thine heart, and with all thy soul, and with all thy might.

And these words, which I command thee this day, shall be in thine heart:

And thou shalt teach them diligently unto thy children, and shalt talk of them when thou sittest in thine house, and when thou walkest by the way, and when thou liest down, and when thou risest up. *(Deuteronomy 6:1-7)*

Train up a child in the way he should go: and when he is old, he will not depart from it. *(Proverbs 22:6)*

When I call to remembrance the unfeigned faith that is in thee, which dwelt first in thy grandmother Lois, and thy mother Eunice; and I am persuaded that in thee also.

All: **Wherefore I put thee in remembrance that thou stir up the gift of God, which is in thee by the putting on of my hands.** *(2 Tim. 1:5-6)*

577
The Church
Matthew 16:13-19; Acts 2:41-47;
Colossians 1:18, 24

Leader: When Jesus came into the coasts of Caesarea Philippi, he asked his disciples, saying, Whom do men say that I, the Son of man am?

Congregation: **And they said, Some say that thou art John the Baptist: some, Elias; and others, Jeremias, or one of the prophets.**

He saith unto them, But whom say ye that I am?

And Simon Peter answered and said, Thou art the Christ, the Son of the living God.

And Jesus answered and said unto him, Blessed art thou, Simon Barjona: for flesh and blood hath not revealed it unto thee, but my Father which is in heaven.

And I say also unto thee, That thou art Peter, and upon this rock I will build my church; and the gates of hell shall not prevail against it.

And I will give unto thee the keys of the kingdom of heaven: and whatsoever thou shalt bind on earth shall be bound in heaven: and whatsoever thou shalt loose on earth shall be loosed in heaven. *(Matthew 16:13-19)*

Then they that gladly received his word were baptized: and the same day there were added unto them about three thousand souls.

And they continued stedfastly in the apostles' doctrine and fellowship, and in breaking of bread, and in prayers.

And fear came upon every soul: and many wonders and signs were done by the apostles.

And all that believed were together, and had all things common;

And sold their possessions and goods, and parted them to all men, as every man had need.

And they, continuing daily with one accord in the temple, and breaking bread from house to house, did eat their meat with gladness and singleness of heart,

Praising God, and having favour with all the people. And the Lord added to the church daily such as should be saved. *(Acts 2:41-47)*

And he is the head of the body, the church: who is the beginning, the firstborn from the dead; that in all things he might have the preeminence.

All: **Who now rejoice in my sufferings for you, and fill up that which is behind of the afflictions of Christ in my flesh for his body's sake, which is the church.** *(Colossians 1:18, 24)*

578
Christian Giving
Malachi 3:8-10; 1 Corinthians 16:1-3;
2 Corinthians 8:1-5; 9:6-7

Leader: Will a man rob God? Yet ye have robbed me. But ye say, Wherein have we robbed thee? In tithes and offerings.

Congregation: **Ye are cursed with a curse: for ye have robbed me, even this whole nation.**

Bring ye all the tithes into the storehouse, that there may be meat in mine house, and prove me now herewith, saith the Lord of hosts, if I will not open you the windows of heaven, and pour you out a blessing, that there shall not be room enough to receive it. *(Malachi 3:8-10)*

(over)

Now concerning the collection for the saints, as I have given order to the churches of Galatia, even so do ye.

Upon the first day of the week let every one of you lay by him in store, as God hath prospered him, that there be no gatherings when I come.

And when I come, whomsoever ye shall approve by your letters, them will I send to bring your liberality unto Jerusalem. *(1 Corinthians 16:1-3)*

Moreover, brethren, we do you to wit of the grace of God bestowed on the churches of Macedonia;

How that in a great trial of affliction the abundance of their joy and their deep poverty abounded unto the riches of their liberality.

For to their power, I bear record, yea, and beyond their power they were willing of themselves;

Praying us with much entreaty that we would receive the gift, and take upon us the fellowship of the ministering to the saints.

And this they did, not as we hoped, but first gave their own selves to the Lord, and unto us by the will of God. *(2 Corinthians 8:1-5)*

But this I say, He which soweth sparingly shall reap also sparingly; and he which soweth bountifully shall reap also bountifully.

All: Every man according as he purposeth in his heart, so let him give; not grudgingly, or of necessity: for God loveth a cheerful giver. *(2 Corinthians 9:6-7)*

579

Stewardship
Matthew 25:14-30

Leader: For the kingdom of heaven is as a man travelling into a far country, who called his own servants, and delivered unto them his goods.

Congregation: **And unto one he gave five talents, to another two, and to another one; to every man according to his several ability; and straightway took his journey.**

Then he that had received the five talents went and traded with the same, and made them other five talents.

And likewise he that had received two, he also gained other two.

But he that had received one went and digged in the earth, and hid his lord's money.

After a long time the lord of those servants cometh, and reckoneth with them.

And so he that had received five talents came and brought other five talents, saying, Lord, thou deliveredst unto me five talents: behold, I have gained beside them five talents more.

His lord said unto him, Well done, thou good and faithful servant: thou hast been faithful over a few things, I will make thee ruler over many things: enter thou into the joy of thy lord.

He also that had received two talents came and said, Lord, thou deliveredst unto me two talents: behold, I have gained two other talents beside them.

His lord said unto him, Well done, good and faithful servant; thou hast been faithful over a few things, I will make thee ruler over many things: enter thou into the joy of thy lord.

Then he which had received the one talent came and said, Lord, I knew thee that thou art an hard man, reaping where thou hast not sown, and gathering where thou hast not strawed:

And I was afraid, and went and hid thy talent in the earth: lo, there thou hast that is thine.

His lord answered and said unto him, Thou wicked and slothful servant, thou knewest that I reap where I sowed not, and gather where I have not strawed:

Thou oughtest therefore to have put my money to the exchangers, and then at my coming I should have received mine own with usury.

Take therefore the talent from him, and give it unto him which hath ten talents.

For unto every one that hath shall be given, and he shall have abundance: but from him that hath not shall be taken away even that which he hath.

All: And cast ye the unprofitable servant into outer darkness: there shall be weeping and gnashing of teeth.

580
World Missions
Isaiah 60:1-5; Matthew 28:19-20;
Romans 10:11-15

Leader: Arise, shine; for thy light is come, and the glory of the Lord is risen upon thee.

Congregation: For, behold, the darkness shall cover the earth, and gross darkness the people: but the Lord shall arise upon thee, and his glory shall be seen upon thee.

And the Gentiles shall come to thy light, and kings to the brightness of thy rising.

Lift up thine eyes round about, and see: all they gather themselves together, they come to thee: thy sons shall come from far, and thy daughters shall be nursed at thy side.

Then thou shalt see, and flow together, and thine heart shall fear, and be enlarged; because the abundance of the sea shall be converted unto thee, the forces of the Gentiles shall come unto thee. *(Isaiah 60:1-5)*

Go ye therefore, and teach all nations, baptizing them in the name of the Father, and of the Son, and of the Holy Ghost:

Teaching them to observe all things whatsoever I have commanded you: and, lo, I am with you alway, even unto the end of the world. Amen. *(Matthew 28:19, 20)*

For the scripture saith, Whosoever believeth on him shall not be ashamed.

For there is no difference between the Jew and the Greek: for the same Lord over all is rich unto all that call upon him.

For whosoever shall call upon the name of the Lord shall be saved.

How then shall they call on him in whom they have not believed? And how shall they believe in him of whom they have not heard? And how shall they hear without a preacher?

All: And how shall they preach, except they be sent? as it is written, How beautiful are the feet of them that preach the gospel of peace, and bring glad tidings of good things! *(Romans 10:11-15)*

581
The Missionary Church
Acts 1:8; Mark 16:15-16;
John 17:18-21; Acts 13:1-5

Leader: But ye shall receive power, after that the Holy Ghost is come upon you: and ye shall be witnesses unto me both in Jerusalem, and in all Judaea, and in Samaria, and unto the uttermost part of the earth. *(Acts 1:8)*

Congregation: And he said unto them, Go ye into all the world, and preach the gospel to every creature.

He that believeth and is baptized shall be saved; but he that believeth not shall be damned. *(Mark 16:15-16)*

As thou hast sent me into the world, even so have l also sent them into the world.

And for their sakes I sanctify myself, that they also might be sanctified through the truth.

Neither pray I for these alone, but for them also which shall believe on me through their word;

That they all may be one; as thou, Father, art in me, and I in thee, that they also may be one in us: that the world may believe that thou hast sent me. *(John 17:18-21)*

Now there were in the church that was at Antioch certain prophets and teachers; as Barnabas, and Simeon that was called Niger, and Lucius of Cyrene, and Manaen, which had been brought up with Herod the tetrarch, and Saul.

As they ministered to the Lord and fasted, the Holy Ghost said, Separate me Barnabas and Saul for the work whereunto I have called them.

And when they had fasted and prayed, and laid their hands on them, they sent them away.

So they, being sent forth by the Holy Ghost, departed unto Seleucia; and from thence they sailed to Cyprus.

All: And when they were at Salamis, they **preached the word of God in the synagogues of the Jews: and they had also John to their minister.** *(Acts 13:1-5)*

582
Regeneration
John 3:1-7; Romans 10:8-11

Leader: There was a man of the Pharisees, named Nicodemus, a ruler of the Jews:

Congregation: **The same came to Jesus by night, and said unto him, Rabbi, we know that thou art a teacher come from God: for no man can do these miracles that thou doest, except God be with him.**

Jesus answered and said unto him, Verily, verily, I say unto thee, Except a man be born again, he cannot see the kingdom of God.

Nicodemus saith unto him, How can a man be born when he is old? Can he enter the second time into his mother's womb, and be born?

Jesus answered, Verily, verily, I say unto thee, Except a man be born of water and of the Spirit, he cannot enter into the kingdom of God.

That which is born of the flesh is flesh; and that which is born of the Spirit is spirit.

Marvel not that I said unto thee, Ye must be born again. *(John 3:1-7)*

But what saith it? The word is nigh thee, even in thy mouth, and in thy heart: that is, the word of faith, which we preach;

That if thou shalt confess with thy mouth the Lord Jesus, and shalt believe in thine heart that God hath raised him from the dead, thou shalt be saved.

For with the heart man believeth unto righteousness; and with the mouth confession is made unto salvation.

All: For the scripture saith, Whosoever believeth on him shall not be ashamed. *(Romans 10:8-11)*

583
Justification
Romans 5:1-11; 8:1-2, 30

Leader: Therefore being justified by faith, we have peace with God through our Lord Jesus Christ:

Congregation: By whom also we have access by faith into this grace wherein we stand, and rejoice in hope of the glory of God.

And not only so, but we glory in tribulations also: knowing that tribulation worketh patience;

And patience, experience; and experience, hope:

And hope maketh not ashamed; because the love of God is shed abroad in our hearts by the Holy Ghost which is given unto us.

For when we were yet without strength, in due time Christ died for the ungodly.

For scarcely for a righteous man will one die: yet peradventure for a good man some would even dare to die.

But God commendeth his love toward us, in that, while we were yet sinners, Christ died for us.

Much more then, being now justified by his blood, we shall be saved from wrath through him.

For if, when we were enemies, we were reconciled to God by the death of his Son, much more, being reconciled, we shall be saved by his life.

And not only so, but we also joy in God through our Lord Jesus Christ, by whom we have now received the atonement. *(Romans 5:1-11)*

There is therefore now no condemnation to them which are in Christ Jesus, who walk not after the flesh, but after the Spirit.

For the law of the Spirit of life in Christ Jesus hath made me free from the law of sin and death.

All: Moreover whom he did predestinate, them he also called: and whom he called, them he also justified: and whom he justified, them he also glorified. *(Romans 8:1-2, 30)*

584
Sanctification
Galatians 5:22-25;
1 Thessalonians 4:1-7

Leader: But the fruit of the Spirit is love, joy, peace, longsuffering, gentleness, goodness, faith,

Congregation: Meekness, temperance: against such there is no law.

And they that are Christ's have crucified the flesh with the affections and lusts.

If we live in the Spirit, let us also walk in the Spirit. *(Galatians 5:22-25)*

(over)

Furthermore then we beseech you, brethren, and exhort you by the Lord Jesus, that as ye have received of us how ye ought to walk and to please God, so ye would abound more and more.

For ye know what commandments we gave you by the Lord Jesus.

For this is the will of God, even your sanctification, that ye should abstain from fornication:

That every one of you should know how to possess his vessel in sanctification and honour;

Not in the lust of concupiscence, even as the Gentiles which know not God:

That no man go beyond and defraud his brother in any matter: because that the Lord is the avenger of all such, as we also have forewarned you and testified.

All: For God hath not called us unto uncleanness, but unto holiness. *(1 Thessalonians 4:1-7)*

For yourselves know perfectly that the day of the Lord so cometh as a thief in the night.

Therefore let us not sleep, as do others; but let us watch and be sober.

For they that sleep sleep in the night; and they that be drunken are drunken in the night.

But let us, who are of the day, be sober, putting on the breastplate of faith and love; and for an helmet, the hope of salvation.

For God hath not appointed us to wrath, but to obtain salvation by our Lord Jesus Christ,

Who died for us, that, whether we wake or sleep, we should live together with him. *(1 Thessalonians 5:2, 6-10)*

All: **And, behold, I come quickly; and my reward is with me, to give every man according as his work shall be.** *(Revelation 22:12)*

585
The Second Coming
Acts 1:10-11; 1 Thessalonians 4:13; 5:2, 6-10; Revelation 22:12

Leader: And while they looked stedfastly toward heaven as he went up, behold, two men stood by them in white apparel;

Congregation: **Which also said, ye men of Galilee, why stand ye gazing up into heaven? This same Jesus, which is taken up from you into heaven, shall so come in like manner as ye have seen him go into heaven.** *(Acts 1:10-11)*

But I would not have you to be ignorant, brethren, concerning them which are asleep, that ye sorrow not, even as others which have no hope. *(1 Thessalonians 4:13)*

586
Christ and Immortality
1 Corinthians 15:19-22, 49-58

Leader: If in this life only we have hope in Christ, we are of all men most miserable.

Congregation: **But now is Christ risen from the dead, and become the firstfruits of them that slept.**

For since by man came death, by man came also the resurrection of the dead.

For as in Adam all die, even so in Christ shall all be made alive. *(1 Corinthians 15:19-22)*

And as we have borne the image of the earthy, we shall also bear the image of the heavenly.

Now this I say, brethren, that flesh and blood cannot inherit the kingdom of God; neither doth corruption inherit incorruption.

Behold, I show you a mystery; We shall not all sleep, but we shall all be changed,

In a moment, in the twinkling of an eye, at the last trump: for the trumpet shall sound, and the dead shall be raised incorruptible, and we shall be changed.

For this corruptible must put on incorruption, and this mortal must put on immortality.

So when this corruptible shall have put on incorruption, and this mortal shall have put on immortality, then shall be brought to pass the saying that is written, Death is swallowed up in victory.

O death, where is thy sting? O grave, where is thy victory?

The sting of death is sin; and the strength of sin is the law.

But thanks be to God, which giveth us the victory through our Lord Jesus Christ.

All: Therefore, my beloved brethren, be ye stedfast, unmoveable, always abounding in the work of the Lord, forasmuch as ye know that your labour is not in vain in the Lord. *(1 Corinthians 15:49-58)*

587
The Judgment
Hebrews 9:27-28; Revelation 20:11-15;
Matthew 13:40-43

Leader: And as it is appointed unto men once to die, but after this the judgment:

Congregation: So Christ was once offered to bear the sins of many; and unto them that look for him shall he appear the second time without sin unto salvation. *(Hebrews 9:27-28)*

And I saw a great white throne, and him that sat on it, from whose face the earth and the heaven fled away; and there was found no place for them.

And I saw the dead, small and great, stand before God; and the books were opened: and another book was opened, which is the book of life: and the dead were judged out of those things which were written in the books, according to their works.

And the sea gave up the dead which were in it; and death and hell delivered up the dead which were in them: and they were judged every man according to their works.

And death and hell were cast into the lake of fire. This is the second death.

And whosoever was not found written in the book of life was cast into the lake of fire. *(Revelation 20:11-15)*

As therefore the tares are gathered and burned in the fire; so shall it be in the end of this world.

The Son of man shall send forth his angels, and they shall gather out of his kingdom all things that offend, and them which do iniquity;

And shall cast them into a furnace of fire: there shall be wailing and gnashing of teeth.

All: Then shall the righteous shine forth as the sun in the kingdom of their Father. Who hath ears to hear, let him hear. *(Matthew 13:40-43)*

588
The Model Prayer
Luke 11:1; Matthew 6:5-15

Leader: And it came to pass, that, as he was praying in a certain place, when he ceased, one of his disciples said unto him, Lord, teach us to pray, as John also taught his disciples. *(Luke 11:1)*

Congregation: **And when thou prayest, thou shalt not be as the hypocrites are: for they love to pray standing in the synagogues and in the corners of the streets, that they may be seen of men. Verily I say unto you, They have their reward.**

But thou, when thou prayest, enter into thy closet, and when thou hast shut thy door, pray to thy Father which is in secret; and thy Father which seeth in secret shall reward thee openly.

But when ye pray, use not vain repetitions, as the heathen do: for they think that they shall be heard for their much speaking.

Be not ye therefore like unto them: for your Father knoweth what things ye have need of, before ye ask him.

After this manner therefore pray ye: Our Father which art in heaven, Hallowed be thy name.

Thy kingdom come. Thy will be done in earth, as it is in heaven.

Give us this day our daily bread.

And forgive us our debts, as we forgive our debtors.

And lead us not into temptation, but deliver us from evil: For thine is the kingdom, and the power, and the glory, for ever. Amen.

For if ye forgive men their trespasses, your heavenly Father will also forgive you:

All: **But if ye forgive not men their trespasses, neither will your Father forgive your trespasses.** *(Matthew 6:5-15)*

589
Growing in Grace
2 Peter 1:2-11; 3:17-18

Leader: Grace and peace be multiplied unto you through the knowledge of God, and of Jesus our Lord,

Congregation: **According as his divine power hath given unto us all things that pertain unto life and godliness, through the knowledge of him that hath called us to glory and virtue:**

Whereby are given unto us exceeding great and precious promises: that by these ye might be partakers of the divine nature, having escaped the corruption that is in the world through lust.

And beside this, giving all diligence, add to your faith virtue; and to virtue knowledge;

And to knowledge temperance; and to temperance patience; and to patience godliness;

And to godliness brotherly kindness; and to brotherly kindness charity.

For if these things be in you, and abound, they make you that ye shall neither be barren nor unfruitful in the knowledge of our Lord Jesus Christ.

But he that lacketh these things is blind, and cannot see afar off, and hath forgotten that he was purged from his old sins.

Wherefore the rather, brethren, give diligence to make your calling and election sure: for if ye do these things, ye shall never fall:

For so an entrance shall be ministered unto you abundantly into the everlasting kingdom of our Lord and Saviour Jesus Christ. *(2 Peter 1:2-11)*

Ye therefore, beloved, seeing ye know these things before, beware lest ye also, being led away with the error of the wicked, fall from your own stedfastness.

All: **But grow in grace, and in the knowledge of our Lord and Saviour Jesus Christ. To him be glory both now and forever. Amen.** *(2 Peter 3:17-18)*

590
Christian Commitment
Romans 12: 1-18

Leader: I beseech you therefore, brethren, by the mercies of God, that ye present your bodies a living sacrifice, holy, acceptable unto God, which is your reasonable service.

Congregation: **And be not conformed to this world: but be ye transformed by the renewing of your mind, that ye may prove what is that good, and acceptable, and perfect, will of God.**

For I say, through the grace given unto me, to every man that is among you, not to think of himself more highly than he ought to think; but to think soberly, according as God hath dealt to every man the measure of faith.

For as we have many members in one body, and all members have not the same office:

So we, being many, are one body in Christ, and every one members one of another.

Having then gifts differing according to the grace that is given to us, whether prophecy, let us prophesy according to the proportion of faith;

Or ministry, let us wait on our ministering: or he that teacheth, on teaching;

Or he that exhorteth, on exhortation: he that giveth, let him do it with simplicity; he that ruleth, with diligence; he that showeth mercy, with cheerfulness.

Let love be without dissimulation. Abhor that which is evil; cleave to that which is good.

Be kindly affectioned one to another with brotherly love; in honour preferring one another;

Not slothful in business; fervent in spirit; serving the Lord;

Rejoicing in hope; patient in tribulation; continuing instant in prayer;

Distributing to the necessity of saints; given to hospitality.

Bless them which persecute you: bless, and curse not.

Rejoice with them that do rejoice, and weep with them that weep.

Be of the same mind one toward another. Mind not high things, but condescend to men of low estate. Be not wise in your own conceits.

Recompense to no man evil for evil. Provide things honest in the sight of all men.

All: **If it be possible, as much as lieth in you, live peaceably with all men.**

591

Love
1 Corinthians 13

Leader: Though I speak with the tongues of men and of angels, and have not charity, I am become as sounding brass, or a tinkling cymbal.

Congregation: **And though I have the gift of prophecy, and understand all mysteries, and all knowledge; and though I have all faith, so that I could remove mountains, and have not charity, I am nothing.**

And though I bestow all my goods to feed the poor, and though I give my body to be burned, and have not charity, it profiteth me nothing.

Charity suffereth long, and is kind; charity envieth not; charity vaunteth not itself, is not puffed up,

Doth not behave itself unseemly, seeketh not her own, is not easily provoked, thinketh no evil;

Rejoiceth not in iniquity, but rejoiceth in the truth;

Beareth all things, believeth all things, hopeth all things, endureth all things.

Charity never faileth: but whether there be prophecies, they shall fail; whether there be tongues, they shall cease; whether there be knowledge, it shall vanish away.

For we know in part, and we prophesy in part.

But when that which is perfect is come, then that which is in part shall be done away.

When I was a child, I spake as a child, I understood as a child, I thought as a child: but when I became a man, I put away childish things.

For now we see through a glass, darkly; but then face to face: now I know in part; but then shall I know even as also I am known.

All: **And now abideth faith, hope, charity, these three; but the greatest of these is charity.**

592

Christian Unity
Psalm 133;
1 Corinthians 12:12-20, 25-27

Leader: Behold, how good and how pleasant it is for brethren to dwell together in unity!

Congregation: **It is like the precious ointment upon the head, that ran down upon the beard, even Aaron's beard: that went down to the skirts of his garments;**

As the dew of Hermon, and as the dew that descended upon the mountains of Zion: for there the Lord commanded the blessing, even life for evermore. *(Psalm 133)*

For as the body is one, and hath many members, and all the members of that one body, being many, are one body: so also is Christ.

For by one Spirit are we all baptized into one body, whether we be Jews or Gentiles, whether we be bond or free; and have been all made to drink into one Spirit.

For the body is not one member, but many.

If the foot shall say, Because I am not the hand, I am not of the body; is it therefore not of the body?

And if the ear shall say, Because I am not the eye, I am not of the body; is it therefore not of the body?

If the whole body were an eye, where were the hearing? If the whole were hearing, where were the smelling?

But now hath God set the members every one of them in the body, as it hath pleased him.

And if they were all one member, where were the body?

But now are they many members, yet but one body. *(1 Corinthians 12: 12-20)*

That there should be no schism in the body; but that the members should have the same care one for another.

And whether one member suffer, all the members suffer with it; or one member be honoured, all the members rejoice with it.

All: **Now ye are the body of Christ, and members in particular.** *(1 Corinthians 12:25-27)*

593

Forgiveness
Matthew 18:21-35; Galatians 6:1;
Ephesians 4:32

Leader: Then came Peter to him, and said, Lord, how oft shall my brother sin against me, and I forgive him? Till seven times?

Congregation: **Jesus saith unto him, I say not unto thee, Until seven times: but, Until seventy times seven.**

Therefore is the kingdom of heaven likened unto a certain king, which would take account of his servants.

And when he had begun to reckon, one was brought unto him, which owed him ten thousand talents.

But forasmuch as he had not to pay, his lord commanded him to be sold, and his wife, and children, and all that he had, and payment to be made.

The servant therefore fell down, and worshipped him, saying, Lord, have patience with me, and I will pay thee all.

Then the lord of that servant was moved with compassion, and loosed him, and forgave him the debt.

But the same servant went out, and found one of his fellowservants, which owed him an hundred pence: and he laid hands on him, and took him by the throat, saying, Pay me that thou owest.

And his fellowservant fell down at his feet, and besought him, saying, Have patience with me, and I will pay thee all.

And he would not: but went and cast him into prison, till he should pay the debt.

So when his fellowservants saw what was done, they were very sorry, and came and told unto their lord all that was done.

Then his lord, after that he had called him, said unto him, O thou wicked servant, I forgave thee all that debt, because thou desiredst me:

Shouldest not thou also have had compassion on thy fellowservant, even as I had pity on thee?

And his lord was wroth, and delivered him to the tormentors, till he should pay all that was due unto him.

So likewise shall my heavenly Father do also unto you, if ye from your hearts forgive not every one his brother their trespasses. *(Matthew 18:21-35)*

Brethren, if a man be overtaken in a fault, ye which are spiritual, restore such an one in the spirit of meekness; considering thyself, lest thou also be tempted. *(Galatians 6:1)*

All: **And be ye kind one to another, tenderhearted, forgiving one another, even as God for Christ's sake hath forgiven you.** *(Ephesians 4:32)*

594
The Christian Hope
Romans 8:18-25

Leader: For I reckon that the sufferings of this present time are not worthy to be compared with the glory which shall be revealed in us.

Congregation: **For the earnest expectation of the creature waiteth for the manifestation of the sons of God.**

For the creature was made subject to vanity, not willingly, but by reason of him who hath subjected the same in hope,

Because the creature itself also shall be delivered from the bondage of corruption into the glorious liberty of the children of God.

For we know that the whole creation groaneth and travaileth in pain together until now.

And not only they, but ourselves also, which have the firstfruits of the Spirit, even we ourselves groan within ourselves, waiting for the adoption, to wit, the redemption of our body.

For we are saved by hope: but hope that is seen is not hope: for what a man seeth, why doth he yet hope for?

All: **But if we hope for that we see not, then do we with patience wait for it.**

595
Spiritual Warfare
Ephesians 6:10-18; Romans 13:12-14

Leader: Finally, my brethren, be strong in the Lord, and in the power of his might.

Congregation: Put on the whole armour of God, that ye may be able to stand against the wiles of the devil.

For we wrestle not against flesh and blood, but against principalities, against powers, against the rulers of the darkness of this world, against spiritual wickedness in high places.

Wherefore take unto you the whole armour of God, that ye may be able to withstand in the evil day, and having done all, to stand.

Stand therefore, having your loins girt about with truth, and having on the breastplate of righteousness;

And your feet shod with the preparation of the gospel of peace;

Above all, taking the shield of faith, wherewith ye shall be able to quench all the fiery darts of the wicked.

And take the helmet of salvation, and the sword of the Spirit, which is the word of God:

Praying always with all prayer and supplication in the Spirit, and watching thereunto with all perseverance and supplication for all saints; *(Ephesians 6:10-18)*

The night is far spent, the day is at hand: let us therefore cast off the works of darkness, and let us put on the armour of light.

Let us walk honestly, as in the day; not in rioting and drunkenness, not in chambering and wantonness, not in strife and envying.

All: **But put ye on the Lord Jesus Christ, and make not provision for the flesh, to fulfil the lusts thereof. (Romans 13:12-14)**

596

Faith
Hebrews 11:1-10

Leader: Now faith is the substance of things hoped for, the evidence of things not seen.

Congregation: **For by it the elders obtained a good report.**

Through faith we understand that the worlds were framed by the word of God, so that things which are seen were not made of things which do appear.

By faith Abel offered unto God a more excellent sacrifice than Cain, by which he obtained witness that he was righteous, God testifying of his gifts: and by it he being dead yet speaketh.

By faith Enoch was translated that he should not see death; and was not found, because God had translated him: for before his translation he had this testimony, that he pleased God.

But without faith it is impossible to please him; for he that cometh to God must believe that he is, and that he is a rewarder of them that diligently seek him.

By faith Noah, being warned of God of things not seen as yet, moved with fear, prepared an ark to the saving of his house; by the which he condemned the world, and became heir of the righteousness which is by faith.

By faith Abraham, when he was called to go out into a place which he should after receive for an inheritance, obeyed; and he went out, not knowing whither he went.

By faith he sojourned in the land of promise, as in a strange country, dwelling in tabernacles with Isaac and Jacob, the heirs with him of the same promise:

All: **For he looked for a city which hath foundations, whose builder and maker is God.**

597

Baptism
Matthew 28:18-20; Romans 6:3-11

Leader: And Jesus came and spake unto them, saying, All power is given unto me in heaven and in earth.

Congregation: **Go ye therefore, and teach all nations, baptizing them in the name of the Father, and of the Son, and of the Holy Ghost:**

Teaching them to observe all things whatsoever I have commanded you: and, lo, I am with you alway, even unto the end of the world. *(Matthew 28:18-20)*

Know ye not, that so many of us as were baptized into Jesus Christ were baptized into his death?

Therefore we are buried with him by baptism into death: that like as Christ was raised up from the dead by the glory of the Father, even so we also should walk in newness of life.

For if we have been planted together in the likeness of his death, we shall be also in the likeness of his resurrection:

Knowing this, that our old man is crucified with him, that the body of sin might be destroyed, that henceforth we should not serve sin.

For he that is dead is freed from sin.

(over)

Now if we be dead with Christ, we believe that we shall also live with him:

Knowing that Christ being raised from the dead dieth no more; death hath no more dominion over him.

For in that he died, he died unto sin once: but in that he liveth he liveth unto God.

All: **Likewise reckon ye also yourselves to be dead indeed unto sin, but alive unto God through Jesus Christ our Lord.** *(Romans 6:3-11)*

598
The Lord's Supper
1 Corinthians 11:23-34

Leader: For I have received of the Lord that which also I delivered unto you, That the Lord Jesus the same night in which he was betrayed took bread:

Congregation: **And when he had given thanks, he brake it, and said, Take, eat: this is my body, which is broken for you: this do in remembrance of me.**

After the same manner also he took the cup, when he had supped, saying, This cup is the new testament in my blood: this do ye, as oft as ye drink it, in remembrance of me.

For as often as ye eat this bread, and drink this cup, ye do shew the Lord's death till he come.

Wherefore whosoever shall eat this bread, and drink this cup of the Lord, unworthily, shall be guilty of the body and blood of the Lord.

But let a man examine himself, and so let him eat of that bread, and drink of that cup.

For he that eateth and drinketh unworthily, eateth and drinketh damnation to himself, not discerning the Lord's body.

For this cause many are weak and sickly among you, and many sleep.

For if we would judge ourselves, we should not be judged.

But when we are judged, we are chastened of the Lord, that we should not be condemned with the world.

Wherefore, my brethren, when ye come together to eat, tarry one for another.

All: **And if any man hunger, let him eat at home; that ye come not together unto condemnation. And the rest will I set in order when I come.**

599
The Christian Death
2 Corinthians 5:1-10;
Revelation 14:13

Leader: For we know that if our earthly house of this tabernacle were dissolved, we have a building of God, an house not made with hands, eternal in the heavens.

Congregation: **For in this we groan, earnestly desiring to be clothed upon with our house which is from heaven:**

If so be that being clothed we shall not be found naked.

For we that are in this tabernacle do groan, being burdened: not for that we would be unclothed, but clothed upon, that mortality might be swallowed up of life.

Now he that hath wrought us for the selfsame thing is God, who also hath given unto us the earnest of the Spirit.

Therefore we are always confident, knowing that, whilst we are at home in the body, we are absent from the Lord:

(For we walk by faith, not by sight:)

We are confident, I say, and willing rather to be absent from the body, and to be present with the Lord.

Wherefore we labour, that, whether present or absent, we may be accepted of him.

For we must all appear before the judgment seat of Christ; that every one may receive the things done in his body, according to that he hath done, whether it be good or bad. *(2 Corinthians 5:1-10)*

All: And I heard a voice from heaven saying unto me, Write, Blessed are the dead which die in the Lord from henceforth: Yea, saith the Spirit, that they may rest from their labours; and their works do follow them. *(Revelation 14:13)*

600
Heaven
Revelation 21:1-3; 7:9-17

Leader: And I saw a new heaven and a new earth: for the first heaven and the first earth were passed away; and there was no more sea.

Congregation: And I John saw the holy city, new Jerusalem, coming down from God out of heaven, prepared as a bride adorned for her husband.

And I heard a great voice out of heaven saying, Behold, the tabernacle of God is with men, and he will dwell with them, and they shall be his people, and God himself shall be with them, and be their God. *(Revelation 21:1-3)*

After this I beheld, and, lo, a great multitude, which no man could number, of all nations, and kindreds, and people, and tongues, stood before the throne, and before the Lamb, clothed with white robes, and palms in their hands;

And cried with a loud voice, saying, Salvation to our God which sitteth upon the throne, and unto the Lamb.

And all the angels stood round about the throne, and about the elders and the four beasts, and fell before the throne on their faces, and worshipped God,

Saying, Amen: Blessing, and glory, and wisdom, and thanksgiving, and honour, and power, and might, be unto our God for ever and ever. Amen.

And one of the elders answered, saying unto me, What are these which are arrayed in white robes? And whence came they?

And I said unto him, Sir, thou knowest. And he said to me, These are they which came out of great tribulation, and have washed their robes, and made them white in the blood of the Lamb.

Therefore are they before the throne of God, and serve him day and night in his temple: and he that sitteth on the throne shall dwell among them.

They shall hunger no more, neither thirst any more; neither shall the sun light on them, nor any heat.

All: For the Lamb which is in the midst of the throne shall feed them, and shall lead them unto living fountains of waters: and God shall wipe away all tears from their eyes. *(Revelation 7:9-17)*

601

Temperance

Proverbs 20:1; Romans 14:1-8,16-23; 1 Corinthians 3:16-17

Leader: Wine is a mocker, strong drink is raging: and whosoever is deceived thereby is not wise. *(Proverbs 20:1)*

Congregation: **Him that is weak in the faith receive ye, but not to doubtful disputations.**

For one believeth that he may eat all things: another, who is weak, eateth herbs.

Let not him that eateth despise him that eateth not; and let not him which eateth not judge him that eateth: for God hath received him.

Who art thou that judgest another man's servant? To his own master he standeth or falleth. Yea, he shall be holden up: for God is able to make him stand.

One man esteemeth one day above another: another esteemeth every day alike. Let every man be fully persuaded in his own mind.

He that regardeth the day, regardeth it unto the Lord; and he that regardeth not the day, to the Lord he doth not regard it. He that eateth, eateth to the Lord, for he giveth God thanks; and he that eateth not, to the Lord he eateth not, and giveth God thanks.

For none of us liveth to himself, and no man dieth to himself.

For whether we live, we live unto the Lord; and whether we die, we die unto the Lord: whether we live therefore, or die, we are the Lord's. *(Romans 14:1-8)*

Let not then your good be evil spoken of:

For the kingdom of God is not meat and drink; but righteousness, and peace, and joy in the Holy Ghost.

For he that in these things serveth Christ is acceptable to God, and approved of men.

Let us therefore follow after the things which make for peace, and things wherewith one may edify another.

For meat destroy not the work of God. All things indeed are pure; but it is evil for that man who eateth with offence.

It is good neither to eat flesh, nor to drink wine, nor any thing whereby thy brother stumbleth, or is offended, or is made weak.

Hast thou faith? Have it to thyself before God. Happy is he that condemneth not himself in that thing which he alloweth.

And he that doubteth is damned if he eat, because he eateth not of faith: for whatsoever is not of faith is sin. *(Romans 14:16-23)*

Know ye not that ye are the temple of God, and that the Spirit of God dwelleth in you?

All: **If any man defile the temple of God, him shall God destroy; for the temple of God is holy, which temple ye are. *(1 Corinthians 3:16-17)***

602

The Upright Man

Psalm 1

Leader: Blessed is the man that walketh not in the counsel of the ungodly, nor standeth in the way of sinners, nor sitteth in the seat of the scornful.

Congregation: **But his delight is in the law of the Lord; and in his law doth he meditate day and night.**

And he shall be like a tree planted by the rivers of water, that bringeth forth his fruit in his season; his leaf also shall not wither; and whatsoever he doeth shall prosper.

The ungodly are not so: but are like the chaff which the wind driveth away.

Therefore the ungodly shall not stand in the judgment, nor sinners in the congregation of the righteous.

All: **For the Lord knoweth the way of the righteous: but the way of the ungodly shall perish.**

603
True Wisdom
Job 28:12-13; Proverbs 3:13-26, 5-6

Leader: But where shall wisdom be found? and where is the place of understanding?

Congregation: **Man knoweth not the price thereof; neither is it found in the land of the living.** *(Job 28:12-13)*

Happy is the man that findeth wisdom, and the man that getteth understanding.

For the merchandise of it is better than the merchandise of silver, and the gain thereof than fine gold.

She is more precious than rubies: and all the things thou canst desire are not to be compared unto her.

Length of days is in her right hand; and in her left hand riches and honour.

Her ways are ways of pleasantness, and all her paths are peace.

She is a tree of life to them that lay hold upon her: and happy is every one that retaineth her.

The Lord by wisdom hath founded the earth; by understanding hath he established the heavens.

By his knowledge the depths are broken up, and the clouds drop down the dew.

My son, let not them depart from thine eyes: keep sound wisdom and discretion:

So shall they be life unto thy soul, and grace to thy neck.

Then shalt thou walk in thy way safely, and thy foot shall not stumble.

When thou liest down, thou shalt not be afraid: yea, thou shalt lie down, and thy sleep shall be sweet.

Be not afraid of sudden fear, neither of the desolation of the wicked, when it cometh.

For the Lord shall be thy confidence, and shall keep thy foot from being taken. *(Proverbs 3:13-26)*

Trust in the Lord with all thine heart; and lean not unto thine own understanding.

All: **In all thy ways acknowledge him, and he shall direct thy paths.** *(Proverbs 3:5-6)*

604
Peace
John 16:32-33; 14:27;
Ephesians 2:14-17; Philippians 4:7-9

Leader: Behold, the hour cometh, yea, is now come, that ye shall be scattered, every man to his own, and shall leave me alone: and yet I am not alone, because the Father is with me.

Congregation: **These things I have spoken unto you, that in me ye might have peace. In the world ye shall have tribulation: but be of good cheer; I have overcome the world.** *(John 16:32-33)*

Peace I leave with you, my peace I give unto you: not as the world giveth, give I unto you. Let not your heart be troubled, neither let it be afraid. *(John 14:27)*

(over)

For he is our peace, who hath made both one, and hath broken down the middle wall of partition between us;

Having abolished in his flesh the enmity, even the law of commandments contained in ordinances; for to make in himself of twain one new man, so making peace;

And that he might reconcile both unto God in one body by the cross, having slain the enmity thereby:

And came and preached peace to you which were afar off, and to them that were nigh. *(Ephesians 2:14-17)*

And the peace of God, which passeth all understanding, shall keep your hearts and minds through Christ Jesus.

Finally, brethren, whatsoever things are true, whatsoever things are honest, whatsoever things are just, whatsoever things are pure, whatsoever things are lovely, whatsoever things are of good report; if there be any virtue, and if there be any praise, think on these things.

All: Those things, which ye have both learned, and received, and heard, and seen in me, do: and the God of peace shall be with you. *(Philippians 4:7-9)*

605
Praising the Lord
Psalm 147

Leader: Praise ye the Lord: for it is good to sing praises unto our God; for it is pleasant; and praise is comely.

Congregation: The Lord doth build up Jerusalem: he gathereth together the outcasts of Israel.

He healeth the broken in heart, and bindeth up their wounds.

He telleth the number of the stars; he calleth them all by their names.

Great is our Lord, and of great power: his understanding is infinite.

The Lord lifteth up the meek: he casteth the wicked down to the ground.

Sing unto the Lord with thanksgiving; sing praise upon the harp unto our God:

Who covereth the heaven with clouds, who prepareth rain for the earth, who maketh grass to grow upon the mountains.

He giveth to the beast his food, and to the young ravens which cry.

He delighteth not in the strength of the horse: he taketh not pleasure in the legs of a man.

The Lord taketh pleasure in them that fear him, in those that hope in his mercy.

Praise the Lord, O Jerusalem; praise thy God, O Zion.

For he hath strengthened the bars of thy gates; he hath blessed thy children within thee.

He maketh peace in thy borders, and filleth thee with the finest of the wheat.

He sendeth forth his commandment upon earth: his word runneth very swiftly.

He giveth snow like wool: he scattereth the hoarfrost like ashes.

He casteth forth his ice like morsels: who can stand before his cold?

He sendeth out his word, and melteth them: he causeth his wind to blow, and the waters flow.

He showeth his word unto Jacob, his statutes and his judgments unto Israel.

All: He hath not dealt so with any nation: and as for his judgments, they have not known them. Praise ye the Lord.

606

The Majesty of God
Psalm 8

Leader: O Lord our Lord, how excellent is thy name in all the earth! Who hast set thy glory above the heavens.

Congregation: **Out of the mouth of babes and sucklings hast thou ordained strength because of thine enemies, that thou mightest still the enemy and the avenger.**

When I consider thy heavens, the work of thy fingers, the moon and the stars, which thou hast ordained;

What is man, that thou art mindful of him? And the son of man, that thou visitest him?

For thou hast made him a little lower than the angels, and hast crowned him with glory and honour.

Thou madest him to have dominion over the works of thy hands; thou hast put all things under his feet:

All sheep and oxen, yea, and the beasts of the field;

The fowl of the air, and the fish of the sea, and whatsoever passeth through the paths of the seas.

All: **O Lord our Lord, how excellent is thy name in all the earth!**

607

Blessings from God
Psalm 103

Leader: Bless the Lord, O my soul: and all that is within me, bless his holy name.

Congregation: **Bless the Lord, O my soul, and forget not all his benefits:**

Who forgiveth all thine iniquities; who healeth all thy diseases;

Who redeemeth thy life from destruction; who crowneth thee with lovingkindness and tender mercies;

Who satisfieth thy mouth with good things; so that thy youth is renewed like the eagle's.

The Lord executeth righteousness and judgment for all that are oppressed.

He made known his ways unto Moses, his acts unto the children of Israel.

The Lord is merciful and gracious, slow to anger, and plenteous in mercy.

He will not always chide: neither will he keep his anger for ever.

He hath not dealt with us after our sins; nor rewarded us according to our iniquities.

For as the heaven is high above the earth, so great is his mercy toward them that fear him.

As far as the east is from the west, so far hath he removed our transgressions from us.

Like as a father pitieth his children, so the Lord pitieth them that fear him.

For he knoweth our frame; he remembereth that we are dust.

As for man, his days are as grass: as a flower of the field, so he flourisheth.

For the wind passeth over it, and it is gone; and the place thereof shall know it no more.

But the mercy of the Lord is from everlasting to everlasting upon them that fear him, and his righteousness unto children's children;

(over)

To such as keep his covenant, and to those that remember his commandments to do them.

The Lord hath prepared his throne in the heavens; and his kingdom ruleth over all.

Bless the Lord, ye his angels, that excel in strength, that do his commandments, hearkening unto the voice of his word.

Bless ye the Lord, all ye his hosts; ye ministers of his, that do his pleasure.

All: **Bless the Lord, all his works in all places of his dominion: bless the Lord, O my soul.**

608
A Psalm of Trust
Psalm 91

Leader: He that dwelleth in the secret place of the most High shall abide under the shadow of the Almighty.

Congregation: **I will say of the Lord, He is my refuge and my fortress: my God; in him will I trust.**

Surely he shall deliver thee from the snare of the fowler, and from the noisome pestilence.

He shall cover thee with his feathers, and under his wings shalt thou trust: his truth shall be thy shield and buckler.

Thou shalt not be afraid for the terror by night; nor for the arrow that flieth by day;

Nor for the pestilence that walketh in darkness; nor for the destruction that wasteth at noonday.

A thousand shall fall at thy side, and ten thousand at thy right hand; but it shall not come nigh thee.

Only with thine eyes shalt thou behold and see the reward of the wicked.

Because thou hast made the Lord, which is my refuge, even the most High, thy habitation;

There shall no evil befall thee, neither shall any plague come nigh thy dwelling.

For he shall give his angels charge over thee, to keep thee in all thy ways.

They shall bear thee up in their hands, lest thou dash thy foot against a stone.

Thou shalt tread upon the lion and adder: the young lion and the dragon shalt thou trample under feet.

Because he hath set his love upon me, therefore will I deliver him: I will set him on high, because he hath known my name.

He shall call upon me, and I will answer him: I will be with him in trouble; I will deliver him, and honour him.

All: **With long life will I satisfy him, and show him my salvation.**

609
The Shepherd Psalm
Psalm 23

Leader: The Lord is my shepherd; I shall not want.

Congregation: **He maketh me to lie down in green pastures: he leadeth me beside the still waters.**

He restoreth my soul: he leadeth me in the paths of righteousness for his name's sake.

Yea, though I walk through the valley of the shadow of death, I will fear no evil: for thou art with me; thy rod and thy staff they comfort me.

Thou preparest a table before me in the presence of mine enemies: thou anointest my head with oil; my cup runneth over.

All: **Surely goodness and mercy shall follow me all the days of my life: and I will dwell in the house of the Lord for ever.**

610

Divine Providence
Psalms 34:1-10, 17-22

Leader: I will bless the Lord at all times: his praise shall continually be in my mouth.

Congregation: **My soul shall make her boast in the Lord: the humble shall hear thereof, and be glad.**

O magnify the Lord with me, and let us exalt his name together.

I sought the Lord, and he heard me, and delivered me from all my fears.

They looked unto him, and were lightened: and their faces were not ashamed.

This poor man cried, and the Lord heard him, and saved him out of all his troubles.

The angel of the Lord encampeth round about them that fear him, and delivereth them.

O taste and see that the Lord is good: blessed is the man that trusteth in him.

O fear the Lord, ye his saints: for there is no want to them that fear him.

The young lions do lack, and suffer hunger: but they that seek the Lord shall not want any good thing. *(Psalm 34:1-10)*

The righteous cry, and the Lord heareth, and delivereth them out of all their troubles.

The Lord is nigh unto them that are of a broken heart; and saveth such as be of a contrite spirit.

Many are the afflictions of the righteous: but the Lord delivereth him out of them all.

He keepeth all his bones: not one of them is broken.

Evil shall slay the wicked: and they that hate the righteous shall be desolate.

All: **The Lord redeemeth the soul of his servants: and none of them that trust in him shall be desolate.** (Psalm 34:17-22)

611

Thanksgiving
Psalms 92:1-5; 95:1-7; 107:40-43

Leader: It is a good thing to give thanks unto the Lord, and to sing praises unto thy name, O most High:

Congregation: **To show forth thy lovingkindness in the morning, and thy faithfulness every night,**

Upon an instrument of ten strings, and upon the psaltery; upon the harp with a solemn sound.

For thou, Lord, hast made me glad through thy work: I will triumph in the works of thy hands.

O Lord, how great are thy works! and thy thoughts are very deep. *(Psalm 92:1-5)*

O come, let us sing unto the Lord: let us make a joyful noise to the rock of our salvation.

Let us come before his presence with thanksgiving, and make a joyful noise unto him with psalms.

(over)

For the Lord is a great God, and a great King above all gods.

In his hand are the deep places of the earth: the strength of the hills is his also.

The sea is his, and he made it: and his hands formed the dry land.

O come, let us worship and bow down: let us kneel before the Lord our maker.

For he is our God; and we are the people of his pasture, and the sheep of his hand. Today if ye will hear his voice; *(Psalm 95:1-7)*

He poureth contempt upon princes, and causeth them to wander in the wilderness, where there is no way.

Yet setteth he the poor on high from affliction, and maketh him families like a flock.

The righteous shall see it, and rejoice: and all iniquity shall stop her mouth.

All: **Whoso is wise, and will observe these things, even they shall understand the lovingkindness of the Lord.** *(Psalm 107:40-43)*

612
God's Everlasting Mercies
Psalm 118:1-9, 21-29

Leader: O give thanks unto the Lord; for he is good: because his mercy endureth for ever.

Congregation: **Let Israel now say, that his mercy endureth for ever.**

Let the house of Aaron now say, that his mercy endureth for ever.

Let them now that fear the Lord say, that his mercy endureth for ever.

I called upon the Lord in distress: the Lord answered me, and set me in a large place.

The Lord is on my side; I will not fear: what can man do unto me?

The Lord taketh my part with them that help me: therefore shall I see my desire upon them that hate me.

It is better to trust in the Lord than to put confidence in man.

It is better to trust in the Lord than to put confidence in princes. *(Psalm 118:1-9)*

I will praise thee: for thou hast heard me, and art become my salvation.

The stone which the builders refused is become the head stone of the corner.

This is the Lord's doing; it is marvellous in our eyes.

This is the day which the Lord hath made; we will rejoice and be glad in it.

Save now, I beseech thee, O Lord: O Lord, I beseech thee, send now prosperity.

Blessed be he that cometh in the name of the Lord: we have blessed you out of the house of the Lord.

God is the Lord, which hath shewed us light: bind the sacrifice with cords, even unto the horns of the altar.

Thou art my God, and I will praise thee: thou art my God, I will exalt thee.

All: **O give thanks unto the Lord; for he is good: for his mercy endureth for ever.** *(Psalm 118:21-29)*

613
The Ideal Mother
Proverbs 31:10-31

Leader: Who can find a virtuous woman? For her price is far above rubies.

Congregation: **The heart of her husband doth safely trust in her, so that he shall have no need of spoil.**

She will do him good and not evil all the days of her life.

She seeketh wool, and flax, and worketh willingly with her hands.

She is like the merchants' ships; she bringeth her food from afar.

She riseth also while it is yet night, and giveth meat to her household, and a portion to her maidens.

She considereth a field, and buyeth it: with the fruit of her hands she planteth a vineyard.

She girdeth her loins with strength, and strengtheneth her arms.

She perceiveth that her merchandise is good: her candle goeth not out by night.

She layeth her hands to the spindle, and her hands hold the distaff.

She stretcheth out her hand to the poor; yea, she reacheth forth her hands to the needy.

She is not afraid of the snow for her household: for all her household are clothed with scarlet.

She maketh herself coverings of tapestry; her clothing is silk and purple.

Her husband is known in the gates, when he sitteth among the elders of the land.

She maketh fine linen, and selleth it; and delivereth girdles unto the merchant.

Strength and honour are her clothing; and she shall rejoice in time to come.

She openeth her mouth with wisdom; and in her tongue is the law of kindness.

She looketh well to the ways of her household, and eateth not the bread of idleness.

Her children arise up, and call her blessed; her husband also, and he praiseth her.

Many daughters have done virtuously, but thou excellest them all.

Favour is deceitful, and beauty is vain: but a woman that feareth the Lord, she shall be praised.

All: **Give her of the fruit of her hands; and let her own works praise her in the gates.**

614
Father's Instructions
Proverbs 4:1-4; 10-27

Leader: Hear, ye children, the instruction of a father, and attend to know understanding.

Congregation: **For I give you good doctrine, forsake ye not my law.**

For I was my father's son, tender and only beloved in the sight of my mother.

He taught me also, and said unto me, Let thine heart retain my words: keep my commandments, and live. (Proverbs 4:1-4)

Hear, O my son, and receive my sayings; and the years of thy life shall be many.

I have taught thee in the way of wisdom; I have led thee in right paths.

When thou goest, thy steps shall not be straitened; and when thou runnest, thou shalt not stumble.

Take fast hold of instruction; let her not go: keep her, for she is thy life.

Enter not into the path of the wicked, and go not in the way of evil men.

Avoid it, pass not by it, turn from it, and pass away.

For they sleep not, except they have done mischief; and their sleep is taken away, unless they cause some to fall.

For they eat the bread of wickedness, and drink the wine of violence.

(over)

But the path of the just is as the shining light, that shineth more and more unto the perfect day.

The way of the wicked is as darkness: they know not at what they stumble.

My son, attend to my words; incline thine ear unto my sayings.

Let them not depart from thine eyes; keep them in the midst of thine heart.

For they are life unto those that find them, and health to all their flesh.

Keep thy heart with all diligence; for out of it are the issues of life.

Put away from thee a froward mouth, and perverse lips put far from thee.

Let thine eyes look right on, and let thine eyelids look straight before thee.

Ponder the path of thy feet, and let all thy ways be established.

All: **Turn not to the right hand nor to the left: remove thy foot from evil.** *(Proverbs 4:10-27)*

615
Christ's Concern for Children
Matthew 18:1-6, 10;
Mark 9:37; 10:13-16

Leader: At the same time came the disciples unto Jesus, saying, Who is the greatest in the kingdom of heaven?

Congregation: **And Jesus called a little child unto him, and set him in the midst of them,**

And said, Verily I say unto you, Except ye be converted; and become as little children, ye shall not enter into the kingdom of heaven.

Whosoever therefore shall humble himself as this little child, the same is greatest in the kingdom of heaven.

And whoso shall receive one such little child in my name receiveth me.

But whoso shall offend one of these little ones which believe in me, it were better for him that a millstone were hanged about his neck, and that he were drowned in the depth of the sea.

Take heed that ye despise not one of these little ones; for I say unto you, That in heaven their angels do always behold the face of my Father which is in heaven. *(Matthew 18:1-6, 10)*

Whosoever shall receive one of such children in my name, receiveth me: and whosoever shall receive me, receiveth not me, but him that sent me.

And they brought young children to him, that he should touch them: and his disciples rebuked those that brought them.

But when Jesus saw it, he was much displeased, and said unto them, Suffer the little children to come unto me, and forbid them not: for of such is the kingdom of God.

Verily I say unto you, Whosoever shall not receive the kingdom of God as a little child, he shall not enter therein.

All: **And he took them up in his arms, put his hands upon them, and blessed them.** *(Mark 9:37; 10:13-16)*

616
The Christian Minister
2 Corinthians 4

Leader: Therefore seeing we have this ministry, as we have received mercy, we faint not;

Congregation: **But have renounced the hidden things of dishonesty, not walking in craftiness, nor handling the word of God deceitfully; but by manifestation of the truth commending ourselves to every man's conscience in the sight of God.**

But if our gospel be hid, it is hid to them that are lost:

In whom the god of this world hath blinded the minds of them which believe not, lest the light of the glorious gospel of Christ, who is the image of God, should shine unto them.

For we preach not ourselves, but Christ Jesus the Lord; and ourselves your servants for Jesus' sake.

For God, who commanded the light to shine out of darkness, hath shined in our hearts, to give the light of the knowledge of the glory of God in the face of Jesus Christ.

But we have this treasure in earthen vessels, that the excellency of the power may be of God, and not of us.

We are troubled on every side, yet not distressed; we are perplexed, but not in despair;

Persecuted, but not forsaken; cast down, but not destroyed;

Always bearing about in the body the dying of the Lord Jesus, that the life also of Jesus might be made manifest in our body.

For we which live are alway delivered unto death for Jesus' sake, that the life also of Jesus might be made manifest in our mortal flesh.

So then death worketh in us, but life in you.

We having the same spirit of faith, according as it is written, I believed, and therefore have I spoken; we also believe, and therefore speak;

Knowing that he which raised up the Lord Jesus shall raise up us also by Jesus, and shall present us with you.

For all things are for your sakes, that the abundant grace might through the thanksgiving of many redound to the glory of God.

For which cause we faint not; but though our outward man perish, yet the inward man is renewed day by day.

For our light affliction, which is but for a moment, worketh for us a far more exceeding and eternal weight of glory;

All: **While we look not at the things which are seen, but at the things which are not seen: for the things which are seen are temporal; but the things which are not seen are eternal.**

617
God's House
Psalm 127:1; 1 Kings 8:8-21; Isaiah 56:7

Leader: Except the Lord build the house, they labour in vain that build it: except the Lord keep the city, the watchman waketh but in vain. *(Psalm 127:1)*

Congregation: **And they drew out the staves, that the ends of the staves were seen out in the holy place before the oracle, and they were not seen without: and there they are unto this day.**

There was nothing in the ark save the two tables of stone, which Moses put there at Horeb, when the Lord made a covenant with the children of Israel, when they came out of the land of Egypt.

And it came to pass, when the priests were come out of the holy place, that the cloud filled the house of the Lord,

So that the priests could not stand to minister because of the cloud: for the glory of the Lord had filled the house of the Lord.

Then spake Solomon, The Lord said that he would dwell in the thick darkness.

I have surely built thee an house to dwell in, a settled place for thee to abide in for ever.

And the king turned his face about, and blessed all the congregation of Israel: (and all the congregation of Israel stood;)

And he said, Blessed be the Lord God of Israel, which spake with his mouth unto David my father, and hath with his hand fulfilled it, saying,

Since the day that I brought forth my people Israel out of Egypt, I chose no city out of all the tribes of Israel to build an house, that my name might be therein; but I chose David to be over my people Israel.

And it was in the heart of David my father to build an house for the name of the Lord God of Israel.

And the Lord said unto David my father, Whereas it was in thine heart to build an house unto my name, thou didst well that it was in thine heart.

Nevertheless thou shalt not build the house; but thy son that shall come forth out of thy loins, he shall build the house unto my name.

And the Lord hath performed his word that he spake, and I am risen up in the room of David my father, and sit on the throne of Israel, as the Lord promised, and have built an house for the name of the Lord God of Israel.

And I have set there a place for the ark, wherein is the covenant of the Lord, which he made with our fathers, when he brought them out of the land of Egypt. *(1 Kings 8:8-21)*

All: **Even them will I bring to my holy mountain, and make them joyful in my house of prayer: their burnt offerings and their sacrifices shall be accepted upon mine altar; for mine house shall be called an house of prayer for all people.** *(Isaiah 56:7)*

618
The Ten Commandments
Exodus 20:1-17

Leader: And God spake all these words, saying,

Congregation: **I am the Lord thy God, which have brought thee out of the land of Egypt, out of the house of bondage.**

Thou shalt have no other gods before me.

Thou shalt not make unto thee any graven image, or any likeness of any thing that is in heaven above, or that is in the earth beneath, or that is in the water under the earth:

Thou shalt not bow down thyself to them, nor serve them: for I the Lord thy God am a jealous God, visiting the iniquity of the fathers upon the children unto the third and fourth generation of them that hate me;

And shewing mercy unto thousands of them that love me, and keep my commandments.

Thou shalt not take the name of the Lord thy God in vain; for the Lord will not hold him guiltless that taketh his name in vain.

Remember the sabbath day, to keep it holy.

Six days shalt thou labour, and do all thy work:

But the seventh day is the sabbath of the Lord thy God: in it thou shalt not do any work, thou, nor thy son, nor thy daughter, thy manservant, nor thy maidservant, nor thy cattle, nor thy stranger that is within thy gates:

For in six days the Lord made heaven and earth, the sea, and all that in them is, and rested the seventh day: wherefore the Lord blessed the sabbath day, and hallowed it.

Honour thy father and thy mother: that thy days may be long upon the land which the Lord thy God giveth thee.

Thou shalt not kill.

Thou shalt not commit adultery.

Thou shalt not steal.

Thou shalt not bear false witness against thy neighbour.

All: **Thou shalt not covet thy neighbour's house, thou shalt not covet thy neighbour's wife, nor his manservant, nor his maidservant, nor his ox, nor his ass, nor anything that is thy neighbour's.**

619

The Beatitudes
Matthew 5:1-12

Leader: And seeing the multitudes, he went up into a mountain: and when he was set, his disciples came unto him:

Congregation: **And he opened his mouth, and taught them, saying,**

Blessed are the poor in spirit: for theirs is the kingdom of heaven.

Blessed are they that mourn: for they shall be comforted.

Blessed are the meek: for they shall inherit the earth.

Blessed are they which do hunger and thirst after righteousness: for they shall be filled.

Blessed are the merciful: for they shall obtain mercy.

Blessed are the pure in heart: for they shall see God.

Blessed are the peacemakers: for they shall be called the children of God.

Blessed are they which are persecuted for righteousness' sake: for theirs is the kingdom of heaven.

Blessed are ye, when men shall revile you, and persecute you, and shall say all manner of evil against you falsely, for my sake.

All: **Rejoice, and be exceeding glad: for great is your reward in heaven: for so persecuted they the prophets which were before you.**

620

Calls to Worship

Psalms 24:1, 9-10; 33:1, 11-12; 84:1-2, 11; 96:1, 3, 8-9; 100:1-2, 4-5; 105:1-3;
107:1-2, 9; 117; 145:3, 17-18; 147:1, 5, 11-12; 150:1-2, 6; Habakkuk 2:20;
Matthew 11:28-30; Colossians 3:16

The earth is the Lord's, and fulness thereof; the world, and they that dwell therein.

Lift up your heads, O ye gates; even lift them up, ye everlasting doors; and the King of glory shall come in.

Who is this King of glory? The Lord of hosts, he is the King of glory.

Rejoice in the Lord, O ye righteous; for praise is comely for the upright.

The counsel of the Lord standeth for ever, the thoughts of his heart to all generations.

Blessed is the nation whose God is the Lord; and the people whom he hath chosen for his own inheritance.

How amiable are thy tabernacles, O Lord of hosts!

My soul longeth, yea, even fainteth for the courts of the Lord: my heart and my flesh crieth out for the living God.

For the Lord God is a sun and shield: the Lord will give grace and glory: no good thing will he withhold from them that walk uprightly.

O sing unto the Lord a new song: sing unto the Lord, all the earth.

Declare his glory among the heathen, his wonders among all people.

Give unto the Lord the glory due unto his name: bring an offering, and come into his courts.

O worship the Lord in the beauty of holiness: fear before him, all the earth.

Make a joyful noise unto the Lord, all ye lands.

Serve the Lord with gladness: come before his presence with singing.

Enter into his gates with thanksgiving, and into his courts with praise: be thankful unto him, and bless his name.

For the Lord is good; his mercy is everlasting; and his truth endureth to all generations.

O give thanks unto the Lord; call upon his name: make known his deeds among the people.

Sing unto him, sing psalms unto him: talk ye of all his wondrous works.

Scriptural Readings

Glory ye in his holy name: let the heart of them rejoice that seek the Lord.

O give thanks unto the Lord, for he is good: for his mercy endureth for ever.

Let the redeemed of the Lord say so, whom he hath redeemed from the hand of the enemy.

For he satisfieth the longing soul, and filleth the hungry soul with goodness.

O praise the Lord, all ye nations: praise him, all ye people.

For his merciful kindness is great toward us: and the truth of the Lord endureth for ever. Praise ye the Lord.

Great is the Lord, and greatly to be praised; and his greatness is unsearchable.

The Lord is righteous in all his ways, and holy in all his works.

The Lord is nigh unto all them that call upon him, to all that call upon him in truth.

Praise ye the Lord: for it is good to sing praises unto our God; for it is pleasant; and praise is comely.

Great is our Lord, and of great power: his understanding is infinite.

The Lord taketh pleasure in them that fear him, in those that hope in his mercy.

Praise the Lord, O Jerusalem; praise thy God, O Zion.

Praise ye the Lord. Praise God in his sanctuary; praise him in the firmament of his power.

Praise him for his mighy acts: praise him according to his excellent greatness.

Let everything that hath breath praise the Lord. Praise ye the Lord.

But the Lord is in his holy temple: let all the earth keep silence before him.

Come unto me, all ye that labour and are heavy laden, and I will give you rest.

Take my yoke upon you, and learn of me; for I am meek and lowly in heart: and ye shall find rest unto your souls.

For my yoke is easy, and my burden is light.

Let the word of Christ dwell in you richly in all wisdom; teaching and admonishing one another in psalms and hymns and spiritual songs, singing with grace in your hearts to the Lord.

621

Offertory Appeals

Genesis 28:20-22; Proverbs 3:9; 19:17; Ecclesiastes 11:1; Malachi 3:8-10;
2 Corinthians 9:6-7; Luke 16:9-13; 21:1-4; Acts 20:35; Romans 12:8;
1 Corinthians 16:2

And Jacob vowed a vow, saying, If God will be with me, and will keep me in this way that I go, and will give me bread to eat, and raiment to put on,

So that I come again to my father's house in peace; then shall the Lord be my God:

And this stone, which I have set for a pillar, shall be God's house: and of all that thou shalt give me I will surely give the tenth unto thee.

Honour the Lord with thy substance, and with the firstfruits of all thine increases.

He that hath pity upon the poor lendeth unto the Lord; and that which he hath given will he pay him again.

Cast thy bread upon the waters: for thou shalt find it after many days.

Will a man rob God? Yet ye have robbed me. But ye say, Wherein have we robbed thee? In tithes and offerings.

Ye are cursed with a curse: for ye have robbed me, even this whole nation.

Bring ye all the tithes into the storehouse, that there may be meat in mine house, and prove me now herewith, saith the Lord of hosts, if I will not open you the windows of heaven, and pour you out a blessing, that there shall not be room enough to receive it.

But this I say, He which soweth sparingly shall reap also sparingly; and he which soweth bountifully shall reap also bountifully.

Every man according as he purposeth in his heart, so let him give; not grudgingly, or of necessity: for God loveth a cheerful giver.

And I say unto you, Make to yourselves friends of the mammon of unrighteousness; that, when ye fail, they may receive you into everlasting habitations.

He that is faithful in that which is least is faithful also in much: and he that is unjust in the least is unjust also in much.

If therefore ye have not been faithful in the unrighteous mammon, who will commit to your trust the true riches?

And if ye have not been faithful in that which is another man's, who shall give you that which is your own?

No servant can serve two masters: for either he will hate the one, and love the other; or else he will hold to the one, and despise the other. Ye cannot serve God and mammon.

———————————————————

And he looked up, and saw the rich men casting their gifts into the treasury.

And he saw also a certain poor widow casting in thither two mites.

And he said, "Of a truth I say unto you, that this poor widow hath cast in more than they all:

For all these have of their abundance cast in unto the offerings of God: but she of her penury hast cast in all the living that she had."

———————————————————

I have shown you all things, how that so laboring ye ought to support the weak, and to remember the words of the Lord Jesus, how he said, "It is more blessed to give than to receive."

———————————————————

Or he that exhorteth, on exhortation: he that giveth, let him do it with simplicity; he that ruleth, with diligence; he that showeth mercy, with cheerfulness.

———————————————————

Upon the first day of the week let every one of you lay by him in store, as God hath prospered him, that there be no gatherings when I come.

———————————————————

622

Benedictions

Numbers 6:24-26; Psalms 19:14; 67:1-2; 1 Thessalonians 5:23, 28;
2 Thessalonians 2:16-17; Ephesians 3:20-21; 2 Corinthians 13:11, 14;
Philippians 4:7; 1 Timothy 1:17; Hebrews 13:20-21; 2 Peter 3:18; Jude 24-25;
Romans 16:20; Galatians 6:18; Ephesians 6:24; 2 Thessalonians 3:16,18;
1 Peter 5:10-11; Revelation 22:21

The Lord bless thee, and keep thee:

The Lord make his face shine upon thee, and be gracious unto thee:

The Lord lift up his countenance upon thee, and give thee peace.

Let the words of my mouth, and the meditation of my heart, be acceptable in thy sight, O Lord, my strength, and my redeemer.

God be merciful unto us, and bless us: and cause his face to shine upon us;

That thy way may be known upon earth, thy saving health among all nations.

And the very God of peace sanctify you wholly; and I pray God your whole spirit and soul and body be preserved blameless unto the coming of our Lord Jesus Christ.

The grace of our Lord Jesus Christ be with you.

Now our Lord Jesus Christ himself, and God, even our Father, which hath loved us, and hath given us everlasting consolation and good hope through grace,

Comfort your hearts, and stablish you in every good word and work.

Now unto him that is able to do exceeding abundantly above all that we ask or think, according to the power that worketh in us,

Unto him be glory in the church by Christ Jesus throughout all ages, world without end. Amen.

Finally, brethren, farewell. Be perfect, be of good comfort, be of one mind, live in peace; and the God of love and peace shall be with you.

The grace of the Lord Jesus Christ, and the love of God, and the communion of the Holy Ghost, be with you all. Amen.

Scriptural Readings

And the peace of God, which passeth all understanding, shall keep your hearts and minds through Christ Jesus.

Now unto the King eternal, immortal, invisible, the only wise God, be honour and glory for ever and ever.

Now the God of peace, that brought again from the dead our Lord Jesus, that great shepherd of the sheep, through the blood of the everlasting covenant,

Make you perfect in every good work to do his will, working in you that which is well-pleasing in his sight, through Jesus Christ; to whom be glory for ever and ever. Amen.

But grow in grace, and in the knowledge of our Lord and Saviour Jesus Christ. To him be glory both now and for ever. Amen.

Now unto him that is able to keep you from falling, and to present you faultless before the presence of his glory with exceeding joy,

To the only wise God our Saviour, be glory and majesty, dominion and power, both now and ever. Amen.

And the God of peace shall bruise Satan under your feet shortly. The grace of our Lord Jesus Christ be with you. Amen.

Brethren, the grace of our Lord Jesus Christ be with your spirit. Amen.

Grace be with all them that love our Lord Jesus Christ in sincerity. Amen.

Now the Lord of peace himself give you peace always by all means. The Lord be with you all.
The grace of our Lord Jesus Christ be with you all. Amen.

But the God of all grace, who hath called us unto his eternal glory by Christ Jesus, after that ye have suffered a while, make you perfect, stablish, strengthen, settle you.
To him be glory and dominion for ever and ever. Amen.

The grace of our Lord Jesus Christ be with you all. Amen.

Meditations

When in sorrow, read John 14

When you have sinned, read Psalm 51

When you are fearful, read Isaiah 40:10

When you are discouraged, read Isaiah 40

When you are impatient, read James 5:7-8

When you are insecure, read Romans 8:31-32

When you are insulted, read Matthew 5:10-12

When you are depressed, read Psalm 34:17-19

When you want to give thanks, read Psalm 138

When your faith needs stirring, read Hebrews 11

When you are being tempted, read James 1:12-13

When you are lonely, read John 14:18 and Psalm 3

When you are seeking direction, read Psalm 25:4-5

When you are seeking peace, read Matthew 11:28-30

When you need empowerment, read Philippians 4:13

When you are seeking righteous living, read Psalm 1

When you want courage for your task, read Joshua 1

When you need courage, read 2 Corinthians 12:1-10

When you are making decisions, read Proverbs 3:5-6

When you want to learn more about God, read Psalm 24

When you want Christian assurance, read Romans 8:1-30

When you are worried, read 1 Peter 5:7 and Luke 12:22-28

When you are feeling guilty, read 1 John 1:9 and Isaiah 1:18

When you are seeking to know the Holy Spirit, read John 16:13

When you are seeking advice, read Isaiah 47:12-14 and James 1:5

When you are seeking family counsel, read Ephesians 5:22-23, 6:1-4

When you feel alone and need comfort during sickness, read Psalm 41

Topical Index for Hymns
Titles not necessarily listed in full

Topical Index for Scriptural Readings

Scripture Index for Hymns

14:3 (77)
14:6 (72)
14:13 (324)
14:14 (343)
14:23 (189)
14:27 (100, 403)
15:4 (247)
15:5 (303)
15:9 (362)
15:13 (62, 378, 432)
15:26 (132)
19:5 (108)
19:17 (137)
19:34 (103, 254)
19:37 (106)
20:22 (126)
20:25 (176)
21:15 (39)

Acts
1:8 (442)
2:2, 4 (128)
2:4 (485)
2:24 (123)
2:38 (196, 312)
3:6 (265)
4:12 (22)
4:21 (12)
8:24 (496)
22:15 (422)
26:14 (169)

Romans
3:24 (163)
5:8 (158, 210, 392)
5:11 (104)
6:18 (174)
8:9 (333)
8:17 (391)
8:18 (286)
8:28 (389)
8:35 (307)
8:37 (160)
10:10 (527)
10:12 (3)
10:13 (42, 184, 388, 534)
14:5 (185)
14:11 (29, 125)

1 Corinthians
1:20 (270)
2:9 (484)
4:2 (436)

10:4 (19)
11:26 (358)
13:12 (467)
15:51 (271)
15:55 (121)
15:57 (143)

2 Corinthians
1:20 (257, 503)
1:24 (409)
3:3 (133)
3:17 (162, 486)
4:6 (368)
5:1 (479)
5:8 (469)
5:17 (364, 452)
6:2 (266)
7:16 (399)
9:7 (351)
9:8 (528)
12:9 (159, 401)
13:11 (501)

Galatians
2:20 (205)
4:7 (249)

Ephesians
1:13 (127)
2:5 (380)
2:8 (154, 161)
2:16 (197)
2:20 (297)
3:17 (273)
4:13 (299)
5:8 (234)
5:19 (521)
5:32 (361)
6:18 (191)

Philippians
1:9 (214)
1:21 (283, 363, 532)
2:5 (156, 543)
2:8 (107)
2:9 (79)
2:10 (63)
2:16 (293)
3:8 (383)
3:10 (145)
4:4 (71)

Colossians
1:3 (336)

1:12 (515)
1:20 (150)
2:2-3 (74)
3:11 (78)
3:16 (370)
3:17 (410)

1 Thessalonians
2:12 (315)
4:1 (309)
4:16 (499)
4:17 (468)
5:10 (227, 279)

2 Thessalonians
1:11 (444)
3:16 (365)

1 Timothy
1:5 (131)
1:15 (167, 418)
4:14 (446)
6:15 (102)
6:15-16 (495)

2 Timothy
1:5 (151)
1:9 (168)
1:12 (397)
2:3 (427)
2:4 (259, 433)
2:7 (288)
3:11 (387)
4:7 (406)

Titus
2:15 (416)

Hebrews
2:9 (76)
2:12 (26)
4:1, 11 (171)
4:16 (164, 264)
6:6 (348)
6:14 (325)
8:9 (305)
10:22 (314, 448, 538)
10:38 (529)
11:16 (478)
12:2 (113, 172, 195)
12:15 (509)
12:22 (471)
13:8 (381)

13:20 (146)

James
1:3 (280)
1:17 (352)
4:8 (173, 317)

1 Peter
2:16 (458)
3:8 (411)
5:4 (105)
5:7 (52, 220, 253)
5:14 (541)

2 Peter
3:9 (414)
3:18 (431)

1 John
1:7 (136, 141, 298, 308, 500)
3:2 (240)
4:4 (311, 382)
4:8 (66)
4:9 (65, 182)
4:10 (120)
4:16 (284)
4:19 (522)
5:2 (208)
5:11 (245)

Jude
24 (47)
25 (34)

Revelation
1:5 (386)
1:8 (38)
2:10 (465)
3:20 (170, 180, 194)
5:12 (25)
6:2 (5)
7:14 (138)
12:11 (140)
17:14 (546)
19:6 (155)
19:14 (517)
21:4 (470, 475)
21:6 (142)
21:10 (544)
22:4 (539)
22:20 (455, 476)
22:21 (558)

General Index

Titles in capital letters, First lines in lower case, Refrains in italics

Key in parentheses

Titles not necessarily listed in full.

A

A CHARGE TO KEEP I HAVE, 436 (C)
A CHILD OF THE KING, 391 (Eb)
A CHRISTIAN HOME, 360 (F)
A MIGHTY FORTRESS IS OUR GOD, 37 (C)
A pilgrim was I, 277 (Eb)
A SHELTER IN THE TIME, 267 (F)
A sunbeam, 510 (G)
A wonderful Savior is Jesus my Lord, 251 (Db)
ABIDE WITH ME, 247 (Eb)
Alas! and did my Savior bleed, 137 (Eb)
ALL CREATURES OF OUR GOD, 33 (Eb)
ALL GLORY, LAUD, AND HONOR, 102 (C)
ALL HAIL, IMMANUEL!, 523 (Bb)
ALL HAIL KING JESUS, 546 (F)
ALL HAIL, (CORONATION), 3 (G)
ALL HAIL, (DIADEM), 5 (Bb)
ALL PEOPLE THAT ON EARTH, 36 (G)
ALL THE WAY MY SAVIOR LEADS, 236 (G)
ALL THINGS COME OF THEE, 356 (F)
All to Jesus I surrender, 198 (Db)
ALLELUIA, 9 (G)
ALMIGHTY FATHER, HEAR, 550 (G)
ALMOST PERSUADED, 185 (G)
ALONE, 115 (F)
AM I A SOLDIER OF THE CROSS?, 259 (F)
AMAZING GRACE (MCINTOSH), 161 (G)
AMAZING GRACE (MARTYRDOM), 163 (G)
Amazing grace shall always be, 162 (C)
AMEN!, 503 (G)
AMERICA, THE BEAUTIFUL, 454 (Bb)
AN EVENING PRAYER, 331 (Ab)
And he walks with me, 116 (Ab)
ANGELS, FROM THE REALMS, 85 (Bb)
ANGELS WE HAVE HEARD, 89 (F)
ANOTHER YEAR IS DAWNING, 453 (G)
ARE YE ABLE, 223 (Ab)
Are you burdened, 191 (Bb)
Are you ready, 480 (G)
ARE YOU WASHED?, 140 (Ab)
ARISE, O YOUTH OF GOD, 518 (Bb)
As I journey through the land, 240 (Ab)
Ask the Savior to help you, 244 (Ab)
ASK WHAT YOU WILL, 258 (C)
AT CALVARY, 144 (C)
AT THE CROSS, 137 (Eb)
AWAY IN A MANGER, 96 (F)
AWESOME GOD, 44 (Em)

B

BALM IN GILEAD, 489 (F)
BATTLE HYMN, 455 (Bb)
Be not a-weary, for labor will cease, 290 (Bb)
Be not dismayed whate'er betide, 52 (Bb)
Be silent, be silent, 177 (Bb)
BE STILL AND KNOW, 50 (C)
BE STILL, MY SOUL, 263 (F)
Beams of heaven as I go, 271 (F)
BEARING HIS CROSS FOR ME, 107 (G)
Beautiful words, 293 (F)
BECAUSE HE LIVES, 120 (Ab)
BEHOLD THE LAMB, 122 (F)
BENEATH THE CROSS OF JESUS, 106 (Db)
Better mind, my sister, 497 (G)
BEYOND THE SUNSET, 471 (Eb)
BLESS HIS HOLY NAME, 4 (Eb)
BLESS THAT WONDERFUL NAME, 71 (G)
BLESS THE LORD, O MY SOUL, 20 (Eb)
Bless the Lord, O my soul, 4 (Eb)
BLESS THOU THE GIFTS, 355 (G)
BLESSED ASSURANCE, 249 (D)
BLESSED BE THE NAME, 35 (Ab)
BLESSED QUIETNESS, 130 (Ab)
BLESSED REDEEMER, 112 (D)
Blessed Savior, Thou wilt guide us, 474 (Ab)
Blessed Savior, we adore Thee, 15 (F)
BLEST BE THE TIE THAT BINDS, 298 (F)
BREAD OF LIFE, 359 (Eb)
BREAK THOU THE BREAD, 295 (Eb)
BREATHE ON ME, 126 (Eb)
BREATHE ON ME, BREATH, 135 (F)
Brightly beams our Father's mercy, 419 (Ab)
Bring ye all the tithes, 353 (Eb)
BRINGING IN THE SHEAVES, 429 (Bb)
Brothers, don't stay away, 179 (Bb)
BURDENS ARE LIFTED, 188 (F)
But it's real, 386 (Db)
By and by, 288 (F)
BY GRACE ARE YE SAVED, 154 (D)

C

Calling today, 171 (Bb)
Calvary, Calvary, 110 (Cm)
CALVARY COVERS IT ALL, 139 (Ab)
CANAAN, 544 (C)
CAN'T NOBODY DO ME, 374 (Ab)

Glossary of Musical Terms

A cappella: Vocal music sung unaccompanied
Accelerando (*accel.*): Becoming faster
Accent: To emphasize; to stress
Accidentals: Sharps, flats, or naturals
Accompaniment: Instrumental support for voice, group, or solo instrument
Acoustics: The science of sound
Ad Libitum (*ad-lib*): At the pleasure of the performer
Allegretto: Moderately quick and lively
Allegro: Quick, lively, and cheerful
Alto: The second highest voice in four-part texture
Anacrusis: A weak or unaccented note that anticipates the downbeat; also called upbeat
Andante: Slow, graceful, walking
Anthem: A choral composition with words from the Bible or other religious text
Arpeggio: A chord in which the notes are played individually in quick succession
Arrangement: The adaptation of a composition for a medium different from that for which it was originally written
Articulation: The manner in which notes are begun and ended
Baritone: Low, adult male voice with a range that lies between tenor and bass voices
Bar line: A vertical line drawn through the staff to separate measures
Bass: The lowest male voice; the lowest part of a choral composition
Beat: The number of counts in a measure
Bridge: A passage in a composition which connects two or more different themes
Cadence: The musical punctuation that separates phrases
Call and Response: A composition in which one person sings a phrase and a group responds
Canon: A strict imitation in which one voice imitates another
Cantabile: An expressive term meaning to sing or singing
Cantata: A religious composition consisting of a number of movements with solo, duet, recitative, and chorus with orchestral or instrumental accompaniment
Changed voices: A change in voice quality experienced by girls and boys between the ages of about 12 and 16. Boys' voices become lower and girls' voices become fuller in sound
Chant: A short musical passage in two or more phrases, often without a melodic line
Chest tone: The lower register of a voice
Choir: An organized group of singers
Chord: The resulting sound when three or more tones are sounded at the same time
Chorus: The musical section of a song that follows a verse, sometimes called a refrain
Clef: A symbol at the beginning of a staff that determines the pitches of that staff
Coda: Additional music performed as an ending to a composition
Con Espressivo: With expression
Con Molto: With spirited movement

Contemporary gospel: An era in gospel music from the 1960s to present

Crescendo (*cresc.*): Gradually increasing in loudness

Decrescendo: Gradually decreasing in loudness (also called diminuendo)

D. C. al Fine: Abbreviation for *da capo al fine*, meaning to return to the beginning and sing until the Fine

Descant: A countermelody played or sung above the basic melody

Diaphragmatic breathing: The act of complete breathing through the upper body which utilizes the diaphragm

Dolce: Sweet and soft

Dominant: The fifth degree of the diatonic scale

Double bar: A barline consisting of two thin vertical lines that denotes a section of a composition such as a Coda or key change

Doxology: A congregational response often sung at the time of the offering, invocation, or benediction

Downbeat: The first beat of a measure

Duet: A musical composition for two voices or instruments

Dynamics: Indications specifying the relative loudness or softness of a note or musical passage

Expression: The general character of a musical passage or composition

Fermata: An indication to prolong or extend a tone or chord

Field song: Composition authored by slaves that were sung in the fields, usually of spiritual influence

Fine bar: A barline consisting of one thin and one thick vertical lines that denotes the end of a composition

Forte (*f*): Loud

Fortissimo (*ff*): Very loud

Fortississimo (*fff*): Extremely loud

Flat (b): Symbol indicating that a note is to be lowered a half-step

Forte piano (*fp*): Loud, then immediately soft

Genre: A general categorization of music that is similar in structure

Giacoso: Joyfully, merrily

Gospel: A song of faith, hope, or life experiences

Gospel band: An instrumental group usually comprised of piano, electric bass, lead guitar, and drum set

Grand staff: A muscial staff consisting of both treble and bass clefs; the standard method of notation for hymns

Harmonize: To provide chordal accompaniment to a melody

Harmony: The sounding of two or more tones at the same time

Head tone: The higher register of a voice

Homophony: A musical texture in which the voices move simultaneously

Hymn: A song of praise or adoration intended to be used in a religious service

Hymn of Invitation: A composition inviting membership or partcipation in a worshipping group

Hymn of Praise: An opening hymn with words of praise, adoration, or thanksgiving

Improvisation: The spontaneous creation of music

Interlude: Music inserted between other compositions or worship activities

Interpretation: The personal and creative elements in the performance of music

Interval: The distance in pitch between two tones

Instrumentation: The instruments used to perform or accompany a composition

Intonation: Singing or playing in tune

Introit: An antiphonal chant of moderately ornate style

Key signature: A grouping of sharps or flats placed at the beginning of a staff to indicate the musical key of the passage or composition

Largo: Broad and dignified tempo

Legato: Connected tones, smoothly joined together

Lento: Slowly

Lyrics: The words of a song

Maestoso: An expressive term meaning majestic

Manual: The designation for any keyboard provided for the hands

Marcato: An expressive term meaning marked

Measure: A regular division of music by beats, indicated by vertical bar lines on the staff; sometimes referred to as a bar

Melisma: An expressive vocal passage of various pitches sung to one syllable

Melody: The predominate musical tones, often sung by the highest voices

Mezzo Forte (*mf*): Moderately loud

Mezzo Piano (*mp*): Moderately soft

Mezzo-Soprano: A woman's voice that lies between soprano and alto in range

Minister of Music: The person responsible for musical activities in a local church

Mixed voices: A combination of men's and women's voices

Moderato: Moderate tempo

Moduation: The process of changing keys

Molto allegro: Very quick, very fast

Monophony: A musical texture consisting of a single voice

Musical style: The result of the interaction of rhythm, melody, harmony, texture, color, and shape of a musical composition

Natural: A symbol which cancels a sharp or flat

Notation: A written method of indicating musical sounds

Notes: Symbols which represent specific musical tones. Different types of notes indicate how long to sing or play a tone.

Octave: The interval between the first and eighth tones of a musical scale; a doubling of acoustic frequency

Offertory Hymn: A composition performed during the gathering of the offering

Oratorio: A semi-dramatic composition for voices and orchestra

Orchestration: The assignment of various melodic and harmonic musical lines to various instruments

Organ: A keyboard instrument that produces pitches by forcing air through pipes of various lengths; most often used in church and religious settings

Ornamentation: Additional notes added to a melody for variation

Ostinato: A pattern of tones or rhythms which is repeated

Percussionist: A performer of a percussion instrument, such as drums or timpani

Phrase: A grouping of a succession of musical notes which produce a specific musical idea or statement; the musical equivalent to a sentence

Piano: A keyboard instrument that produces pitches by the use of felt hammers striking metal strings

Piano (*p*): Soft
Pianissimo (*pp*): Very soft
Pianississimo (*ppp*): Extremely soft
Pitch: The relative highness or lowness of a musical note
Poco a poco: Little by little, gradually
Polyphony: A musical texture in which the individual voices move independent of each other
Postlude: Music played at the end of a worship service
Praise: To sing or extol honor and adoration
Prelude: Music played at the beginning of a worship service
Presto: Nimble, quick tempo
Processional: Vocal or instrumental music used to begin a religious service; often used to accompany the entrance of the choir into the sanctuary
Psalms: Sacred songs utilizing text from the book of Psalms
Quartet: A musical composition for four voices or instruments
Quintet: A musical composition for five voices or instruments
Range: The extent of the pitches within which a voice or instrument can sound
Recessional: Vocal or instrumental music used to close a religious service: often used to accompany the exit of the choir from the sanctuary
Recitative: A musical style consisting of a melodic line sung freely to a simple accompaniment; often used in operas and oratorios
Refrain: The musical section of a song that follows the verse, sometimes called a chorus
Repeat sign: Shows what part of the music is to be sung or played twice
Repertoire: A collection of music that a performer is prepared to perform
Response: A musical reply to a prayer sung by choir or congregation
Rest: A symbol indicating silence
Rhythm: The grouping of notes which are sounded in a specific pattern
Ritardando (*rit.*): Gradually becoming slower
Sacred: Music of a religious, reverent, and consecrated nature
Scale: A series of eight tones, resembling a musical ladder
Sharp (#): A symbol indicating that a note is to be raised a half-step
Slave song: Chants or work songs of the field hand slave
Slur: Singing or playing two or more different notes without articulation between them; notated by the use of a curved line connected the notes
Soprano: The highest female voice
Sostenuto: Sustaining a tone to or beyond its normal value
Spiritual: Slave utterances, chants, moans, cries for deliverance
Spiritoso: With spirit
Staccato: Detached, cut short
Stanza: Poetic units two lines or longer in length sung to the same music; also called a verse
Staff: A five-line system on which musical pitches and rhythms are notated
Subito: Suddenly
Syncopation: An alteration of the normal pulse of music in which notes are performed on weak beats
Tempo: The pace at which a musical composition is performed

Tenor: The highest male voice

Texture: The musical weave of a composition

Theme: A melodic unit on which a composition is based

Tie: The connecting of two or more notes of the same pitch; notated with a curved line between the notes.

Timbre: The individual tone quality of a specific voice or instrument

Time signature: A notational indication, similar to a fraction, which appears at the beginning of a composition and specifies the meter. The bottom number defines which kind of note receives each beat or pulse, and the top number defines how many notes of that particular value appear in each measure.

Tone: A single musical sound

Tonic: The first degree of the diatonic scale

Traditional gospel: An era in gospel music from the 1920s to the 1950s

Transcription: An arrangement or reduction of an orchestral or vocal work

Treble: The highest part of a choral composition

Triad: Three tones, forming two intervals of thirds, sounded simutaneously

Trill: A rapid alteration of two tones, often used as an ornament

Trio: A composition for three voices or instruments

Unchanged voices: The high voices of younger children

Upbeat: A weak or unaccented note that anticipates the downbeat; also called anacrusis

Urban gospel: An era in gospel music from the 1990s to present

Variation: A modification or altered version of a musical passage

Vivace: Brisk, lively tempo

Vocalization (*vocalise*): A long melody sung on a vowel to exercise the voice

Volume: The quantity or power of sound

Walking bass: A bass line that moves steadily in a constant rhythm

Simple meter	Compound meter